An Invitation

TO JOIN THE ROYAL MINT COIN CLUB

In order to satisfy the demands of the modern collector, the Royal Mint has established its own Coin Club to provide its members with the latest information on new coins from both home and abroad. Recognised as the supreme examples of the minter's art, Royal Mint collector coins form a tangible record of our heritage.

Some of the benefits of becoming a Coin Club member are:

FREE
Coin Club Membership.
No COMMITMENT TO PURCHASE
whatsoever.
ROYAL MINT GUARANTEE
return your coins within 30 days for an immediate refund.
FREE
Quarterly
Coin Club Magazine.
FREE
Postage & Packing
on all purchases.
INTEREST-FREE
Payments on selected high-value products.

ROYAL MINT

ADVANCE NOTIFICATION
of rare and limited-edition issues.
OPPORTUNITY
to purchase products which are NOT offered to the general public.
SPECIAL PRE-ISSUE PRICES
(subject to status).
The **confidence** that you are dealing with one of the most prestigious and reputable numismatic organisations in the world with a history spanning over 1100 years.

A TRADITION OF EXCELLENCE

To receive your free brochure, please telephone (01443 62 34 56)
or write to the address detailed below, quoting ref: CYBOO
Royal Mint Coin Club, FREEPOST, PO Box 500, Cardiff, CF1 1YY.

1

Coins, Medals and Banknotes

REGULAR SALES: LIVE AND ON-LINE AT WWW.SOTHEBYS.COM

For information on buying, selling and valuations without obligation, please contact the Coin and Medal department:

James Morton
james.morton@sothebys.com

Tom Eden
tom.eden@sothebys.com

Paul Wood
paul.wood@sothebys.com

Tel: +44 (0)20 7293 4436
Fax: +44 (0)20 7293 5973

Elizabeth I, Fifth Coinage sovereign
Estimate: £3,000-4,000

SOTHEBY'S
34-35 New Bond Street
London W1A 2AA

www.sothebys.com

SOTHEBY'S
Founded 1744

Tel: 01543 473073 between 1pm and 9pm	# J. WELSH P.O. Box 150, Burton-on-Trent Staffs DE13 7LB Callers by appointment only as all coins banked	Est. 1968 Fax No. (24 hrs) 01543 473234

COINS FOR SALE

HAMMERED GOLD
James I ¼ Laurel NVF/VF £250.00
James I ¼ Laurel EF Excellent portrait
£450.00

£5 & £2 PIECES
1911 Pr. £2 GEM FDC Rare £575.00
1937 Pr. £5 UNC £625.00

GUINEAS
1678 2 Guinea Charles II EL Below Nice
EF/VUNC Extr. rare £1,750.00
1685 James II Gn. Nice NEF £850.00
1686 James II GN. Nice UNC . £2,250.00
1688 James II Gn. Nice UNC . £2,250.00
1700 Wm. III GN. Nice UNC ... £2,250.00
1714 Anne Gn. Nice UNC £1,950.00
1745 Geo. II Gn. EF/AUNC £995.00
1790 GN. Nice BU Scarce £350.00
1792 Gn. Nice BU Rare £350.00
1813 Military, Nice BU £995.00

½ GUINEAS
1786 Nice BU Rare £325.00
1813 ½ Gn. Superb BU £295.00

SOVEREIGNS
George III 1760-1820
1820 BU GEM £575.00

George IV 1821-1830
1825 Plain edge, Nice BU, very few
minted
.... £2,500.00
1826 Pr. BU GEM £2,000.00
1826 VF £150.00

William IV 1831-1837
1832 Superb BU £695.00

Victoria 1838-1887
Young Head Shield Rev.
1852 GVF £85.00
1855 Sydney NVF Extr. rare £595.00
1864 EF £90.00
1864 GVF £75.00
1866 NEF £72.00
1866 Syd. VF £100.00
1866 EF DN 4 .... £80.00
1869 EF DN 60 .... £80.00
1877 S BU £140.00
1877 S Nice VF £75.00
1878 S Nice BU Rare £250.00
1884 M Nice BU Scarce £195.00
1884 S ABU £100.00
1885 A ABU/BU £100.00

Veiled Head 1893-1901
1893 L Nice BU £90.00
1894 M EF £68.00

1894 S EF £70.00
1896 M BU £85.00
1899 M NEF/EF £62.00
1899 L EF £68.00
1899 L BU £90.00
1899 L ET £68.00
1901 M NEF/EF £65.00
1901 L NEF £62.00
2000 BU GEM £55.00

HALF SOVEREIGNS
1817 F £60.00
1817 Nice BU £225.00
1817 Superb BU/FDC £200.00
1820 Superb BU/FDC Scarce £275.00
1825 Geo. IV Laur. BU £30.00
1828 Geo. IV Superb BU/FDC Proof like
Exeptional £595.00
1835 Wm. IV Nice BU Very rare . £550.00
1837 Wm. IV Nice BU Very rare . £650.00
1839 Pr. Nice UNC Extr. rare £850.00
1853 BU GEM Extr. rare in this grade
£350.00
1873 M Nice VF Rare £65.00
1880 GF £48.00
1887 Pr. Nice BU Extr. rare £250.00
1887 BU £70.00
1902 MP UNC £70.00
1982 ABU/BU £30.00
1982 BU GEM £33.00
2000 BU GEM £34.00
2000 Pr. GEM/FDC orig. R.M. Box£70.00
1oz Kruger BU GEM £210.00

CROWNS
1662 Rose Below NVF £110.00
1662 Rose Below GF £80.00
1664 GF £85.00
1667 GF £80.00
1679 Vir. EF £475.00
1688 GF Rare £145.00
1696 NVF/VF £75.00
1696 VF £95.00
1794 CM Doll. Nice ABU £375.00
1795 DOLL. Oval C/M GEM UNC£575.00
1818 LIX Nice UNC £250.00
1818 UNC £225.00
1819 LIX Nice UNC £225.00
1821 NEF/EF £125.00
1821 UNC Toned £375.00
1845 EF £195.00
1847 Gothic UNC Nice £700.00
1887 Nice BU £65.00
1902 EF £70.00
1902 Superb UNC £120.00
1930 Nice BU Rare £195.00
1933 NVF/VF £68.00
1835 BU GEM £14.00
1935 EF £9.00
1937 BU GEM £16.00

1959 BU £5.00
1960 BU £5.00

HALFCROWNS
James I 3rd C. VF £325.00
1676 EF Nice tone £295.00
1685 GF/NVF £125.00
1686 James II GF Rare £100.00
1687 James II F £65.00
1687 NVF Rare £100.00
1689 Wm. & Mary EF Nice £250.00
1689 NVF/VF £75.00
1696 B GF £48.00
1700 Duo Nice BU Rare £450.00
1708 ABU £350.00
1709 NVF/VF £65.00
1715 F/GF £125.00
1723 SSC Nice GVF+ Rare £295.00
1735 VF Rare £150.00
1736 Vir. UNC Very rare, nice ... £450.00
1746 Pr. GEM UNC Toned Extr. rare
£850.00
1817 LH Nice UNC £125.00
1820 SH GEM UNC Very rare £250.00
1826 Pr. UNC Nice tone Extr. rare
£495.00
1831 Pr. UNC Nice tone Extr. rare
£595.00
1874 EF £50.00
1879 BU GEM Very rare £225.00
1887 Jub. Hd. BU £20.00
1887 EF £12.00
1893 BU £55.00
1902 Superb UNC £85.00
1920 EF Rare £14.00
1928 BU £15.00
1947 BU £4.00

FLORINS
1849 Nice UNC £120.00
1870 BU GEM Very rare £250.00
1881 Nice BU £175.00
1885 Nice BU Rare £140.00
1887 BU £20.00
1900 Nice BU £50.00
1902 BU £50.00
1920 EF Rare £12.00
1905 BU Very rare £350.00
1925 BU GEM Very rare £195.00

SHILLINGS
Charles I S. 2785 VF £85.00
James I GF £45.00
1715 BU Rare £250.00
1718 BU Rare £250.00
1758 BU £50.00
1763 North Fine Very rare £150.00
1763 North Nice UNC £450.00
1787 BU £40.00
1839 Pr. Superb Pl. edge £225.00
1887 NICE UNC £12.00
1902 BU £26.00

4

"THE I.A.P.N. dealer, your guide to the world of numismatics"

"More than one hundred of the world's most respected coin dealers are members of the I.A.P.N. (International Association of Professional Numismatics).

I.A.P.N. members offer the collector an exceptional selection of quality material, expert cataloguing, outstanding service, and realistic pricing. The I.A.P.N. also maintain the International Bureau for the Suppression of Counterfeit Coins (I.B.S.C.C.) which, for a fee can provide expert opinions on the authenticity of coin submitted to it. A booklet listing the name, address and specialities of all I.A.P.N. members is available without charge by writing to the I.A.P.N. Secretariate". Jean-Luc van der Schueren, 14, Rue de la Bourse, B-1000, Bruxelles.

Tel: +32–2–513 3400   Fax: +32–2–512 2528   E-mail: iapnsecret@compuserve.com   Web site: http://www.iapn.ch

ARGENTINA
DERMAN, Alberto José, Avenida Corrientes 368, BUENOS AIRES

AUSTRALIA
NOBLE NUMISMATICS Pty Ltd (Jim Noble), 169 Macquarie Street, SYDNEY NSW 2000

AUSTRIA
HERINEK, G., Josefstädterstrasse 27, A–1082 WIEN VIII
MOZELT, Erich, Postfach 19, A–1043 WIEN

BELGIUM
ELSEN SA, Jean, Avenue de Tervuren 65, B–1040 BRUXELLES
FRANCESCHI & Fils, B, 10, Rue Croix-de-Fer, B–1000 BRUXELLES
VAN DER SCHUEREN, Jean-Luc, 14, Rue de la Bourse, B–1000 BRUXELLES

CANADA
WEIR LTD., Randy, PO Box 64577, UNIONVILLE, Ontario, L3R 0M9

EGYPT
BAJOCCHI, Pietro 45 Abdel Khalek Sarwat Street, 11111 CAIRO

ENGLAND
BALDWIN & SONS LTD., A.H. ,11 Adelphi Terrace, LONDON WC2N 6BJ
DAVIES LTD, Paul, PO Box 17, ILKLEY, West Yorkshire LS29 8TZ
CHRISTOPHER EIMER, PO Box 352, LONDON NW11 7RF
FORMAT OF BIRMINGHAM LTD 18 Bennetts Hill, BIRMINGHAM B2 5QJ
KNIGHTSBRIDGE COINS, 43 Duke Street. St. James's, LONDON SW1Y 6DD
LUBBOCK & SON LTD, 315 Regent Street, LONDON W1R 7YB
RUDD , Chris, PO Box 222. Aylsham, NORFOLK NR11 6TY
SPINK & SON LTD, 69, Southampton Row, Bloomsbury, LONDON WC1B 4ET

FRANCE
BOURGEY, Sabine, 7, Rue Drouot, F–75009 PARIS
BURGAN, Claude—Maison Florange, 8, Rue du 4 Septembre, F–75002, PARIS
MAISON PLATT SA, BP 2612, F–75026, Cedex 01, PARIS
NUMISMATIQUE et CHANGE DE PARIS, 3, Rue de la Bourse, F–75002 PARIS
O.G.N., 64, Rue de Richelieu, F–75002 PARIS
A POINSIGNON-NUMISMATIQUE, 4, Rue des Francs Bourgeois, F–67000 STRASBOURG
SILBERSTEIN, Claude, 39, Rue Vivienne, F–75002 PARIS
VINCHON-NUMISMATIQUE, Jean 77, Rue de Richelieu, F–75002 PARIS
WEIL, Alain, SPES NUMISMATIQUE, 54, Rue de Richelieu, F–75001 PARIS

GERMANY
DILLER, Johannes, Postfach 70 04 29, D–81304 MÜNCHEN
GARLICH, Kurt B, Albert Schweizer Strasse, 24A, D–63303, DREIEICH-GOTZENHAIN
GIESSENER MÜNZHANDLUNG DIETER GORNY GmbH, Maximiliansplatz 20, D–80333 MÜNCHEN
HIRSCH, NACHF., Gerhard, Promenadeplatz 10/11, D–80333 MÜNCHEN
JACQUIER,Paul-Francis, Honsellstrasse 8, D–77694 KEHL
KAISER, Rüdiger, Münzfachgeschaft, Mittelweg 54, D–60318 FRANKFURT

KRICHELDORF Nachf., H.H.Gunterstalstrasse 16, D–79102 FREIBURG i.Br.
KÜNKER, Fritz Rudolf, Münzenhandlung, Gutenbergstrasse 23, D–49076 OSNARBRUCK
KURPFALZISCHEMÜNZENHANDLUNG— KPM, Augusta-Anlage 52, D–68165 MANNHEIM
Numismatik LANZ, Luitpoldblock-Maximiliansplatz 10, D–80333 MÜNCHEN
MENZEL, Niels, Dachsteinweg 12, D–12107, BERLIN-MARIENDORF

MÜNZENETAGE–ANTIKE NUMISMATIK (Herrn Dr. M. Brandt), Marktplatz 14, D–70173 ,STUTTGART
MÜNZEN-UND MEDAILLENHANDLUG STUTTGART, Charlottenstrasse 4, D–70182 STUTTGART
NEUMANN, Ernst, Watteplatz 6, Postfach 1423, D–89312, GUNZBÜRG
PEUS NACHF., Dr. Busso Bornwiesenweg 34, D–60322 FRANKFURT/M,
Münzhandlung RITTER GmbH Postfach 24 01 26, D–40090 DÜSSELDORF
TIETJEN + CO, Spitalerstrasse 30, D–20095 HAMBURG
WESTFALISCHE AUKTIONSGESELLSCHAFT ohG, Nordring 22, D–59821, ARNSBERG

ISRAEL
EIDELSTEIN, Adolfo, 61 Herzl St., HAIFA, Postal address: POB 5135, 31051 Haifa
QEDAR, Shraga, 3, Granot Street, Entrance 6, JERUSALEM. Postal address: PO Box 520, 91004 Jerusalem

ITALY
BARANOWSKY s.a.s, Via del Corso 184, I–00187, ROMA
BERNARDI, Giulio, Via Roma 3 & 22c, PO Box 560, I–34 121 TRIESTE
CARLO CRIPPA s.n.c., Via degli Omenoni 2 (angolo Piazza Belgioioso). I–20121 MILANO
DE FALCO, Corso Umberto 24, I–80138 NAPOLI
FALLANI , Via del Babuino 58a, I–00187, ROMA
MARCHESI GINO &Figlio (Guiseppe Marchesi), V. le Pietramellara 35, I–40121, BOLOGNA
PAOLUCCI, Raffaele, Via San Francesco 154, I–35121 PADOVA
RINALDI & Figlio, O.,Via Cappello 23 (Casa di Giulietta), I–37121 VERONA

JAPAN
DARUMA INTERNATIONAL GALLERIES, 2–16-32-301, Takanawa, Minato-ku, JP-TOKYO 108-0074
WORLD COINS, 1-15-5, Hamamatsu-cho, Minato-Ku, TOKYO 105-0013.

LUXEMBOURG
LUX NUMIS, 20, rue J. P Kommes, L–6988 HOSTERT, LUXEMBOURG

MONACO
GADOURY Editions Victor, 57 rue Grimaldi, Le Panorama, MC–98000 MONACO
LE LOUIS D'OR, 9, Ave. des Papalins, MC–98000 MONACO

THE NETHERLANDS
MEVIUS NUMISBOOKS Int. BV Oosteinde 97, NL 7671
VRIEZENVEEN SCHULMAN BV, Laurens, Brinklaan 84a, NL–1404 GM BUSSUM
WESTERHOF, Jille Binne, Trekpad 38–40, NL–8742 KP, Burgwerd

NORWAY
OSLO MYNTHANDEL AS, (Jan Aamlid) Postboks 355, Sentrum, N–0101, OSLO

PORTUGAL
NUMISPORTO LDA, Mr. Ferreira Leite, Av. Combatentes Grande Guerra 610 LJ6, P–4200 PORTO

SINGAPORE
TAISEI STAMPS & COINS (S) PTE LTD, 116 Middle Road, #09–02, ICB Enterprise House, SINGA- 188972

SPAIN
CALICO, X. & F., Plaza del Angel 2, E–08002 BARCELONA
CAYON, Juan R., JANO S.L., Alcala 35, E–28014 MADRID
SEGARO, Fernando P, Plaza Mayor 26, E–28012, MADRID
VICO SA, Jesus, Jorge Juan, 83 Duplicado, E–28009 MADRID

SWEDEN
AHLSTRÖM MYNTHANDEL, AB, Norrmalmstorg 1, 1, PO Box 7662, S–103 94 STOCKHOLM
NORDLINDS MYNTHANDEL AB, ULF, Karlavagen 46, PO Box 5132, S–102 43 STOCKHOLM

SWITZERLAND
HESS, Adolph A. G (H. J. Schramm) Postfach 7070, CH-8023, ZÜRICH
HESS—DIVO AG, Postfach 7070, CH-8023, ZÜRICH
LEU NUMISMATIK AG, Postfach 4738, CH-8022 ZÜRICH
MÜNZEN UND MEDAILLEN AG, Malzgasse 25, BASEL. Postal address: Postfach 3647, CH–4002 BASEL
NUMISMATICA ARS CLASSICA AG, Niederdorfstrasse 43, Postfach 745, CH–8025 ZÜRICH
STERNBERG AG, Frank Schanzengasse 10 (Bhf. Stadelhofen), CH–8001 ZÜRICH

UNITED STATES OF AMERICA
BASOK, Alexander, 1954 First Street #186, HIGHLAND PARK, IL 60035
BERK, LTD., Harlan J, 31 North Clark Street, CHICAGO, IL 60602
BULLOWA, C.E. COIN HUNTER, 1616 Walnut Street, PHILADELPHIA, PA 19103
COIN AND CURRENCY INSTITUTE INC, PO Box 1057, CLIFTON, NJ 07014
COIN GALLERIES, 123 West 57 Street, NEW YORK, NY 10019
CRAIG, Freeman, PO Box 4176, SAN RAFAEL, CA 94913
DAVISSON'S LTD, COLD SPRING, MN 56320
DUNIGAN, Mike, 5332 Birchman, Fort Worth, TX 76107
FORD, John J. Jr, PO Box 10317, PHOENIX, AZ 85064
FREEMAN & SEAR, PO Box 641352, LOS ANGELES, CA 90064–6352
FROSETH INC., K.M., PO Box 23116, MINNEAPOLIS, MN 55423
GILLIO Inc., Ronald J., 1103 State Street, SANTA BARBARA, CA 93101
HARVEY, Stephen, PO Box 3778, BEVERLEY HILLS, CA 90212
HINDERLING, Wade, PO Box 606 MANHASSET, NY 11030
KERN, Jonathan K. Co., 441, S. Ashland Avenue, Lexington, KY 40502
KOLBE, George Frederick, PO Drawer 3100, CRESTLINE, CA 92325–3100
KOVACS, Frank L., PO Box 25300 SAN MATEO, CA 94402
KREINDLER, Herbert, 15, White Birch Drive, Dix Hills, NY11746
MALTER & CO. Inc., Joel L., 17005 Ventura Blvd., ENCINO, CA 91316
MARGOLIS, Richard, PO Box 2054, TEANECK, NJ 07666
MARKOV, Dmitry, Coins & Medals, PO Box 950, NEW YORK, NY 10272
MILCAREK, Dr. Ron, PO Box 1028, Greenfield, MA 01302
PONTERIO & ASSOCIATES, Inc, 1818 Robinson Ave., SAN DIEGO, CA 92101–1683
RARE COIN COMPANY OF AMERICA, Inc, 6262 South Route 83, WILLOWBROOK, IL 60514
RARE COIN GALLERIES, Robert van Bebber, 228, South Brand Boulevard, GLENDALE, CA 91204
ROSENBLUM, William M., EVERGREEN, CO. 80437–0355
RYNEARSON, Dr Paul, PO Box 4009, MALIBU, CA 90264
SINGER, Dr Gordon Andreas, PO Box 235, GREENBELT, MD20768–0235
STACK'S, 123 West 57 Street., NEW YORK, NY 10019
STEPHENS Inc., Karl, PO Box 3038, Fallbrook, CA 92088
STREINER, Eric Inc, 119 West 57th Street, Suite 1218, NY 10019, NEW YORK
SUBAK Inc., 22 West Monroe Street, Room 1506, CHICAGO, IL 60603
TELLER NUMISMATIC ENTERPRISES 16027 Ventura Blvd., Suite 606, ENCINO, CA 91436
WADDELL, Ltd., Edward J., Suite 316, 444 N. Frederick Ave., GAITHERSBURG, MD 20877
WORLD-WIDE COINS OF CALIFORNIA, PO Box 3684, SANTA ROSA, CA 95402

VENEZUELA
NUMISMATICA GLOBUS, Apartado de Correos 50418 CARACAS 1050–A

6

THE
COIN
YEARBOOK
2001

Edited by

James Mackay, MA, DLitt
John W. Mussell
and the Editorial Team of COIN NEWS

ISBN 1 8701 92 36 2

Published by
TOKEN PUBLISHING LIMITED

Orchard House, Duchy Road, Heathpark, Honiton, EX14 1YD
Telephone: 01404 46972   Fax: 01404 44788
e-mail: info@coin-news.com. Website: http://www.coin-news.com

Printed in Great Britain by Polestar Wheatons Ltd., Exeter EX2 8RP

Contents

Index to advertisers

9

Selling your Coins/Banknotes?

Highest Prices

Warwick & Warwick can obtain the highest prices through our Private Treaty Service. Whether you have a specialised collection, proof sets, surplus material, from £100 to £100,000, we can sell them for you.

All Material

We have clients keen to purchase material in any quantity, in any condition, from fair to FDC from any country – even unpopular and obscure material.

Whatever you have, Warwick and Warwick can sell it – dealers' stocks, hoards, old accumulations, single coins of individual value, bullion.

Free Valuation

Warwick & Warwick provide written valuations free of charge and without obligation. If you decline our valuation you owe us nothing except the return postage or transport costs. You will receive the full amount tendered in the valuation with no commission or service charge deducted.

Free Visits

Warwick & Warwick will, completely free of charge and without obligation, arrange to visit sellers of more valuable collections anywhere in the country within 48 hours. Visits abroad can also be arranged.

Smaller collections are transported to our offices for valuation by insured security courier at no expense to the vendor.

Act Now

Telephone us today with details of your property. Write to us or fax us if you prefer. Remember we can be with you in 48 hours.

Warwick & Warwick

Warwick & Warwick Limited, Chalon House, Scar Bank, Millers Road, Warwick, England. CV34 5DB.
Tel: 01926-499031. Fax: 01926-491906

Foreword

WELCOME to the eighth edition of the COIN YEARBOOK. There is an old saying that "good gear goes in small bulk" and this is certainly true of this volume whose format has been widely welcomed by collectors and dealers alike, enabling people to carry it in their pocket or bag to coin fairs or when browsing round the coin shops. We continue to give serious thought to ways and means of improving the blue pages which are at the core of this volume. The prices are constantly under review and revised in light of market movements detected in the saleroom or through the medium of the lists produced regularly by the specialist dealers in each field.

During the past year sterling remained remarkably stable against the dollar and the Euro, although at the time of writing (early August 2000) the value of sterling had begun to drop, providing welcome relief to British exporters and industry generally, if not such good news for collectors and dealers intent on buying abroad. The converse also applies and before the end of the 1999/2000 season there were clear indications that overseas bidders were beginning to make their presence more keenly felt in the London and even provincial salerooms.

The recovery of the far eastern markets generally, and in Japan, Taiwan and Korea in particular, has been reflected in the marked upswing in prices realised at the major sales in Singapore and Hong Kong, while the dealers attending the international coin shows in these numismatic centres report a new vibrancy in the market which is now having a knock-on effect in Europe and America as well.

Politically the past year has been of immense interest for the introduction of devolution in several parts of the United Kingdom. A full year has now elapsed since the Scottish Parliament and the Welsh Assembly were called into being and while the performance of these legislatures has not been without controversy and criticism, overall there is a feeling in these countries that democracy is now being seen in action. The situation with regard to Northern Ireland, however, has not been so positive although there are now signs at last of a breakthrough in what had seemed to be an intractable position, both sides beginning to give a little from their previously fiercely entrenched positions. And now even London has its own elected mayor and democratic government for the first time in recorded history. If London were an independent country it would probably rank quite high in the world league table in terms of population alone, and probably up there with the major powers if wealth were the criterion. All that remains surely is to accord to England generally the degree of autonomy now being enjoyed by London and the other countries of the United Kingdom.

Numismatically, of course, self-government for Scotland and Wales has not yielded anything of note so far, although the Scots continue to have their own banknotes, including a pound note of the Royal Bank featuring the new Scottish Parliament. When it comes to a superabundance of coinage, commemorative and otherwise, the offshore islands seem to provide more than enough, now that Alderney, a dependency of Guernsey, has established itself as a regular issuer of crowns and the Isle of Man continues to produce its attractive thematic sets.

The introduction of the single European currency last year has not had as great an impact on numismatics as was anticipated and the disappointing performance of the Euro itself against sterling and the American dollar seems to have had a somewhat dampening effect on the new currency. Nevertheless, the countries of the European Community which have pledged themselves to replace national currencies by the Euro are forging ahead.

Elsewhere the easing of the regulations governing Value Added Tax on gold bullion coins has already encouraged the Royal Mint to resume the striking of sovereigns and half sovereigns for this market. While the impact of these bullion pieces on numismatics is marginal, anything which makes easier the handling of coins, bullion or otherwise, is to be welcomed.

When putting together a publication such as the COIN YEARBOOK we inevitably have to call on a number of experts for advice and assistance. We are indebted to the many people who have helped in the production of this year's publication, particularly to Nick Swabey for providing us with a completely new authoritative price guide to Maundy coins and sets, also Royston Norbury of West Essex Coins, Steven Mitchell of Studio Coins, Chris Rudd, John Cummings and numerous other dealers who have generously given advice on the pricing of coins and Pam West for pricing the banknote section. Thanks also to the various auction houses and dealers who have allowed us to reproduce illustrations from their publications.

11

12

That was
the year
that was!

An at-a-glance résumé of the main events and occurrences that affected the coin hobby during the past months, as reported in COIN NEWS . . .

July 1999

Her Majesty the Queen formally inaugurates the Scottish Parliament, the first in almost 300 years. Immediately there is an outcry regarding the award of a bronze medal to MSPs, struck by the Royal Mint to mark the occasion. Apart from MSPs, the medal is awarded to the 162 babies born in Scotland on the inaugural day.

The Royal Mint and the British Art Medal Society join forces to produce a Millennium medal designed by Felicity Fuller (see picture below), showing a dandelion clock on the obverse. Purchasers have the option of a reverse with blank central field for engraving to personal specifications.

Dr Carol Homden is appointed Director of Marketing and Public Affairs at the British Museum. Her primary responsibility is to launch the Great Court, London's first fully funded Millennium project.

Tesco's SchoolNet 2000 project is launched with plans to have 38,000 web pages from 14,500 UK schools registered by the end of 1999. As part of the scheme, the pupils of Tonysguboriau Junior School, Talbot Green plan a project documenting a "day in the life" of the Royal Mint.

Presveis, a joint venture of the British Museum and the Athens Numismatic Museum, co-sponsored by the European Commission and the Hellenic Ministry of Culture, launches a cyber exhibition on the Internet covering all aspects of coinage from its origins to the latest Euro currency.

Jos F. M. Eijsermans of Holland is appointed European Director of MoneyWorld Asia Pte Ltd

Celtic dealer Chris Rudd is elected to membership of the International Association of Professional Numismatists.

August 1999

To commemorate the Cutty Sark Tall Ships Race and the visit of the ships to Shetland, Shetland Landmark release a set of ten coloured crown-sized kroner coins depicting the ten Class A Tall Ships participating in the race.

The Royal Mint announces plans to strike commemorative coins within the Millennium Dome when it opens in 2000. An exhibit will feature a press striking the special £5 coins.

To celebrate the Rugby World Cup, the Royal Mint strikes a special £2 coin depicting a football and goalposts.

Celtic dealer Chris Rudd who was elected to the International Association of Professional Numismatists in July 1999.

The Royal Mint publishes its annual figures, indicating a fall in operating profit, from £13m in 1997–98 to £5.8 in 1998–99. Sales were down 18 per cent at £91.4m (comparable to 1996–97 levels). Capital expenditure rose to £12.7m, an increas of £3.1m over the previous year. An all-time production record was set, the Mint producing 3,832 million circulating coins and blanks for the UK and 58 overseas countries.

Joe Cribb, Curator of Coins and Medals at the British Museum, is awarded the silver medal of the Royal Numismatic Society in recognition of his distinguished services to numismatics.

A new world record was created on August 30 at the Bowers & Merena sale of the Walter H. Childs collection in New York, when a Class I silver dollar of 1804 in "gem proof" condition realised a staggering $4,140,000 (including 15 per cent buyer's premium). This figure eclipses the previous world record for a US coin, also an 1804 silver dollar at a Bowers & Merena sale in 1997 when it sold for $1,815,000.. The record-breaking coin is believed to be the specimen which was presented in 1853 to the Sultan of Oman by the US government.

September 1999

The Museum of London launches a major exhibition devoted to the life and times of Alfred the Gereat, to remain open until January 9, 2000.

The exhibition coincides with the 11th centenary of Alfred's death on October 26, 899.

The second annual show for collectors of coins, banknotes, phonecards and other collectables, Sberatel, takes place in Prague, September 10-12.

Croydon Coin Auctions and Simmons Gallery both launch websites.

Havering Numismatic Society produce the winning design for their Millennium medal, the reverse depicting the Millennium Dome and St. Andrew's Church, Havering.

The London Coin Fair takes place at the Cumberland Hotel on September 11.

The Royal Albert Museum in Exeter opens an exhibition on September 18 entitled "From Script to Print to Hypertext", a celebration of Devon's written heritage, and including the museum's collection of inscribed Celtic coins.

Coincraft's long-awaited *Standard Catalogue of the Coins of Scotland, Ireland, Channel Islands and the Isle of Man* is published to wide acclaim.

October 1999

Baldwin's auction the collection of numismatic material pertaining to the Channel Islands formed by Antony McCammon, author of *Currencies of the Anglo-Norman Isles* and a *DIY History of the World*.

At Sotheby's on October 14 the set of gold coins marking the coronation of the first Qajar Shah of Persia, fetches £528,000, more than twice the pre-sale estimate, a record price for a coin sold outside the USA.

Reading Museum acquires a hoard of 25 British gold staters which was discovered by a metal detectorist, Gerald Fletcher, in August 1998 at Jealott's Hill Farm near Bracknell.

Money Week (October 23–31) at the British Museum is adjudged a great success, more than 500 visitors attending the Wednesday show alone, when the Museum's experts were on hand to identify and expertise coins brought along by the public.

Lindner coin albums and accessories appoint the West Cornwall Stamp Centre as their UK agency.

Benjamin R. Bell joins the cataloguing department of the Classical Numismatic Group at their head office in Lancaster, Pennsylvania.

At an exhibition of Aboriginal Art, held at the Hermitage Museum, St. Petersburg, the Perth Mint present a series of gold proof coins covering the period from 1997 and including the coins for the forthcoming Olympic Games in Sydney.

Canada's Millennium souvenir set includes a nickel

medal designed by Alf Gamble, its symbolic motif alluding to the country's provinces.

Coincraft stage their 14th annual sale on October 24–30, now widely regarded as one of the coin world's leading events, with crowds queuing all round the block before the grand opening.

Mick Vort-Ronald, Australian correspondent of *Coin News*, is appointed Editor of *Australian Coin Review*.

The Royal Mint launched a World Millennium collection consisting of 24 silver crowns or crown-sized coins.

The Sierra Leone crown portraying Princess Diana and Mother Teresa, issued in 1997, is voted "most inspirational" coin of 1997 in the Coins of the Year Awards, organised by Krause Publications.

The World Proof Numismatic Association celebrates its 35th birthday.

Wing Commander Geoffrey Porter, a veteran member of Bexley Coin Club and BANS Congresses, dies on October 28.

November 1999

At an inquest early in November coroner Michael Rose declares a hoard of silver denarii treasure trove. The coins were discovered by Kevin Elliott on his father's farm at Shapwick, Somerset in August, using a metal detector for the very first time. The hoard consists of 9,377 denarii buried about AD 230 and believed to be the largest Roman hoard found in Britain.

The Classical Numismatic Group hold their third annual Triton Sale on November 30–December 1, featuring the Sinton and Vermeule collections of classical coins among others. The total realised is a record $4,781,080 with 92 per cent of the lots sold.

At a sale in Sydney on November 17–18, Noble Numismatics establish a new record price for the famous 1930 proof Australia penny. The coin, sold by a vendor in Melbourne, was once in the possession of the British Museum and was acquired in 1981 by exchange. Of the six other pennies, three are in institutions and the others in private hands.

Guernsey and Alderney release gold and silver coins to mark the 125th anniversary of the birth of Sir Winston Churchill, both sets being struck by the Royal Mint.

December 1999

The Millennium medal from the Bigbury Mint has the designer's own small daughter as the model. The medal was designed by David Holland and the obverse shows Ella trying to embrace the whole world.

Phillips, Britain's third largest auction house which includes the specialist coin saleroom Glendining's, is acquired by Bernard Arnault, owner of the French luxury goods company Louis Vuitton Moet Hennessy, reputedly for about £70m.

The new issue department of Spink & Son is taken over by Groth AG of Switzerland.

The contract to manufacture the winners' medals for the Sydney Olympic Games is split between the Royal Australian Mint and the Perth Mint. The standard reverse, designed by Wojciech Pietranik, features the Sydney Opera House, the Olympic torch and rings, while the obverse shows Nike, goddess of victory, and Olympic symbols.

Michael Harrison, proprietor of Coins International of Leeds for more than 30 years, dies after a long illness.

The artist's daughter was the subject of the Bigbury Mint's Millennium medal issued in December 1999.

January 2000

British Customs and Excise abolish Value Added Tax on investment gold coins. As a result, the Royal Mint announce plans to strike bullion sovereigns and half-sovereigns for the first time since 1982.

Well-known coin dealer David Butler of Cheltenham dies on January 6 at the age of 56.

The Royal Mint unveils details of the crown-sized £5 coin to be released this year to celebrate the hundredth birthday of Her Majesty Queen Elizabeth the Queen Mother, designed by Ian Rank-Broadley.

Basel 2000, the World Money Fair and 29th International Coin Show, takes place on January

The reverse of the £5 crown to celebrate Her Majesty the Queen Mother's centenary is unveiled in January 2000.

21–23, with dealers and mints from 30 countries participating.

The Royal Mint unveil details of a 50p coin to celebrate the 150th anniversary of British Public Libraries.

Richard Lobel celebrates 25 years membership of the prestigious Professional Numismatic Guild and the fulfillment of Coincraft's 405,000th order since 1992. The mail order side of the business now caters to customers in 60 countries

February 2000

The Long Beach Coin and Collectibles Expo is held in California February 10–13. A highlight of the show is the Ship of Gold, featuring treasure salvaged from the wreck of the SS *Central America* from the California gold rush period. The $10m exhibit attracted over 17,500 visitors during the four-day show.

One of Florida's most prominent numismatists, Richard "Dick" Parker, dies at Las Vegas on February 13. Originally a lawyer, he turned to coin dealing later in life, specialising in US and British coins of all periods.

The Irish International Coin, Banknote and Medal Fair organised by the auctioneer Whyte's, takes place at the Gresham Hotel, Dublin, over the weekend of February 26–27. A major sale of coins, medals and militaria is staged simultaneously.

The Young Friends of the British Museum fund the acquisition of the "Turk" Collection of East Asian charms by the Department of Coins and Medals. The collection, comprising some 412 items mainly from China and Japan, makes a significant addition to the Museum's holding of Asian charms. A preview of the collection is held on Children's Study Day on February 18.

March 2000

Auctioneers B. Frank & Son celebrate their 50th

sale of coins and medals by reducing vendors' commission on pre-decimal British milled coins by 50 per cent.

Australia releases its first coloured coin, a 50 cent piece with the national flag in red, white and blue on the reverse, to mark the Millennium.

Spink & Son move from King Street, St. James's to 69 Southampton Row in Bloomsbury. The firm's new headquarters was formerly the West Central District Office of the Post Office and provides greatly enhanced accommodation and the latest state-of-the-art technical facilities.

The 14th Singapore International Coin Show takes place at the Raffles City Convention Centre March 24–26, with eight mints participating as well as dealers from around the world. As a prelude to the show Baldwin-Gillio-Monetarium stage a huge sale of coins and banknotes on March 23. Both are a resounding success, reflecting the significant upturn in the Asian economy in recent months.

Judging of the Coin of the Year Awards in New York accords the overall winner to an Austrian silver coin celebrating book printing, issued in 1998. The 500 schilling coin was also chosen as best silver coin in the preliminary round of voting. Other winners were Portugal's 200 escudos for the 500th anniversary of Vasco da Gama's voyage to India (most historically significant), Israel's silver 2 sheqalim marking the 50th anniversary of independence (best contemporary coin), Singapore's Year of the Tiger $250 (best gold coin), Portugal's Ocean Expo silver 1,000 escudos (best trade coin), Canada's silver dollar for the Mounted Police (most popular coin), Andorra's silver 10 diners showing Europa in a chariot (most artistic coin), Bosnia's silver 14 Euro "peace dove" (most inspirational coin) and the three-nation $2 issued by Fiji, the Cook Islands and Western Samoa (most innovative coin).

Auctions with online bidding commences at www.sothebys.amazon.com, bringing the 226-year-old auction house into the 21st century.

The long-awaited Sacagawea dollar goes into general circulation in the USA. It takes its name from the portrait of the 15-year-old Shoshone Indian girl who served as guide to the Lewis and Clark Expedition. The gold-coloured coin is the first attempt by the USA to get a base-metal dollar into general circulation since the abortive Anthony dollar back in the 1970s.

Olympic coins from the Solomon Islands depict Kenny the Kangaroo, Kylie the Koala and Eddie the Emu, cartoon characters by Brian Sage, believed to be the first time that a cartoon treatment has been used for an entire series of coins.

To mark the Millennium Zambia releases coins in an upright elongated format. Although this shape is familiar to collectors of "pressed pennies", this is believed to be the first time that an elliptical format is used for coinage.

At Dreweatt Neate's sale three tokens from the Worcester Porcelain Company, distributed to factory workers in the 1770s and 1780s, realise almost £5,000.

Noble Numismatics of Sydney achieve a world record price for a bronze coin when a 1930 proof penny of Australia fetches a staggering $281,750, surpassing that sold in November 1999. The corresponding proof halfpenny makes a highly respectable $39,100.

The 1930 Australian proof penny sold by Noble on March 29, 1999 for the world record price of A$281,750.

April 2000

The British Association of Numismatic Societies' annual Congress takes place at Dalrymple Hall, University of Glasgow over the weekend of April 7–9, organised and hosted by the Glasgow and West of Scotland Numismatic Society.

"Paid in Burnt Silver'" is the title of an exhibition devoted to the wealth and power of the Viking Age which opens at the British Museum's Department of Coins and Medals on April 12 and runs until August 13.

One of the finest hoards of Roman coins from Wales goes on display in the Coins and Medals Gallery at the National Museum and Gallery, Cardiff, thanks to the sponsorship of BG Transco, the national gas pipeline and emergency company. The hoard was discovered during the laying of a Transco pipeline near Bridgend in 1994. One of the largest hoards found in Britain, it contained over

1,400 Roman copper-alloy nummi and was buried in a home-made pot around AD 130.

The Millennial Collection, a special auction of coins and medals organised by Patrick Finn and handled by Whyte's of Dublin, takes place on April 29. Unfortunately Patrick was taken seriously ill immediately before the sale and was unable to attend.

Australia's 50 cent coin marking the Queen's visit, has a new obverse designed by local artist Vladimir Gottwald. This is the first time that an effigy of the reigning monarch has been used for an Australian coion since 1936.

May 2000

The "ultimate collectors fair" takes place at the NEC, Birmingham over the weekend of May 26–28. About 475 dealers covering every aspect of collectables take part.

Spink move to new premises in Bloomsbury in March 2000. The entrance in Southampton Row (left) belies the size of the spacious accommodation (below).

The annual Money World Asia show takes place at the Convention and Exhibition Centre, Hong Kong on May 26–28

The Royal Mint includes the four Maundy silver coins in the year set for the first time in over 60 years as part of the celebrations marking the Millennium. Remarkably, the Maundy coins retain the Mary Gillick profile of the Queen, first used in 1953.

Stephen Fenton of Knightsbridge Coins and Ron Gillio of Long Beach Collectables join with 13 other international numismatists to form Renaissance Auctions, whose first sale is scheduled to take plate at Philadelphia in August.

The summer exhibition at the Simmons Gallery in London is entitled "Freerange" and reflects the exceedingly diverse styles and techniques adopted by contemporary medallists with works on display by John Mills, Ian Rank-Broadley, Avril Vaughan and Ron Dutton. The exhibition opens on May 30 and continues until July 7.

The Royal Canadian Mint announces its second highest financial earnings ever for the year ended in mid-1999. Profits totalling over $22 million were achieved mainly by the Mint's successful efforts to create innovative products, notably the range of collectables associated with the Millennium. The only year to notch up a larger profit was 1980 when profits were boosted by the volatility of the bullion market (gold briefly reaching $900 an ounce).

June 2000

15-year-old Laura Paxton from Thunder Bay, Ontario becomes the world's youngest coin designer, when she wins a national children's competition to design the Celebration 25 cent coin in Canada's Millennium series.

Chicago hosts the IAPN Congress, attended by delegates from 12 countries including a strong British presence. Among the 41 members present are four from the UK, while a fifth, Christopher Eimer, is elected to membership. Paul and Bente Withers of the UK take the bronze award for their book *British Copper Tokens 1811-1820*.

Format of Birmingham introduce a new style of list, now divided into British and World sections which, it is hoped, will be of greater convenience to the more specialised collector.

The Ormskirk and West Lancashire Numismatic Society celebrates its 30th anniversary.

London Coin Auctions hold their biggest sale ever on June 6, realising a total of £51,400.

The National Museum of Scotland produced an interactive CD-rom cataloguing the museum's

Interactive CD-rom issued by the National Museum of Scotland in June 2000.

extensive coin collection dating from the 12th century to the present day.

The June 24 sale by Jean Elsen in Brussels contains an exceptional range of coins of the Low Countries, including an extremely rare lion d'or of Anthony of Burgundy and the famous Robustus Daalder of Brabant in 1584.

The Royal Mint produces three alternative designs for a new £2 coin to celebrate the centenary of the first trans-Atlantic radio signals by Marconi, and solicits the opinions of the general public, through the medium of the *Radio Times*, as to which design should be used. The decision was to be taken on June 15.

Trevor Bird and Jonathan Clemes discover a crock containing 80 Roman bronze and silver coins in a riverbank in Cornwall.

Bonham's coin and medal department winds down, although the services of Daniel Fearon as a consultant are retained. The decision to close the coin department is all the more surprising as the company is currently expanding its activitives in other areas of antiques and collectables, although the location of the department in Lots Road is blamed for its demise.

The Royal Canadian Mint admit to an error in the production of their Millennium souvenir sets. Medallions which accompany the set were struck with the effigy of the Queen instead of a map of the country. Efforts are made to retrieve the erroneous sets from the market but inevitably a few get into the hands of collectors. It is believed that fewer than 25,000 sets, out of a total of 500,000, were affected.

The Royal Mint launches a Millennium time capsule, enabling members of the public to salt away coins and other mementoes of the year 2000 in a special metal box, with separate compartments for a year set of coins and souvenirs or historic documents.

July 2000

The third part of the mammoth sale of world tokens takes place at Noble Numismatics of Sydney on July 11–13. The sale is so huge that it requires a two-volume catalogue to detail all the lots.

The York Coin & Stamp Fair at the Racecourse Grandstand on July 28–29 is the biggest so far, with a record number of dealers and collectors in attendance.

Zambia announces the release of a set of three oval-shaped coins with photographic reverses, a major technical breakthrough appropriately applied to the celebration of the 100th birthday of the Queen Mother.

Classic Forum launch a website specially designed for coin collectors.

From July 22 to September 24 the Birmingham Museum and Art Gallery stages "The Money Show", a comprehensive social history of money and how it has affected our lives. Coins, banknotes, tokens and other currency items are displayed in themes that include "Funny Money", "Alternative Money" and "I Can't Believe It's Not Money". There is also an exhibit of DIY Money, devoted to William Booth, Birmingham's most notorious forger who was hanged for counterfeiting in 1812—not once but twice.

The National Art Collections Fund pledges £60,000 towards the purchase of the Shapwick

The Royal Mint's Millennium Time Capsule which contains a 2000 year set including the Millennium crown.

coin hoard for the Somerset County Museum. The hoard, believed to be the largest accumulation of denarii ever found in Britain, was discovered by metal detectorists in September 1998 and consists of 9,213 Roman silver coins dating from 32 BC to AD 224. The total cost of acquiring the hoard is estimated at £265,000.

August 2000

To celebrate the hundredth birthday of the Queen Mother the Royal Mint, Debden Security Printing and the Royal Mint join forces to produce a unique souvenir, consisting of a first day cover bearing the Royal Mail £5 stamp featuring Windsor Castle, a special £5 note of the Bank of England with the prefix QM100 and the £5 Queen Mother coin.

An exhibition at the British Museum entitled "Illegal Tender: Counterfeit Money Through the Ages" opens at the Coins and Medals Gallery on August 16 and runs until January 7, 2001.

On August 21 the Museum of London stages a demonstration of coin production, enabling visitors to have a go themselves for a mere 50p. The event forms part of the Museum's "High Street Londinium" exhibition which runs from July 21 till January 2001.

Niels Hagemann is appointed Sales Director for the Royal Mint's Coin Club activities in the UK, USA and Canada. Formerly with Richard Borek, the well-known German dealer, he and his family relocate in Britain.

Well-known coin and token dealer John Whitmore is elected Vice President of the Conder Token Collectors Club of America. The name "Conder" is derived from an early American student of British trade tokens which came to be used as a nickname for tokens in general.

September 2000

The annual Token Congress takes place at the Fairweather Centre of the University of Wales Institute, Cardiff on September 1–3.

To celebrate the golden jubilee of the Commune of Riccione, the annual numismatic show on September 9–10 is the biggest event of its kind ever staged in Italy.

The London Coin Fair on September 9 gets the 2000–2001 numismatic season off to a fine start, returning to its original venue at the Carlisle Suite of the Cumberland Hotel, Marble Arch while the hotel's banqueting suite is renovated.

The bronze medals marking the Sydney Olympic Games are struck from metal recycled from large quantities of the obsolete 1c and 2c coins.

A. F. BROCK & CO . LTD
Auctioneers & Valuers

* Coins * Medals * Banknotes * Stamps
* Postcards * Cigarette & Trade Cards
* Jewellery * Silverware
* Antiques & Collectibles

Auction Venue:
The Acton Court Hotel,
Buxton Road, Stockport

Our buying department will always be pleased to make an offer of purchase, if preferred.

Retail Jewellery & Jewellery Repairs Pawnbroking Service

AUCTION CALENDAR 2001

January 23
March 6
April 10
May 22
July 10
August 21
October 2
November 13

Complimentary catalogues available (UK only)
Entries welcomed for forthcoming sales

269 London Road, Hazel Grove,
Stockport, Cheshire SK7 4PL
Tel: 0161 456 5050
Tel/Fax: 0161 456 5112
E-mail: info@afbrock.co.uk
www.afbrock.co.uk

Opening Hours: Monday to Saturday 9.00am – 5.00pm
Half day closing Wednesday 1.00pm

The
best
and worst

of recent coin designs

Undoubtedly the event of the period under review is the Millennium; the present tense seems appropriate in view of the fact that coins marking this outstanding event are still pouring forth and will probably still be making their appearance at the end of the year 2000, which many believe marks the end of the second Millennium and the dawn of the third, and not the end of December 1999. Mathematicians and astronomers have been pointing out that there is no such thing as the year zero and therefore the end of the 20th century does not occur until December 31, 2000. Be that as it may, there is something manifestly sexy about round numbers and the world's mints needed little incentive to go into overdrive as 1999 drew to a close.

From a purely aesthetic viewpoint the best in this line-up were probably the coins from Sierra Leone which concentrated, oddly enough, on Chinese history of the past 2000 years, but which at least afforded the possibility of focusing on some of the most sublime works of art in different media.

The accolade for the most imaginative use of new technology must surely go to the Seychelles whose montage of timepieces through the ages incorporated a new technique for latent imaging in order to create an overall three-dimensional effect with the year 1999 changing to 2000 when the coin is tilted to the light.

Austria's answer was to depict a gold computer chip in the centre of a silver coin , with a titanium centre on the reverse. This recognises the fact that we are going through a revolution every bit as momentous as the Industrial Revolution of two centuries ago. The day is surely not far off when there will be coins with real computer chips in them—"smart" coins designed for the vending machines of the future.

Few countries remembered that the Millennium represented the 2000th birthday of Jesus Christ, although the Vatican remained steadfast to the observance of the anniversary as a Holy Year, both in the year set of definitive coins and in the special series of silver coins that traced the life of Christ and culminated in the coins showing the Resurrection and Pentecost. These coins, released in pairs over the past five years, represent the very acme of contemporary numismatic art, combining the skills of the master craftsmen and the technical

Sierra Leone chose 200 years of Chinese history to celebrate the Millennium

Seychelles chose a latent "2000" image.

Austria depicted a microchip in titanium.

facilities of the Italian State Mint. Truly this is coin design and production of the very highest order, as befits the occasion.

Slovakia produced a pair of gold and silver coins celebrating the 500th anniversary of the minting of the first thaler at Kremnica. The obverses showed the medieval process of striking coins and the first Kremnica guldiner, with the arms of Hungary, while the reverses showed the reverse of the first guldiner and a panoramic view of the town which was at the centre of the mining industry. These coins form a worthy addition to the select band with the theme of minting and coin production or "coins on coins". If you cannot afford the genuine, original article then you can make do with the coins that commemorate and reproduce them so well. In the same genre is Austria's cupro-nickel 20 schilling celebrating the 150th anniversary of the first stamps, with a reverse reproducing the 9 kreuzer stamp of 1850. Stamps have seldom been featured on coins, so this is a relatively new theme that might appeal to philatelists and thus draw them into the sister hobby.

The prize for originality, however, has to go to Alderney whose £2 coin showed a pair of rather bemused gannets roosting during the eclipse of the sun on August 11, 1999, believing that night had fallen. But as an event, an eclipse of the sun is hardly of world rank, though the fact that this one occurred in western Europe probably gave it greater importance than it really deserved.

Just as there was an anticipatory atmosphere about much of the Millennium fare, so also there was a marked tendency to jump the gun where the most celebrated member of the British Royal Family was concerned. Her Majesty Queen Elizabeth the Queen Mother celebrated her hundredth birthday on August 4, 2000 but the rush to issue coins in her honour began almost as soon as she had reached her 99th birthday; indeed,

Slovakia celebrated the 500th anniversary of the minting of the first thaler.

The Vatican series on the life of Christ deserves acclaim.

Stamp collectors could well be attracted to Austria's 20 schilling coin depicting their first postage stamp.

the Pobjoy Mint produced a set of four crowns for Gibraltar before even that magic anniversary was attained. With an almost infinite gallery of press photographs and portraits to choose from, there was always going to be immense variety in the subjects for Queen Mother coins, although predictably they ranged from girlhood to marriage to motherhood to the poignant war years as Queen Consort and the even more poignant years of long widowhood. At one end of the spectrum was the British £5 crown, struck in various metals and finishes, from cupro-nickel to 22 carat gold, with a prosaic but workmanlike motif which incorporated a recent profile with her autograph signature. The design would have been immeasurably improved if the clutter of flag-waving admirers had been omitted; nor did the concentric inscriptions with double dates and value in words help to mitigate the fussiness of the design. At the other extreme were the three coins from Zambia (likewise in cupro-nickel, silver and gold) whose upright elongate shape not only departed radically from the conventional circular format, but had reverse designs which were photographically transferred to a raised background. It remains to be seen whether either of these gimmicks catches on.

Meanwhile there seemed no end to the coins in tribute to the late lamented Diana, Princess of Wales, while not a few celebrated the nuptials of her erstwhile brother-in-law, Prince Edward, to Miss Sophie Rhys-Jones, now the Earl and Countess

Top marks for originality goes to Alderney for an issue in celebration of the eclipse of the sun.

of Wessex. Unlike the Queen Mum, there did not appear to be much to choose from in selecting suitable portraits of the bridal pair, with the result that the reproductions on coins tended to be rather stereotyped. The Isle of Man's offering, for example, using rather uncertain three-quarter facing portraits, would have been infinitely better without the pairs of wedding bells dangling in space like earrings that have suddenly become detached. Admittedly, these coins were a decided improvement over the reverse motif from Gibraltar which showed full-face portraits of the bridal pair, neither of which were at all lifelike. Full-face portraiture seldom works successfully within the paramaters of a coin.

The political changes in Europe continue to reverberate in coin design. While the Czech Republic celebrated the 50th anniversary of NATO with a silver 200 crowns coin showing the modernistic sculpture that stands in front of NATO headquarters, Poland marked its accession to the Alliance with a stirring reverse motif of a helicopter and two NATO soldiers on peace-keeping duties in the former Yugoslavia. Who could have imagined that the countries of the Warsaw Pact would one day be clamouring to join the opposition? Perhaps the day is not too far off when Russia itself joins the alliance which is now proving its worth as a force for peace and stability in Europe rather than as a defensive bulwark of one of the power blocs.

Old and new: Bishop Gellert an 11th century monk appears on Hungary's 3,000 forint coin (left) whilst computer technology is used by Israel.

Meanwhile neighbouring Hungary issued a 3,000 forint coin showing Bishop Gellert, the medieval cleric who did so much to consolidate the recent conversion of Hungary to Christianity and integrate it within the hierarchy of the Papacy. That this was intended as a metaphor for something else much closer to our own times was revealed in the legend which referred to the integration of Hungary into the European Union, truly a consummation devoutly to be wished.

In a country that sets great store by tradition, not to mention conservatism in religious matters, Israel sometimes shows a quirky penchant for the secular in the design of its coins. Having celebrated the 50th anniversary of independence in 1998 it produced a set of three coins in 1999 with a standard obverse and reverse. For the obverse, the state emblem of the menorah or candelabra was rendered in computerised digital form, while the reverse was dominated by the image of a printed circuit. The coins were probably designed by a computer as well; more and more computer-generated graphics and lettering are replacing the traditional skills of the engraver and sculptor, although it is extremely doubtful whether this will lead to any real improvement in the aesthetics of coin design.

The vogue for bimetallic coins continued to increase in popularity and there must be few countries these days that do not include one or more such confections in its line-up. What is infinitely more intriguing, however, is the increased use of a second alloy for a part of the design, intended to give greater prominence to a particular feature or emphasise a symbolic motif. This was done to great effect in the 100 pataca silver coin from Macau marking its new-found status as a special administrative region of the People's Republic of China, a 24-carat gold ellipse depicting the temple of Ma Gao as an insert in a stirring scene of a Portuguese caravel and a Chinese

Gibraltar attempted full face portraits of the Royal couple.

NATO was the subject handled in completely different ways by the Czech Republic (above) and Poland (left).

junk, symbolising the meeting of two cultures more than 400 years ago. Most bimetallic coins consist of a central disc and an outer ring of contrasting metals, but a nice variant on this was provided by Switzerland's Fete des Vignerons coin showing the natural outline of a gold bunch of grapes.

Gold and silver bimetallic combinations are no longer dramatic enough, and nothing less that full colour will suffice, in an age when everything from television to Sunday supplements has to be a riot of colour. Even the Royal Mint got in on this act, with the second Eclipse coin from Alderney whose reverse had a gaudy image of the Sun passing over the face of the Moon with solar segments of the design in a particularly bilious shade of yellow. There is a real danger of overdoing things, of using colour as a cover-up for a fundamentally mediocre design. Colour is definitely here to stay, but its use should be restrained and appropriate to the subject or event, such as Australia's 50c Millennium coin with the national flag tastefully depicted in red, white and blue. We suppose that the ultimate would be bimetallic coins which also have a full-colour area, and inevitably that concept has already come close to fruition, in the guise of Australia's second issue for the new Millennium; the $20 is bimetallic while the accompanying dollar is multicoloured. It won't be long at this rate till the two gimmicks appear on the same coin.

Joint issues of stamps are now commonplace, but this is still a relatively new concept where coinage is concerned. Norway and Canada, however, participated in a joint venture to mark the 1000th anniversary of Leif Eiriksson's discovery of the New World, although a different reverse was used in each case. Thus Canada chose a motif showing Leif the Lucky's Viking longship approaching L'Anse-aux-Meadows at the northern tip of Newfoundland, while Norway settled for a static view of the prow of a Viking hull. Both Iceland and Greenland could potentially get involved in the same celebration, not to mention the USA where Leif and his pals are believed to

Neither Denmark's effigy of Queen Margrethe II or Canada's portrayal of Queen Elizabeth II on the "Millennium—Birth of Nunavut" coin are very flattering efforts.

have penetrated as far south as Maine and northern Massachusetts. It is an interesting idea, and a reminder that there is more than one millennium being celebrated at this time. Conversely, although Belgium and the Netherlands co-hosted the European Cup, the coins released in both countries to mark the occasion were quite distinctive even if they tended to be marketed abroad as a complete package. Not especially felicitous was the Dutch 5g which, not content with a football on the reverse, placed the profile of Queen Beatrix against a football.

Oddest coin of the year was the tiny 10 litu from Lithuania which was trumpeted as the world's smallest gold coin, but which, with a diameter of 13.92mm, was well above the 4mm pieces from some of the former Indian princely states. The reverse, appropriately, bore a stylised image of a coin being struck.

Arguably the worst coin design of the year was the obverse of Canada's Millennium $2, which reduced the Queen's effigy to ludicrous proportions. Why was it necessary to surround this skimpy profile by an inner ring and then devote so much space to the outer legend? Had the inner ring been removed or reduced and the central disc enlarged, a much more pleasing and dignified coin would have resulted. This decision was probably dictated for technical reasons and the need to maintain a certain proportion between the two alloys in this bimetallic coin; but other bimetallics have overcome the limitations of the outer and inner ring principle without a sacrifice to appearance. Admittedly, Denmark came a pretty close second with the coins celebrating the 60th birthday of Queen Margrethe II, which portrayed this Nordic beauty with uncharacteristically coarse features, although, in mitigation, the elaborately jewelled hairstyle had probably not helped the designer.

For their joint project Canada and Norway chose different ways to portray the same subject.

26

Books
of the year

Every coin collector knows that knowledge is the key to forming a good collection and each year new books or new editions of older works, as well as standard reference works, are up-dated by dedicated specialists. Here we list the most important numismatic titles that have appeared during the past year. Most have been reviewed in COIN NEWS.

BENET'S ARTEFACTS OF ENGLAND AND THE UNITED KINGDOM by Paul G. Murawski. Casebound. 300 pages. Published by the author, 13 Benet Street, Cambridge, CB2 3PT.

Aside from the odd title (we always thought that England was part of the United Kingdom and not distinct from it), this is a very handsome production with over 1,000 full-colour photographs. The objects are arranged in sections by period, from the Stone Age to Norman, Medieval, Tudor and Post-Tudor times, the last-named in fact pretty well encompassing everything from 1603 to the present day (the sole criterion for inclusion being that it is something dug out of the ground). Each section has a brief introduction outlining the period and the sort of artefacts one is likely to find relating to it. The greater part of the book is taken up with the illustrations accompanied by brief captions giving price ranges.

BRITISH COPPER TOKENS 1811-1820 by Paul and Bente Withers. Casebound. 257 pages, Fully illustrated. Galata Print. Price £75.00.

The husband and wife team set out originally to produce a reprint of W. J. Davis' *The Nineteenth Century Token Coinage* but very quickly realised that so much new material had come to light since that book appeared in 1904 that nothing less than a completely fresh approach to the subject was required, This handsome volume comprehensively deals with the tokens of England, Scotland and the Channel Islands from 1811 to 1820 and the Isle of Man from 1805 to 1830. Each item is fully described and catalogued, the listings being in alphabetical order by town in each regional section. No fewer than 50 different edge types are recorded alone. There is an excellent but concise introductory text explaining the reasons for this series and tracing its history and economic impact.

CHINESE CASH by David Jen. Softbound. 341 pages. Krause Publications. Price $42.95.

Covering more than 3,000 years of numismatic history, this detailed book reveals the complicated history of one of the world's oldest civilisations through the coins issued by every major ruler from the Xia dynasty of 2200 BC to the fall of the Qing dynasty in 1911. The book encapsulates the historical background, with a chronology of the emperors and dynasties, and offers a rare insight into Chinese culture and politics. Virtually every coin is represented by a clear line drawing, from the cowrie sheel and knife and spade money to the more familiar square-holed copper cash. All coins are valued in two different grades, making this an essential handbook for any collector interested in the Chinese series.

COINCRAFT'S COIN CHECKLISTS, 1656-1816 and 1816 to Date. Paperback. 128 pages and 126 pages respectively. Coincraft. Price £6.95 each.

These handly little volumes are more or less self-explanatory, providing rudimentary details on all British coins from the Commonwealth to the present day and forming the ideal travelling companion when going on a quest for new specimens at fairs and coin shops. Both are based on Coincraft's own distinctive numbering system, and contain spaces for noting the grade and acquisition details of each coin.

COINCRAFT'S STANDARD CATALOGUE OF THE COINS OF SCOTLAND, IRELAND, CHANNEL ISLANDS AND ISLE OF MAN. Casebound. 438 pages. Coincraft. Price £34.50.

The companion volume to the foregoing encompasses more than a thousand years or numismatic history, from the Viking and Hiberno-Norse periods to the present day. This is the first volume for more than 15 years to deal with the other coinages of the British Isles and its appearance should be warmly welcomed, for it was certainly well worth waiting for. It is an admirably concise account of the different coinages with comprehensive introductory notes which are of immense value to the beginner and advanced collector alike. It contains a vast amount of useful data on material which has hitherto been rather neglected.

COINCRAFT'S STANDARD CATALOGUE OF ENGLISH AND UK COINS. Casebound. 760 pages. Coincraft. Price £19.95.

This book of epic proportions provides the fullest details yet available in a single volume on all coins of England from 1066 onwards as well as the coinage of Britain and the United Kingdom right down to the present time. The Millennium edition includes a greatly expanded section on hammered and milled patterns as well as a new chapter on touchpieces. All coin prices have been revised and there are literally thousands of illustrations.

ENGLISH PATTERN TRIAL AND PROOF COINS IN GOLD 1547-1968 by Alex Wilson and Mark Rasmussen. Casebound. 537 pages. Alexander Publishing. Price £85.

This impressive book is a distillation of many years research by Mark Rasmussen during his time at Spink, aided and abetted during the past seven years by Alex Wilson. The resultant volume catalogues all known English pattern and proof coins struck in gold, together with off-metal strikes (i.e. Coins normally struck in silver or base metal but struck in gold), as well as unofficial fantasy pieces in gold. Included are English coins from Edward VI to Elizabeth I (1547-1603) and British coins from 1604 to 1968. The authors have also included all known gold patterns, the design essays prepared at some stage but never actually taken to the point of general production, as well as unofficial 'fantasies' produced privately.

THE GOLD SOVEREIGN by Michael A. Marsh. Casebound. 118 pages. Illustrated throughout. Published by the author, 25A St. Neots Road, Hardwick, Cambridgeshire CB3 7QH. Price £12.95.

A much revised and expanded second edition of the seminal work on the British gold sovereign, including a wealth of new material pertaining to the earlier coins as well as covering the issues of the past two decades since the first editionw as published in 1980. The original work was a remarkable tour de force which, at the time, one could scarcely have been improved upon, but Michael Marsh has truly surpassed himself in this new work, a 'must' for all collectors of British coins in general and the sovereign in particular.

LOST TREASURE SHIPS OF THE TWENTIETH CENTURY by Nigel Pickford. Casebound. 192 pages including 70 colour, 70 black and white plates and 20 maos. Pavilion. Price £25.00.

For thousands of years people were accustomed to transport their valuables by sea. Sadly, a fair proportion of these valuables now lie on the sea bed or the ocean floor as a result of innumerable shipwrecks. The author has here presented a graphic, and at times extremely poignant, record of shipwrecks of the 20th century which among

them must account for a sizable amount of the world's wealth in real terms. This book chronicles eighteen famous shipwrecks from the *Islander* of 1901 to the Japanese ship *Awa Maru* torpedoed by an American submarine in April 1945. The story of each ship and its final voyage are unfolded in detail. Herein are detailed the fabulous riches which sank with the *Titanic*, the *Lusitania*, the *Hampshire* and the *Empress of Britain* among others. The text is rounded off with a gazetteer dealing with cargo routes and other technical data. Inevitably there are numismatic aspects of these, from the gold coins transported by the *Tubantia* and the *Hampshire* to the medals that commemorated the *Republic*, the *Lusitania* and the *Titanic*.

MEDIEVAL ARTEFACTS, CATALOGUE AND PRICE GUIDE by Nigel Mills. Laminated card covers. 114 A4 pages. Greenlight Publishing, 119 Newlands Street, Witham, Essex, CM8 1WF.

This book has a very informative text setting the historical background to the Middle Ages and then provides useful notes for collectors, followed by chapters on buckles, strapends, brooches, buckles, seal matrices, pilgrim badges, finger rings, knives, pottery, arrowheads, harness pendants, locks, keys, weights, spoons, spurs and edged weapons, purses, pins, buttons, mirrors, whistles and last, but by no means elast, ecclesiastical objects. The introduction, recounting the author's own experiences as a mudlark and later a successful metal detectorist, makes fascinating and highly entertaining reading, and will probably inspire many others to have a go.

ROMAN COINS AND THEIR VALUES Volume I by David R. Sear. Casebound. 532 pages. Spink, £45.

Volume one of this two-volume standard work covers the coins of the Republic and the twelve

Caesars of the Empire, from 280 BC to AD 96. It is 12 years since the fourth edition appeared so this new edition, with extensive revision amounting to a wholesale reworking of the text, is very welcome. In particular, the catalogue entires have been expanded to include a virtually complete listing of the entire Republican series. Greater emphasis is now placed on precise chronology and place of minting for each type. Extensive coverage is now given to the billon and bronze coins of Alexandria. As well as listing almost 3,000 coins, with more than 1,200 black and white pictures, this volume brings the valuations right up to date, based on auction realisations and dealers' lists.

introductory essay on 'Coins and History, the Changing Face over Two Millennia'. Certain sections have been entirely rewritten in light of recent research, notably those dealing with the coinages of Edward I and II and the early silver of Edward III. The gold coinage of Richard II and the silver coins of the Oxford Mint under Charles I have been completely revised. Numerous varieties have been added to the section on milled coinage, and full details have been provided for all issues from the Royal Mint down to the year 2000. This remains the only single reference work that encompasses every major coin type from Celtic to the present day.

SPINK STANDARD CATALOGUE OF BRITISH COINS, COINS OF ENGLAND AND THE UNITED KINGDOM. Casebound. 500 pages. Spink, £15.00.

This is the 35th edition of an old-established favourite, substantially revised and expanded as befits a Millennium project. The prices have been extensively revised throughout in light of the market and many new illustrations have been included. Peter Clayton has contributed an

And of course the Token Publishing titles:

BANKNOTE YEARBOOK. Softbound. 232 pages. Price £14.95.

COIN YEARBOOK. Softbound. 300 pages. Price £9.95.

MEDAL YEARBOOK. Softbound. 472 pages. Price £16.95.

For further information on these three popular annual titles please contact our Order Department.

Advertising
on coins

DENZIL WEBB looks at coins that have been put to another use other than that for which they were originally intended . . .

In the 1870s and '80s the 5 and 10 centimes French coins of Napoleon III and the later 5 and 10 centimes pieces of the French Third Republic were widely accepted in the United Kingdom as pennies and halfpennies, which were virtually the same size. Thomas J. Barrett, the proprietor of Pears' Soap and one of the most audacious advertisers of the time, is still remembered as the buyer of Sir John Millais' famous picture *Bubbles*, and putting it to a use for which it was not intended and also for cozening the Post Office into allowing him (for a short time) to print his advertisements on the backs of the penny and halfpenny stamps.

Barrett was well aware that the law in England against the defacement of "Coin of the Realm" did not apply to foreign coins, and he therefore imported 250,000 French bronze 10 centimes pieces, and had them overstamped PEARS' SOAP (in two lines), which he put into circulation nationwide at a rate of 14 to the shilling. This alarmed the government who attempted to prohibit the circulation of foreign money in Britain. The prohibition had little immediate effect, however, and French "pennies and halfpennies" continued to be used until the First World War, when the disastrous inflation of the franc made it very profitable to import them for circulation here.

Advertising reached extremes in Victorian Britain with billboards and signs filling every available space . . . including coins!

Despite the government's grave concern, to advertise his Pears' Soap Thomas J. Barrett overstruck French 10 centimes coins, thousands of which were already in circulation in Great Britain.

Aware that the country might well be flooded with these pieces, a law was passed to prohibit the importation of foreign copper coins into Britain.

Another firm to countermark the 10 centimes coins of Napoleon III, were the makers of Borwick's Baking Powder. BORWICK'S/ BAKING/POWDER is found in three lines across the obverse of the pieces. Both of these advertisements are readily obtained from dealers in paranumismatica, and they may still be encountered in junk shops or on flea market stalls, together with the unmarked issues. Apart from the advertising interest, attention is drawn to the various mintmarks appearing on the Napoleon III coinage, seven in all, consisting of block capital letters except for that of Marseilles—MA in the form of a monogram. The others are: A—Paris, B—Rouen, BB—Strasbourg, D—Lyons, K—Bordeaux and W—Lille. Also worth looking out for are the various types of lettering which form the words PEARS' SOAP, which occurs with and without a dot after the P in SOAP.

Earlier in the 19th century, Edward Lloyd, who founded the *Lloyds's Weekly Newspaper* in 1842, hit upon the idea of advertising his newspaper by counterstamping George III "Cartwheel' pennies of 1797 and halfpennies of 1806–7, both of which were still in circulation. In order that the incuse impressions would stand out clearly, he chose only badly worn specimens. At the time of their issue at the close of the 18th century, it was the rule that all coins, including base metal issues, should have a face value equal to the market value of the metal used. The result was the issue of one penny and twopence coins weighing 1 oz and 2 oz respectively. Needless to say, they were highly unpopular because of their size, and when the

price of copper rose many found their way into the melting pot—a nice little earner for those with worthwhile quantity to sell at 1¼d and 2½d each! Having said that, specimens of both coins in Very Fine or Extremely Fine condition turn up in dealers' offerings, and their rarity is reflected in the prices asked. Badly worn specimens are only worth collecting with the Lloyds advertisements, and these are generally reasonably priced.

The government was slow to take action against Edward Lloyd's illegal activities, but they eventually did so, prohibiting the circulation of the defaced coins, and funds were voted to replace them. The "Cartwheel" twopence had been demonetised by this time, but it would appear that the "Cartwheel" penny (which had been minted in vast quantities) and the halfpenny coppers, most of which were hardly recognisable as coins, remained current until 1869 and the introduction of bronze coinage

Edward Lloyd overstruck pennies and halfpennies of George III with an advertisement for his Weekly Newspaper but the government prohibited their circulation.

35

Talking
Tokens

Strictly speaking, a token is any piece of money whose intrinsic value is less than its face value. In that sense, therefore, all modern coins are mere tokens, because their metallic worth is invariably less than their nominal, legal tender value. Until the 19th century, however, most countries issued coins which contained metal up to the value at which they circulated. This applied mainly to gold and silver coins, but it should be noted that Britain's first copper penny and twopence (1797) were so cumbersome because they contained one and two ounces of metal respectively, copper being then valued at a penny an ounce.

The desire for parity between intrinsic and nominal value led to copper coins containing a small plug of silver to bring them up to their full value. The UK abandoned full value in 1816; as a result of the recoinage of that year the gold sovereign became the absolute standard and all silver and copper coins became mere tokens. The difference between real and nominal value widened in subsequent years with the debasement of silver coins and finally the replacement of silver altogether by cupro-nickel and other base alloys. Oddly enough, there have been many instances of small copper or bronze coins in recent years which had a greater intrinsic value than their face value and actually cost twice as much to produce as they were worth in circulation.

A token is an outward sign or pledge, something given or shown as a guarantee of authority or good faith. The word comes from German *zeichen* and Old English *tacen*, meaning a sign or mark. From this developed the notion of a promise, symbol or keepsake. In the numismatic sense, however, the term is restricted to any coinlike object, either issued by a body other than a government, or something which is used in place of money and can be exchanged for specified goods and services. Broadly speaking, tokens include any unofficial coins supplied by local bodies or occasionally even private individuals and tolerated in general circulation at times of shortage of government issues of small change.

Tokens go back a surprisingly long way. The earliest issues in base metal with limited local

validity were produced by Sicily in the middle of the fifth century BC, the bronze litra being easier to handle than its tiny silver counterpart. Himera was one of the first towns to issue such tokens, but by the end of the century many Sicilian towns had adopted small bronze pieces as token currency, the intrinsic value of which was considerably below the circulating value placed on them by the issuing authorities.

This concept gradually spread to all other parts of the Greek world. Under the Roman Empire, base-metal tokens were issued from the time of Augustus to the late third century AD. Sometimes referred to as quasi-autonomous coinage, these pieces were struck mostly in bronze with the nominal value of drachmae or sestertii, and have portraits of local deities instead of the Roman emperor and members of his family. These tokens were struck by every town and city and their range and variety is enormous.

This concept survived the fall of the Roman Empire and many towns in medieval Europe continued to strike small base-metal pieces for use as local currency. They were usually accorded a measure of legality because they were authorised by the royal or imperial government, even if their actual design and metal content were decided by the municipal authorities. In addition to the tokens which served as small change there are other categories of coinlike material which deserve comment.

Jetons (from French *jeter*, to throw) originated in medieval France as counters used on the chequerboard by merchants and bankers as well as royal treasurers to do their monetary calculations. These pieces spread rapidly all over Europe, but found their greatest expression at Nuremberg where, in the hands of Hans Krauwinckel (flourished 1580–1620), they attained the status of an art form and were often produced in thematic sets.

While many jetons were struck in gold or silver and were eventually used (especially in France) as a form of New Year bonus to servants, the vast majority of them were struck in debased silver alloys (billon) or in copper, bronze, brass or pewter. Base-metal Nuremberg jetons, in fact, often circulated as small change in countries where there was a shortage of total lack of government issues of small change. This situation arose in England early in the 14th century, Nuremberg jetons circulating freely until 1335 when they were banned by statute.

English tokens

The first indigenous tokens in England were cast or struck in lead and have been recorded as circulating in 1404. For many years these local farthings and half-farthings were tolerated but had no official sanction. They were certainly well-established in Tudor times and it was not until 1598 that any attempt was made to regulate them. Queen

17th century tokens come in a variety of shapes and sizes.

The prolific issues of 18th century tokens were banned on the introduction of the "Cartwheel" coinage in 1797.

Elizabeth then licensed Bristol to issue lead tokens, to be valid within a ten-mile radius of the city. At the same time, private tokens were expressly forbidden, so that the municipal tokens were given a monopoly. By the end of the Civil War (1649) was an acute shortage of small change, and illicit tokens, mainly in lead and including pewter, brass, copper or even leather pieces, were revived in England and Wales.

Almost 4,000 types of token were issued in London alone, by tradesmen and shopkeepers of all kinds, often circulating no farther than the end of the street. As the vast majority were produced before the Great Fire of 1666 they form an invaluable record of London streets and their occupants from this period. Following the introduction of regal copper farthings and halfpence in 1672 these tradesmen's tokens were banned, but they continued in some parts of England until 1674, and survived in Ireland until 1679. By contrast there was virtually no need for tokens in 17th century Scotland because of an abundant supply of copper coinage, and only two Scottish tokens (c. 1668) have so far been recorded.

In many ways tokens benefited the poor, who were no longer compelled to purchase more than they actually required because the smallest coin available was a penny. Tokens were also used as alms, as people would gladly give a farthing but would think twice about giving a halfpenny or penny. For this reason many tokens of the 17th century were inscribed "Remember the Poore",

"For the Poore's Advantage" or "For Change & Charitie" or some other pious slogan.

There were even tokens inscribed in verse: "To supply the poore's need is charitie indeed". Other poetic inscriptions include "When you please, I'll change thee", "Although but brass, yet let me pass", "Welcome you be to trade with me" or "Take these that will, I'll change them still".

Eighteenth century tokens

Tokens were revived in the British Isles in 1787 to fill a gap in the regal coinage. Silver pennies for general circulation were only sporadically produced in the reign of George III and none at all was minted after 1786. The dearth of copper halfpence and farthings was even greater as none was minted after 1775. On this occasion the way was led by the Angelsey Copper Mining Company which began striking pennies with the effigy of a Druid on the obverse. This triggered off an immense deluge of token pennies, halfpennies and farthings. The range was not as great as it had been in the 17th century as fewer individual shopkeepers now issued them.

There was a greater concentration of tokens issued by municipal authorities and the more important merchant companies. On the other hand, the quality of design and execution improved beyond all recognition and latterly they were aimed at the contemporary collector market, with emphasis on heraldry, landmarks, scenery, historic events and portraits of local and national celebrities. These tokens enjoyed a decade of use before they were banned following the introduction of the "Cartwheel" coinage in 1797.

Nineteenth century tokens

Silver tokens were issued between 1804 and 1816 as a result of a continuing shortage of silver coins. At first countermarked Spanish dollars and half-dollars were issued but in 1811–12 the Bank of England released silver pieces inscribed BANK TOKEN on the reverse, with the value and date below. The obverse portrayed George III and had his name and titles round the circumference like the proper silver coins. Denominations of 1s6d and 3s were issued; though 9d pieces exist they were only patterns. The Bank of Ireland had silver tokens in the same period, but denominated in a decimal system of 5, 10 and 30 pence, as well as 6 shillings. Many private silver tokens were issued in 1811–12 in denominations from 3d to 5s, mainly by private banks, local authorities and large companies.

Copper or bronze tokens were again issued in the British Isles from 1811 to the 1830s. As no copper subsidiary coins were issued between 1807

and 1821 (no halfpence or pennies until 1825–26) the range of tokens in this period was far greater than ever. Significantly a high proportion of these tokens were now issued by banks rather than by private individuals.

Other types of tokens

Tokens have been produced in most countries at some time or another. Very extensive series, for example, were produced in Canada and Australia before these countries introduced subsidiary coinage. They were also produced on a number of occasions in the USA, from the revolutionary period onwards, and notably during the Hard Times (1834–44) during a shortage of copper cents and half-cents. There was a further spate of local tokens during the Civil War (1861–65), often with patriotic motifs and having a propaganda purpose as well as filling the gap in the coinage. Many countries issued tokens during and after the First World War, every type of material from pasteboard and wood to leather and even rubber being pressed into service. A special category consists of trade dollars issued all over Canada. These are often commemorative or intended as tourist mementoes, but they have a nominal value, redeemable for cash within a certain area and over a fixed period, usually twelve months. They are immensely

Banks and local authorities produced hundreds of different tokens in the early 19th century.

Hop tokens, although simple and sometimes crudely made, can make an interesting collection.

Another vast area consists of the checks and tokens issued by co-operative societies, often in proportion to the money spent by the member in the societies' stores, as a form of dividend. When a certain quantity of checks had been accumulated they could be exchanged for goods or services. The same concept underlay the discount schemes, premium giveaways and trading stamps of more recent items.

Tokens of metal, pasteboard or even plastic have been used as a method of controlling the use of public transport by employees of companies, the Post Office or local authorities, being given out whenever it was necessary for an employee to travel on official business. Such tokens were produced by local authorities or the private companies operating buses, ferries, trams and other services. At the other end of the spectrum are the tokens and passes, often in silver or even gold, or ivory, which were issued to directors of the railway companies to enable them to travel free of charge. Tokens in the same materials, and for the same purpose, were produced for the use of the directors and shareholders of theatres and other places of entertainment, and were often highly ornate in design.

popular and now have a wide following in North America.

In Britain from the 18th century onwards tokens were often issued by textile mills, collieries, iron foundries and other industrial undertakings in exchange for a day's work. These tokens could only be used to obtain goods from the company stores, and were eventually outlawed by the Truck Act in 1844. Nevertheless they survived in various parts of Britain, often in specific forms of labour. A very prolific series, for example, consists of hop-pickers' tokens, associated mainly with the hopfields of Kent and Sussex. In Scotland, however, fruit-pickers' tokens were also issued by many of the farms in the Clyde Valley and the fruit-growing areas of Perthshire and Angus.

Gaming tokens

This is another vast field, ranging from the brass halfpenny and penny tokens issued by many pubs and taverns in the 19th century for use in games of chance, to the modern tokens, often in cupro-nickel, bronze or aluminium-bronze, used in one-armed bandits and fruit machines. These tokens range from the fairly utilitarian designs showing perhaps a company name and a unit of value only, to the very elaborate tokens used by casinos and gaming clubs, often with special security features built into their design and composition. Many of the gaming tokens of more recent years have a quasi-commemorative or publicity character.

A new world record price for a British token was set at Noble Numismatic's sale on July 7/8, 1998, when Richard Orchard's Sawbridgeworth token realised £24,400.

The Trial of
The Pyx

DENZIL WEBB recalls the background to this ancient and colourful ceremony which takes place regularly to determine the fineness (i.e. metal content) and therefore the value of the British national coinage.

The Pyx Trial determines publicly the exact metal content and, therefore, the value of the national coinage. Samples of each batch of coinage produced during the previous year are placed in the pyx (the word pyx means box) or chest awaiting "trial"—i.e. weighing and assaying. This testing of the coinage was important in the middle ages as the law required that there should be one coinage of a single standard and weight which the sovereign himself was responsible for issuing—nothing else could be used. Merchants therefore had to take any foreign silver coin or scrap silver to be officially weighed and assayed for fineness, receiving in exchange current English coin of equal value (less seignorage, a charge

The Trial of the Pyx—an ancient tradition that still survives today.

41

for administrative expenses—a varying sum of about one shilling and four pence for every pound weight). Thus as they paid in by weight and received payment "by tale" in coins, it was important to know that the weight and fineness of the coins they received was reliable. Equally, in his dealings with foreign merchants, the Englishman would need to know the intrinsic value of the money he was reckoning in. The King also needed to be certain of the reliability of the coinage. He was personally and legally responsible as his head and name were on the coins.

In the widely scattered mints of Anglo-Saxon and Norman England moneyers could be unscrupulous over the weight and fineness of the coins they minted. Henry II (1154–89) considerably reduced the number of mints, and introduced the office of "Assay Master" in an attempt to obtain reliability and uniformity; it is even possible that something equivalent to the pyx trial was operated about 1180.

In 1248 under Henry III (1216–72) there was a public trial when the mayor and citizens of London were ordered to appoint 12 citizens and 12 skilful goldsmiths to go before the barons of the Exchequer to examine *"the old and the new money of the realm"*. However, the first recorded trial on modern lines was that of 1281 under Edward I (1272–1307) since which time it has never been discontinued.

At the same time trial plates—an essential component in the trial—began to be used. A silver plate of 1279, when a new coinage was ordered for Edward I, is still in existence. The earliest gold plate to survive is one of 1477 (Edward IV) but English gold coinage substantially dates from Edward III (1327–77), over 130 years earlier. The purpose of such plates is clear from an entry in the Red Book of the Exchequer (referring to the new money of 1279): *"the money shall be made according to the form of the standard and of the same fineness"*. The Red Book goes on, *"There must be a box with two keys, one of which the Master of the Mint must keep and the Warden the other. And in the box must be put one silver penny out of each ten pounds coins, to make the assay"*.

The Pyx Chamber in Westminster Abbey. It is part of the original building started by Edward the Confessor in 1065; the view shows the altar in the north-east corner, probably of c. 1240 when Henry III was rebuilding the Abbey Church.

Gold and silver trial plate of 1649. In the first year of the Commonwealth the Goldsmiths' Company were charged with preparing trial plates of Crown gold (22 carats) and silver. This is the gold plate with the reverse impression of a half-broad (10s).

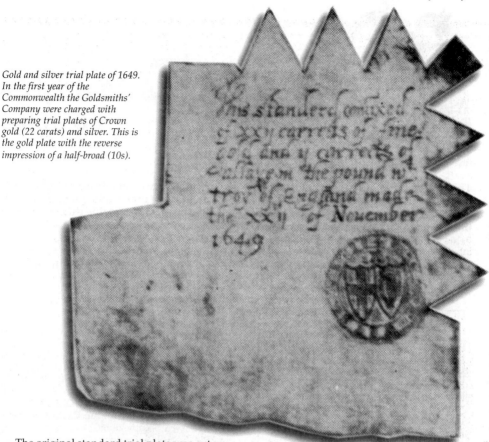

The original standard trial plate was cut up and divided so that certain officials and each mint, if more than one was involved, would hold a part. The strange methods of dividing the plate—in an undulating or toothed fashion—were laid down in the Record Books of the Goldsmith's Company. The shape of the cut was a type of authentication as each piece should fit into the original plate rather like a jigsaw puzzle. The Exchequer kept the trial plates in the Pyx Chamber within the precinct of Westminster Abbey and they remained there until 1843, since when they have been kept at the Royal Mint.

The Pyx Chamber was part of the Palace of Westminster and from at least 1249 had been a royal treasury. The chests (pyxes) containing the coins for trial were also kept there until taken to the Star Chamber (now within the Houses of Parliament) where the trial was generally conducted.

The trials were held at varying intervals, sometimes quarterly, sometimes after an interval of years, but and now they take place annually. Since the reign of Elizabeth I (1558–1603) the jury has been entirely provided from members of the Goldsmiths' Company, sworn in by the Queen's Remembrancer. The object of the trial was to establish publicly, and through experts not involved in making the coins, the actual weight and fineness of coins by reference to the standard. In 1840 Ruding wrote that the intervals between trials were too long and felt it *"to be absolutely necessary that this trial should be restored to its pristine form"*. This has now been done, although the everyday use of notes instead of gold coins and of cupro-nickel instead of silver coinage have made the matter one of less urgency.

Dates
on coins

The vast majority of modern coins bear the date prominently on one side. In most cases dates are expressed in modified Arabic numerals according to the Christian calendar and present no problem in identification. There have been a few notable exceptions to this general rule, however. Morocco, for example, has used European numerals to express dates according to the Moslem calendar, so that a coin dated 1321 actually signifies 1903. Dates are almost invariably written from left to right—even in Arabic script which writes words from right to left. An exception, however, occurred in the Philippines quarto of 1822 where the date appeared as 2281, and the "2s" back to front for good measure.

	ARABIC-TURKISH	CHINESE, JAPANESE KOREAN, ANNAMESE (ORDINARY)	CHINESE, JAPANESE KOREAN, ANNAMESE (OFFICIAL)	INDIAN	SIAMESE	BURMESE
1	١	一	壹	٩	၈	၁
2	٢	二	貳	٢	๒	၂
3	٣	三	叄	٣	๓	၃
4	٤	四	肆	٥	๔	၄
5	٥	五	伍	५	๕	၅
6	٦	六	陸	٤	๖	၆
7	٧	七	柒	٧	๗	၇
8	٨	八	捌	८	๘	၈
9	٩	九	玖	٩	๙	၉
0	٠			٥	๐	၀
10	١٠	十	拾		๑๐	
100	١٠٠	百			๑๐๐	
1000	١٠٠٠	千				

Dates in Roman numerals have been used since 1234 when this practice was adopted by the Danish town of Roskilde. Such Roman numerals were used sporadically throughout the Middle Ages and in later centuries and survive fitfully to this day. This was the system used in England for the first dated coins, the gold half-sovereigns of Edward VI struck at Durham House in 1548 (MDXLVIII). This continued till 1550 (MDL) but thereafter Arabic numerals were used, beginning with the half-crown of 1551. Notable exceptions of more recent times include the Gothic coinage of Queen Victoria (1847–87).

The first coin with the date in European numerals was a plappart of St Gallen, Switzerland dated 1424, but this was an isolated case. In 1477 Maria of Burgundy issued a guldiner which bore a date on the reverse, in the form of two pairs of digits flanking the crown at the top. The numerals in this instance were true Gothic, an interesting transition between true Arabic numerals and the modified Arabic figures now used in Europe. The Tyrolese guldengroschen of 1484–6 were the first coins to be regularly dated in European numerals and thereafter this custom spread rapidly.

For the numismatist, the problem arises when coins bear a date in the numerals of a different alphabet or computed according to a different era. Opposite is a table showing the basic numerals used in different scripts. The various eras which may be found in coin dates are as listed and explained overleaf.

Hijra

The era used on Moslem coins dates from the flight of Mohammed from Mecca to Medina on July 15, 622 and is often expressed as digits followed by AH (*Anno Hegirae*). Moslems employ a lunar calendar of twelve months comprising 354 11/30 days. Tipu Sultan of Mysore in 1201 AH (the fifth year of his reign)introduced a new era dating from the birth of Mohammed in AD 570 and using a luni-solar system. Tipu also adopted the Hindu cycle of sixty years (the Tamil Brihaspate Cycle), but changed this two or three years later, from Hijra to Muludi.

Afghan coins used the lunar calendar until 1920 and during 1929–31, but at other times have used the solar calendar. Thus the Democratic Republic began issuing its coins in SH 1358 (1979).

To convert an AH date to the Christian calendar you must translate the Arabic into European numerals. Taking an Arabic coin dated 1320, for example, first deduct 3% (to convert from the Moslem lunar year to our solar year). This gives 39.6 which, rounded up to the nearest whole number, is 40. Deduct 40 from 1320 (1280), then add 622. The answer is 1902.

There have been a few notable exceptions. Thus the Khanian era of Ilkhan Ghazan Mahmud began on 1st Rajab 701 AH (1301). This era used a solar calendar, but was shortlived, being confined to coins of Mahmud and his nephew Abu Said down to year 34 (1333).

The era of Tarikh Ilahi was adopted by the Mughal emperor Akbar in the thirteenth year of his reign (922 AH). This era dated from his accession on 5th Rabi al-Sani 963 AH (February 19, 1556). The calendar had solar months and days but no weeks, so each day of the month had a different name. This system was used by Akbar, Jahangir and Shah Jahan, often with a Hijra date as well.

Saphar

The era of the Caesars began on January 1, 38 BC and dated from the conquest of Spain by Augustus. Its use on coinage, however, seems to have been confined to the marabotins of Alfonso VIII of Castile and was expressed in both Latin and Arabic.

Samvat

The era of Vikramaditya began in 57 BC and was a luni-solar system used in some Indian states. Coins may be found with both Samvat and Hijra dates. Conversion to the Christian date is simple; merely subtract 57 from the Samvat to arrive at the AD date.

Saka

This originated in the southwestern district of Northern India and began in AD 78. As it used the luni-solar system it converts easily by adding 78 to the Saka date.

Nepal

Nepalese coins have used four different date systems. All coins of the Malla kings were dated in Nepal Samvat (NS) era, year 1 beginning in 881. This system was used briefly by the state of Cooch Behar. Until 1888 all coins of the Gurkha dynasty were dated in the Saka era (SE) which began in AD 78. After 1888 most copper coins were dated in the Vikram Samvat (VS) era from 57 BC. With the exception of some gold coins struck in 1890 and 1892, silver and gold coins only changed to the VS era in 1911, but now this system is used for all coins struck in Nepal. Finally, dates in the Christian era have appeared on some commemorative coins of recent years.

Ethiopian

This era dates from August AD 7, so that EE 1885 is AD 1892. Ethiopian dates are expressed in five digits using Amharic numerals. The first two are the digits of the centuries, the third is the character for 100, while the fourth and fifth are the digits representing the decade and year. On modern coins dates are rendered in Amharic numerals using the Christian era.

Thailand

Thai coins mainly use the Buddhist era (BE) which dates from 543 BC, but some coins have used dates from the Chula-Sakarat calendar (CS) which began in AD 638, while others use a Ratanakosind Sok (RS) date from the foundation of the Chakri dynasty in AD 1781.

Hebrew

The coins of Israel use the Jewish calendar dating from the beginning of the world (Adam and Eve in the Garden of Eden) in 3760 BC. Thus the year 1993 is rendered as 5753. The five millennia are assumed in dates, so that only the last three digits are expressed. 735 therefore equates with AD 1975. Dates are written in Hebrew letters, reading from right to left. The first two characters signify 400 and 300 respectively, totalling 700. The third letter denotes the decades (*lamedh* = 30) and the fourth letter, following the separation mark (") represents the final digit (*heh* = 5). The Jewish year runs from September or October in the Christian calendar.

Dates from the creation of the world

This system was also used in Russia under Ivan IV. The dating system *Anno Mundi* (AM) was established by the Council of Constantinople in AD 680 which determined that the birth of Christ had occurred in 5508 AM. Ivan's coins expressed the date as 7055 (1447).

Dynastic dates

The system of dating coinage according to regnal years is a feature of Chinese and Japanese coins. Chinese coins normally have an inscription stating that they are coins of such and such a reign period (not the emperor's name), and during the Southern Sung dynasty this was joined by the numeral of the year of the reign. This system was continued under the republic and survives in Taiwan to this day, although the coins of the Chinese Peoples Republic are dated in western numerals using the Christian calendar.

Early Japanese coins bore a reference to the era (the title assumed by each emperor on his accession) but, like Chinese coins, could not be dated accurately. From the beginning of the Meiji era (1867), however, coins have included a regnal number. The Showa era, beginning in 1926 with the accession of Hirohito, eventually ran to sixty-three (expressed in western numerals on some denominations, in Japanese ideograms on others) to denote 1988, although the rest of the inscription was in Japanese characters.

Dynastic dates were used on Korean milled coins introduced in 1888. These bore two characters at the top *Kae Kuk* (founding of the dynasty) followed by quantitative numerals. The system dated from the founding of the Yi dynasty in 1392. Curiously enough, some Korean banknotes have borne dates from the foundation of the first dynasty in 2333 BC.

Iran adopted a similar system in 1975, celebrating the 15th anniversary of the Pahlavi regime by harking back to the glories of Darius. The new calendar dated from the foundation of the Persian Empire 2535 years earlier, but was abolished only three years later when the Shah was overthrown.

Political eras

France adopted a republican calendar in 1793 when the monarchy was abolished. Coins were then inscribed L'AN (the year) followed by Roman numerals, but later Arabic numerals were substituted. This continued to the year 14 (1806) but in that year the Emperor Napoleon restored the Christian calendar.

The French system was emulated by Haiti whose coins dated from the revolution of 1803. The date appeared as AN followed by a number until AN 31 (1834) on some coins; others had both the evolutionary year and the Christian date from 1828 until 1850 (AN 47). Coins with a date in the Christian calendar appeared only in 1807–9 and then from 1850 onwards.

Mussolini introduced the Fascist calendar to Italy, dating from the seizure of power in October 1922. This system was widely employed on documents and memorials, but was first used on silver 20 lire coins of 1927 and then only in addition to the Christian date and appearing discreetly as Roman numerals. Subsequently it was extended to gold 50 lire and 100 lire coins in 1931 and the subsidiary coinage in 1936, being last used in the year XXI (1943).

Around the *World*

Listed here are the names of all the coins of the world, many of which have been around for hundreds of years, others are no longer in use. Some of the denominations have been introduced only recently, whilst others are familiar household words. A number of the names are shared by different countries and a few have even been used by different civilisations.

Abazi Caucusus
Abbasi, Abbassi Afghanistan, Georgia, Persia
Ackey Gold Coast
Adli Altin Ottoman Empire
Afghani Afghanistan
Agnel France
Agora (ot) Israel
Ahmadi Mysore, Yemen
Akce Turkey
Akcheh Turkestan
Albertusdaler Denmark
Albus German States, Swiss Cantons
Altin, Altun Egypt, Turkey
Altinlik Turkey
Altyn, Altynnik Russia
Amani Afghanistan
Amman Cash Mewar Udaipur, Pudukota, India
Angel England, Scotland, Isle of Man
Angelet France
Angelot France
Angster Lucerne
Anna Burma, India, Pakistan, Kenya, Muscat & Oman
Antoninianus Rome
Ardite Navarre
Argentino Argentina
Ariary Malagasy Republic
As Rome
Asarfi Nepal
Ashrafi Afghanistan, Awadh, Bahawalpur, Egypt, Hyderabad
Asper Algeria, Egypt, Libya, Trebizond, Tunisia, Turkey
Asses Luxembourg
At Laos
Atia Portuguese India
Atribuo Frankfurt
Att Cambodia, Laos, Siam (Thailand)
August d'Or Saxony

Augustale Sicily
Aurar (plural **Eyrir**) Iceland
Austral Argentina
Avo Macau, Timor
Bagarone Bologna
Bagattino Venice
Baggliangster Lucerne
Baht Thailand

Baiocco (plural **Baiocchi**) Papal States
Baisa Oman
Baiza Kuwait
Baizah Muscat & Oman
Balboa Panama
Ban (plural **Bani** or **Banu**) Roumania
Banica Croatia
Barbarina Mantua
Barbonaccio Lucca
Barbone Lucca
Barbuda Portugal
Barilla Philippines
Batzen German States, Swiss Cantons
Bawbee Scotland
Bazaruco Portuguese India
Bazaruk Dutch Settlements in India
Belga Belgium
Benduqi Morocco
Besa (plural **Bese**) Ethiopia, Somalia
Beshlik Soviet Central Asia
Bezant Byzantine Empire, Cyprus, Jerusalem
Bezzo Italian States

Bianco (plural **Bianchi**)   Bologna, Papal States
Biche   French Indian Settlements
Binio   Roman Empire
Bipkwele   Equatorial Guinea
Bir (r)   Ethiopia
Bisti   Caucasia
Bit   Guyana, West Indies
Bitt   Danish Virgin Islands
Black Dog   Nevis
Blaffert   Switzerland
Blanc   France
Blodsklipping   Sweden
Bluzger   Swiss Cantons
Bodle   Scotland
Bogach   Yemen
Bolivar   Venezuela
Boliviano   Bolivia
Bolognino   Papal States
Bonk   Ceylon, Dutch East Indies
Bonnet   Scotland
Boo   Japan
Braspenning   Flanders
Broad   England
Bu   Japan
Budju   Algeria
Buqsha   Yemen Arab Republic
Burbe(ns)   Tunisia
Butut   Gambia
Cache   French Indian Settlements
Cagliareso   Italian States
Calderilla   Spain
Candareen   China
Carbovanetz   Ukraine
Carlin   Sicily
Carlino   Papal States
Carolin   Austria,German States, Sweden
Cash   China, Hong Kong, India, Mysore,
    Travancore, Turkestan, Vietnam
Cassathaler   German States
Cauri   Guinea
Ceitil   Portugal
Cent   Australia, Bahamas, Barbados, Belize,
    Bermuda, Botswana, British East Caribbean
    Territories, British Honduras, British North
    Borneo, British Virgin Islands, Brunei,
    Canada, Cayman Island, Ceylon, China,
    Cochin China, Cocos (Keeling) Islands, Cook
    Islands, Curacao, Cyprus, Danish West Indies,
    East Africa, Ethiopia, Fiji, French Indochina,
    Gilbert and Ellice Islands, Guyana, Hawaii,
    Hong Kong, Indonesia, Jamaica, Kenya, Kiao
    Chau (Kiatschau), Kiribati, Laos, Liberia,
    Malaya, Malaysia, Malta, Mauritius,
    Netherlands, Netherlands Antilles,
    Netherlands Indies, New Zealand, Nova
    Scotia, Panama, Prince Edward Island,
    Sarawak, Seychelles, Sierra Leone, Singapore,

Solomon Islands, South Africa, Sri Lanka,
    Straits Settlements, Suriname, Swaziland,
    Tanzania, Trinidad and Tobago, Tuvalu,
    Uganda, United States of America, Virgin
    Islands, Zanzibar, Zimbabwe
Centas (plural **Centa, Centu**)   Lithuania
Centavo   Angola, Argentina, Bolivia, Brazil,
    Cape Verde Islands, Chile, Colombia, Costa
    Rica, Cuba, Dominican Republic, Ecuador, El
    Salvador, Guatemala, Guinea-Bissau,
    Honduras, Mexico, Mozambique, Nicaragua,
    Paraguay, Peru, Philippines, Portugal,
    Portuguese Guinea, Portuguese India, Puerto
    Rico, St Thomas and Prince Islands, Timor,
    Venezuela
Centecimo   Bolivia
Cententionalis   Roman Empire
Centesimo   Bolivia, Chile, Dominican Republic,
    Ethiopia, Italian East Africa, Italy, Panama,
    Paraguay, San Marino, Somalia, Uruguay,
    Vatican
Centime   Algeria, Antwerp, Belgian Congo,
    Belgium, Cambodia, Cameroon, Cochin
    China, Comoro Islands, Djibouti, France,
    French Equatorial Africa, French Guiana,
    French Indochina, French Oceania, French
    Polynesia, French Somali Coast, French West
    Africa, Guadeloupe, Guinea, Haiti, Laos,
    Monaco, Morocco, New Caledonia, Reunion,
    Senegal, Switzerland, Togo, Tunisia, Vietnam,
    Westphalia, Yugoslavia, Zaire
Centimo   Costa Rica, Mozambique, Paraguay,
    Peru, Philippines, Puerto Rico, St Thomas and
    Prince Islands, Spain, Venezuela
Centu   Lithuania
Chaise   Antwerp, Bavaria, France
Chervonetz (plural **Chervontzy**)   Russia
Chetrum   Bhutan
Cheun   South Korea
Chiao   China, Formosa, Manchukuo
Chi'en   China
Chio   China
Cho-gin   Japan
Chomseh   Yemen
Chon   Korea
Christian d'Or   Denmark
Chuckram   Travancore
Colon   Costa Rica, El Salvador
Condor   Chile, Colombia, Ecuador
Cordoba   Nicaragua
Cornado   Spain
Cornuto   Savoy
Coroa de Prata   Portugal
Coroin   Eire
Corona   Austrian provinces of Italy, Naples
Coronato   Castile, Naples
Couronne d'Or   France

Crocione   Italian States
Crossazzo   Genoa
Crown   Ascension, Australia, Bermuda, England, Ghana, Gibraltar, Ireland, Isle of Man, Jamaica, Jersey, Malawi, New Zealand, Nigeria, Rhodesia, Rhodesia and Nyasaland, St Helena, Scotland, Southern Rhodesia, Tristan da Cunha, Turks and Caicos Islands
Cruzadinho   Brazil, Portugal
Cruzado   Brazil, Portugal
Cruzeiro   Brazil
Cuartillo, Cuartino   Mexico
Cuarto   Bolivia, Spain
Daalder   Netherlands
DakBler   Danish West Indies, Denmark, Sweden
Dam   Afghanistan, India, Nepal
Daric   Persia
Dauphin   France
Decime   France
Decimo   Argentina, Chile, Colombia, Ecuador, Galapagos
Decussis   Roman Republic
Dekadrachm   Syracuse, Hellenistic kingdoms
Dekanummion   Byzantine Empire
Dekobolon   Greece
Demareteion   Syracuse
Demer   France
Demy   Scotland
Denar   Hungary
Denarius   Rome
Denaro   Italian States
Denga   Russia
Dengi   Roumania
Denier   France and colonies, Haiti, Swiss Cantons
Denning   Denmark
Deut   Rhineland, Westphalia
Deutschemark   Germany
Dhofari Riyal   Yemen
Diamante   Ferrara
Diamantino   Ferrara
Dicken   Swiss Cantons
Didrachm   Greece
Dime   Canada, Hawaii, USA
Dinar   Afghanistan, Algeria, Bahrain, Hejaz, Iraq, Kuwait, Morocco, Persia, Saudi Arabia, Serbia, Tunisia, Turkey, Yugoslavia
Diner   Andorra
Dinero   Peru, Spain
Diobol   Greece
Dirham   Jordan, Libya, Morocco, United Arab Emirates
Dirhem   Dubai, Iraq, Morocco, Qatar
Dio, Diu   Portuguese India
Disme   USA
Dobla   Genoa, Naples and Sicily

Doblado   Spanish colonies
Doblenca, Doblenga   Aragon, Barcelona
Dobler   Mallorca
Doblon   Chile, Spain, Urugay
Dobra   St Thomas and Prince
Dodekadrachm   Carthage
Doit   Netherlands, Netherlands Indies, Indonesia
Dokdo   Junagadh, Kutch, Nawanagar (Indian States)

Dollar   Anguilla, Antigua and Barbuda, Australia, Bahamas, Belize, Bermuda, Canada, Cayman Islands, China, Cocos (Keeling) Islands, Cook Islands, East Caribbean Territories, Fiji, Great Britain, Grenada, Guyana, Hawaii, Hong Kong, Indonesia, Jamaica, Japan, Kiribati, Liberia, Malaysia, Mauritius, Montserrat, Newfoundland, New Zealand, Panama, St Kitts-Nevis, St Lucia, St Vincent, Scotland, Sierra Leone, Singapore, Solomin Islands, Straits Settlements, Trinidad and Tobago, Tuvalu, USA, Virgin Islands, Western Samoa, Zimbabwe
Dolya   Russia
Dong   Annam, Vietnam
Doppia   Italian States
Doppietta   Sardinia
Double   Guernsey
Dou Dou   French Indochina
Douzain   France
Drachma   Crete, Greece
Dram   Armenia
Dreibatzner   Austria, German States
Dreigroscher   Lithuania, Prussia
Dreiling   German States
Dub   Hyderabad, India
Dubbeltje   Holland
Ducat   Austria, Austrian States, Courland, Czechoslovakia, Denmark, German States, Hungary, Italian States, Liechtenstein, Liege, Netherlands,Poland, Roumania, Sweden, Swiss Cantons, Russia, Yugoslavia
Ducaton   Belgium, Netherlands
Ducatone   Italian States
Dudu   India
Duetto   Italian States

Duit   Ceylon, German States, Netherlands,
Netherlands Indies
Dukat   Czechoslovakia, German States,
Hungary, Poland, Sweden, Yugoslavia
Duplone   Swiss Cantons
Duro   Spain
Dyak   Nepal
Ecu   Belgium, Bosnia, France, Gibraltar
Ekuele   Equatorial Guinea
Elisabeth d'Or   Russia
Emalangeni   Swaziland
Escalin   Belgium, Guadeloupe, Haiti, Liege,
Martinique
Escudillo   Spain
Escudo   Angola, Argentina, Azores, Bolivia,
Cape Verde Islands, Central American
Republic, Chile, Colombia, Costa Rica,
Ecuador, Guadeloupe, Guatemala, Guinea-
Bissau, Madeira, Mexico, Mozambique, Peru,
Portugal, Portuguese Guinea/India, St
Thomas and Prince Islands, Spain, Timor
Espadin   Portugal
Esphera   Goa
Excelente   Spain
Eyrir (singular **Aurar**) Iceland
Fals   Iraq
Faluce   Ceylon
Falus   Afghanistan, China, India, Iran, Morocco,
Turkestan
Fanam   Ceylon, Dutch East Indies, Travancore
Fano   Tranquebar (Danish Indian Settlements)
Fanon   French Indian Settlements
Farthing   Antigua, Ceylon, Great Britain, Isle of
Man, Jamaica, Malta, Scotland, South Africa
Fels   Algeria
Fen   People's Republic of China, Manchukuo
Fenig (ow)   Poland
Feoirling   Eire
Ferding   Courland, Livonia
Filiberto   Savoy
Filippo   Italian States
Filler   Hungary
Fils   Bahrain, Iraq, Jordan, Kuwait, South
Arabia, United Arab Emirates, Yemen
Fiorino   Italian States
Flitter   South German States
Floirin   Eire
Florin   Australia, Austria, East Africa, Fiji,
Great Britain, Hungary, Ireland, Malawi, New
Zealand, Rhodesia and Nyasaland, South
Africa, Swiss Cantons
Follis   Rome, Byzantine Empire
Forint   Hungary
Franc   Algeria, Belgian Congo, Belgium,
Burundi, Cambodia, Cameroon, Central
African Republic, Chad, Comoro Islands,
Congo, Danish West Indies, Djibouti,

Dominican Republic, Ecuador,
France, French colonies, Gabon, Guadeloupe,
Guinea, Ivory Coast, Katanga, Luxembourg,
Madagascar, Malagasy Republic, Mali,
Martinique, Mauretania, Monaco, Morocco,
New Caledonia, New Hebrides, Reunion,
Ruanda-Urundi, Rwanda, St Pierre and
Miquelon, Senegal, Switzerland, Togo,
Tunisia, West African States
Francescone   Italian States
Franchi   Switzerland
Franco   Dominican Republic, Ecuador, Italian
States, Swiss Cantons
Frang   Luxembourg
Frank(en)   Belgium, Liechtenstein, Saar,
Switzerland, Westphalia
Franka Ara   Albania
Frederik d'Or   Denmark
Friedrich d'Or   German States
Fyrk   Sweden
Gabellone   Papal States
Gayah   Sumatra
Gazetta   Venice
Genovino   Genoa, Florence, Venice
Genevoise   Geneva
George Noble   England
Georgstaler   German States
Gersh   Ethiopia
Gigliato   Hungary, Naples, Rhodes
Gigot   Brabant, Flanders
Gin   Japan
Giorgino   Ferrara, Modena
Giovannino   Genoa
Girsh   Hejaz, Nejd, Saudi Arabia, Sudan
Giulio   Italian States
Golde   Sierra Leone
Goldgulden   German States, Swiss Cantons
Goldpfennig   German States
Goryoban   Japan
Gourde   Haiti
Gourmier   Morocco
Gram   Afghanistan
Gramme   Burma
Gramo   Bolivia, Tierra del Fuego
Grana   Italian States

Grano   Italian States, Mexico,
   Sovereign Order of Malta
Grenadino   Colombia, New Granada
Greschl   Roumania, Transylvania
Grivenka   Russia
Grivennik   Russia
Grivna (plural **Grivny**)   Ukraine
Groat   Great Britain
Groeschl   Bohemia
Groot   Netherlands
Gros   France
Groschel   German States
Groschen   Austria, German States, Poland,
   Swiss Cantons
Groshen   Austria, German States
Grossetto   Dalmatia, Illyria, Venice
Grosso   Italian States
Grossone   Italian States
Grosspfennig   Pomerania, Rhineland
Grossus   Courland, Poland
Grosz (plural **Grosze** or **Groszy**)   Poland
Grote   German States
Grush   Albania
Guarani   Paraguay
Guerche   Egypt, Saudi Arabia
Guinea   Great Britain, Saudi Arabia
Gulden   Austria, Curacao, German States,
   Netherlands, Netherlands Indies, Swiss
   Cantons
Guldiner   Austria, South German States, Swiss
   Cantons
Gutegroschen   North and Central German
   States
Guterpfennig   German States
Habibi   Afghanistan
Halala   Saudi Arabia, Yemen
Halbag   Frankfurt
Haler (plural **Halere, Haleru**)   Czechoslovakia,
   Czech Republic
Halierov   Slovakia
Haller   Swiss Cantons
Hao   China, Vietnam
Hapalua   Hawaii
Hardhead   Scotland
Hardi   France, Turin
Hau   Tonga
Hayrir Altin   Iraq, Turkey
Hekte   Lesbos, Mytilene
Heller   Austria, German States, German East
   Africa
Helm   England
Henri d'Or   France
Hryvnia   Ukraine
Hsien   China
Hvid   Denmark
Hwan   Korea
Hyperpyron   Byzantine Empire

Ichibu-gin   Japan
Ikilik   Russia
Imadi   Yemen
Imami   Mysore
Imperial   Russia
Isabella   Spain
Ischal   Russia
Ishu Gin   Japan
Jacondale   France
Jawa   Nepal
Jeon   Korea
Jerome d'Or   Westphalia
Jiao   People's Republic of China
Jedid   Egypt
Jefimok (plural **Jefimki**)   Russia
Joachimico   Italy
Joachimik   Poland
Joachimstaler   Bohemia
Joao   Portugal
Johanna   Portugal
Johannes   Portugal
Jokoh   Kelantan, Malaysia
Judenpfennig   Frankfurt
Justo   Portugal
Kapang   Sarawak
Kapeikas   Latvia, Belarus
Karolin   German States
Kas   Danish Indian Settlements
Kasu   Mysore
Kazbeg   Caucasia, Safavid Persia
Khayriya   Egypt
Khoum   Mauretania
Kin   Japan
Kina   Papua New Guinea
Kip   Laos
Koban   Japan
Kobo   Nigeria
Kopec   Poland
Kopejek   Outer Mongolia (Tannu Tuva)

Kopek   Russia
Kori   Kutch**Korona**   Bohemia and Moravia,
   Hungary, Slovakia
Kortling   German States
Korun(a) (plural **Koruny** or **Koruncic**)
   Czechoslo-vakia
Koula   Tonga
Krajczar   Hungary
Kran   Iran, Persia

Kreu(t)zer   Austria, Austrian States,
Czechoslovakia, German States, Hungary,
Liechtenstein, Poland, Roumania, Swiss
Cantons
Krona (plural Kronor or Kronur)   Iceland,
Sweden
Krona (plural Kroner or Kronen)   Austria,
Denmark, German States, Greenland,
Liechtenstein, Norway
Kroon(i)   Estonia
Krugerrand   South Africa
Kuna (plural Kune)   Croatia
Kupang   Malaysia, Thailand
Kurus   Turkey
Kuta   Congo-Kinshasa, Zaire
Kwacha   Malawi, Zambia
Kwanza   Angola
Kwartnik   Poland
Kyat   Burma, Myanmar
Kyrmis   Russia
Lang   Annam
Laree, Lari, Lariat or Larin   Maldive Islands
Lati, Lats   Latvia
Laurel   England
Lei   Roumania
Lek (plural Leke or Leku)   Albania
Lempira   Honduras
Leone   Sierra Leone
Leopard   England
Lepton (plural Lepta)   Crete, Greece, Ionian
Islands
Leu (plural Lei)   Roumania
Lev(a)   Bulgaria
Li   Manchukuo
Liang   China, Laos
Liard   Belgium, France, Luxembourg
Libra   Peru
Licente   Lesotho
Likuta   Zaire
Lilangeni   Swaziland
Lion   Scotland
Lion d'Or   Austrian Netherlands

Lira (plural Lire)   Eritrea, Italian East Africa,
Italy, San Marino, Syria, Turkey, Vatican
Lira (plural Lirot)   Israel
Lisente   Lesotho

Litas (plural Litai or Litu)   Lithuania
Litra   Sicily, Syracuse
Livre   France, Guadeloupe, Lebanon,
Martinique, Mauritius, Reunion
Louis d'Argent   France
Louis d'Or   France
Luhlanga   Swaziland
Lumma   Armenia
Lweis   Angola
Mace   China
Macuta   Angola
Magdalon d'Or   Aix-en-Provence, Tarascon
Mahalek   Ethiopia
Mahallak   Harar
Mahbub   Egypt, Ottoman Empire
Mahmudi   Saudi Arabia
Makuta   Zaire
Maloti   Lesotho
Manat   Azerbaijan
Manghir   Crimea
Marabotin   Moorish kingdoms, Southern Spain
Maravedi   Spain
Marchetto   Italian States
Marck   German States
Marengo   France
Mariengroschen   German States
Mark   Germany, German States, German New
Guinea, Norway, Poland, Sweden
Marka   Estonia
Markka(a)   Finland
Mas   Malaysia
Masriya   Egypt
Masson   Lorraine and Bar
Mat   Burma
Matapan   Venice
Mathbu   Morocco
Maticaes   Mozambique
Matona   Ethiopia
Mattier   German States
Maximilian d'Or   German States
Mazuna   Morocco
Medin   Egypt
Mehmudiye Altin   Ottoman Empire
Meinhard   Austria, German States
Melgarejo   Bosnia
Merk   Scotland
Metica   Mozambique
Meung   Japan
Mil   Cyprus, Hong Kong, Israel, Malta, Palestine
Milan d'Or   Serbia
Miliarense   Byzantine Empire
Milesima   Spain
Millieme   Egypt, Libya
Millime   Tunisia
Milreis   Brazil
Miscals   China
Mohar   Nepal

Mohur Afghanistan, Bikanir, Cooch Behar, Gwalior, Hyderabad, India (Mughal Empire), Maldive Islands, Netherlands Indies, Rajkot
Moidore (Moeda de ouro) Portugal
Momme Japan
Mon Japan, Ryukyu Islands
Mongo Mongolia
Mouton d'Or France
Mu Burma
Mun Korea
Mung Mongolia
Munzgulden Swiss Cantons
Muzuna Algeria
Naira Nigeria
Nami-sen Japan
Napoleon France
Naya Paisa Bhutan, India
Negotiepenning Netherlands
Neugroschen German States
New Pence Gibraltar, Great Britain, Guernsey, Isle of Man, Jersey
Ngultrum Bhutan
Ngwee Zambia
Nisar Afghanistan, India
Nisfiya Egypt
Noble Austria,England, Scotland, Isle of Man
Nomisma Byzantine Empire
Nonsunt Scotland
Nummion (plural Nummia) Byzantine Empire
Oban Japan
Obol Greece, Ionian Islands
Ochavo Spain
Octavo Mexico, Philippines
Omani Oman
Onca Mozambique
Oncia Italian States
Onlik Crimea
Onluk Turkey
Onza Bolivia, Chile, Costa Rica, Mexico
Or Sweden
Ore Denmark, Faroe Islands, Greenland, Norway, Sweden
Ort(e) Poland, Prussia
Ortug (plural Ortugar) Sweden
Ouguiya Mauretania
Pa'anga Tonga
Pagoda India (Madras)
Pahlavi Iran
Pai India, Siam (Thailand)
Paisa Afghanistan, Bhutan, India, Nepal, Pakistan
Panchia India
Pano Portuguese Africa
Paoli Italian States
Papetto Papal States
Para (plural Paras or Parades) Crimea, Egypt, Greece, Iraq, Libya, Nejd, Roumania, Saudi

Arabia, Serbia, Sudan, Syria, Turkey, Walachia, Yugoslavia
Pardao Portuguese India
Parisis d'Or France
Pataca Macau
Pataco Portugal
Patagon Belgium
Patrick Ireland
Pavillon d'Or France
Pe Burma, Cambodia
Peca Portugal
Pengo Hungary
Penni(a) Finland
Penning(ar) Denmark, Sweden
Penny (plural Pence) Australia, Bahamas, Barbados, Bermuda, Biafra, British Guiana, British East Africa British West Africa, Canada, Ceylon, Falkland Islands, Fiji, Gambia, Ghana, Gibraltar, Gold Coast, Great Britain, Guernsey, Ireland, Isle of Man, Jamaica, Jersey, Malawi, Montserrat, New Guinea, New Zealad, Nigeria, Rhodesia and Nyasaland, St Helena, St Kitts-Nevis, South Africa, Southern Rhodesia, Trinidad & Tobago, Tristan da Cunha, Zambia
Pentekontalitron Sicily
Pentekontedrachm Hellenistic kingdoms
Pentenummion Byzantine Empire
Perper(a) Montenegro
Pesa German East Africa
Peseta Andorra, Equatorial Guinea, Peru, Spain
Pesewa Ghana
Peso Argentina, Bolivia, Cambodia, Chile, Colombia, Costa Rica, Cuba, Dominican Republic, El Salvador, Guatemala, Guinea-Bissau, Honduras, Mexico, Netherlands Antilles, Nicaragua, Paraguay, Peru, Philippines, Puerto Rico, Uruguay, Venezuela
Pessa Yemen (Lahej), Zanzibar
Petermannchen Trier
Pfennig(e) Austria, Bohemia, Germany, German States, Poland, Swiss Cantons
Pfenning Austrian States, German States
Philippeioi Macedon
Phoenix Greece
Piastra Italian States
Piastre Annam, Cambodia, Cochin China, Cyprus, Denmark, Egypt, French Indochina, Hejaz, Iraq, Khmer, Lebanon, Libya, Nejd, Saudi Arabia, Syria, Sudan, Tonkin, Tunisia, Turkey, Vietnam, Yemen
Piataltynny Russia
Picciolo Sovereign Order of Malta
Piccolo Italian States
Pice Bhutan, Ceylon, East Africa, India, Kenya, Malaysia

Pinto   Portugal
Piso   Philippines
Pistole   France, German States, Ireland,
   Scotland, Swiss Cantons
Pitis   Brunei, Java, Sumatra, Siam
Plack   Scotland
Plappart   Switzerland
Poisha   Bangladesh
Poltina   Russia
Poltura   Hungary, Roumania
Poludenga   Russia
Polupoltinnik   Russia
Polushka   Russia
Pond   Transvaal

Pound   Ascension, Australia, Biafra, Cyprus,
   Egypt, Falkland Islands, Ghana, Gibraltar,
   Great Britain, Guernsey, Iran, Isle of Man,
   Israel, Jersey, Malta, Nigeria, Rhodesia, St
   Helena, South Arabia, South Africa, Sudan,
   Syria
Protea   South Africa
Pruta(ot)   Israel
Puffin   Lundy
Pul   Afghanistan, China, Turkestan
Pula   Botswana
Puli   Caucasia
Pultorak   Poland
Pya(t)   Burma
Pysa   Zanzibar
Qindar(ka)   Albania
Qiran   Afghanistan
Qirsh   Egypt
Quadrans   Roman Republic
Quan   Annam
Quart   Gibraltar, Swiss Cantons
Quart d'Ecu   France
Quartenses   Silesia
Quartillo   Spain
Quartinho   Portugal
Quarto   Ecuador, Mexico, Philippines, Spain
Quartuncia   Rome
Quaternio   Rome
Quattrino   Italian States
Qepiq   Azerbaijan
Quetzal   Guatemala
Quinarius   Rome

Quint   USA
Quinto di Scudo   Papal States
Rand   South Africa
Rappen   Switzerland
Rasi   Netherlands Indies
Reaal   Curacao
Real(es)   Argentina, Bolivia, Central American
   Republic, Chile, Colombia, Costa Rica,
   Dominican Republic, Ecuador, El Salvador,
   Venezuela
Real Batu   Indonesia
Reichsmark   Germany
Reichspfennig   Germany
Reichsthaler   Germany
Reis   Angola, Azores, Brazil, Madeira,
   Mozambique, Portugal, Portuguese India
Reisedaler   Denmark
Rentenmark   Germany
Rentenpfennig   Germany
Reul   Eire
Rial   Iran, Morocco, Muscat and Oman, Oman,
   Persia, Yemen Arab Republic
Rider   Scotland
Riel   Kampuchea
Rigsbankdaler   Denmark
Rigsbankskilling   Denmark
Rigsdaler,   Denmark, Norway
Rigsmontskilling   Denmark
Rijder   Friesland, Guelderland, United Provinces
Rijksdaalder   Netherlands
Riksdaler   Sweden
Riksdaler Riksmynt   Sweden
Riksdaler Specie   Sweden
Rin   Japan
Ringgit   Malaysia
Rio   Japan
Rixdollar   Ceylon
Riyal   Iran, Iraq, Saudi Arabia, United Arab
   Emirates, Yemen Arab Republic
Rose Noble   England
Rouble   Russia, USSR
Royal d'Or   France
Royalin(er)   Tranquebar, Danish Indian
   Settlements
Rub   Ethiopia
Rubel   German occupation of Russia
Rubiya   Egypt
Ruble   Poland, Transnistria
Rublis   Latvia
Rufiyaa   Maldive Islands
Rumi Altin   Ottoman Empire
Rupee   Afghanistan, Andaman Islands, Bhutan,
   Burma, China, Cocos Keeling Islands, India,
   Iran, Kenya, Mauritius, Nepal, Pakistan, Saudi
   Arabia, Seychelles, Sri Lanka, Tanzania, Tibet,
   United Arab Emirates, Yemen
Rupia   Portuguese India, Somalia

Rupiah Indonesia
Rupie German East Africa
Ruspone Italian States
Ryal England, Hejaz, Iran, Muscat and Oman,
Nejd, Oman, Persia, Quaiti State, Saudi
Arabia, Yemen, Zanzibar
Ryo Japan
Rytterpenning Denmark, Hanseatic League
Saidi Oman
Saiga Merovingian Empire
Salung Siam (Thailand)
Salut d'Or France
Sampietrino Papal States
Sanar Afghanistan
Sanese Siena
Santa Croce Italian States
Santim(at) Morocco
Santims (plural **Santimi** or **Santimu**) Latvia
Sapeque Annam, Cochin China, French
Indochina
Sar Sinkiang
Sarrazzino Crusader kingdoms
Satang Siam (Thailand)
Sceat Anglo-Saxon England
Scellino Somalia

Schilling Austria, German States, Poland,
Swiss Cantons
Schoter Breslau, Silesia
Schwaren German States
Scilling Eire
Scudo Bolivia, Italian States, Mexico, Malta,
Papal States, Peru, San Marino
Sechsling German States
Semis Rome
Semuncia Rome
Sen Brunei, Cambodia, Indonesia, Irian Barat,
Japan, Kampuchea, Malaysia, Riau Lingga,
West New Guinea
Sene Samoa
Sengi Zaire
Seniti Tonga
Sent Estonia
Sente Lesotho
Senti Estonia, Somalia, Tanzania
Sentimo Philippines

Serebrnik Bulgaria
Sertum Bhutan
Sesena Spain
Sesino Italian States
Sestertius Rome
Sestino Italian States
Shahi Afghanistan, Iran, Turkestan
Sheqal(im) Israel
Shilingi Tanzania
Shilling Australia, Biafra, British West Africa,
Canada, Cyprus, East Africa, Fiji, Gambia,
Ghana, Great Britain, Grenada, Guernsey,
Ireland, Isle of Man, Jamaica, Jersey, Kenya,
Malawi, Malta, New Guinea, New Zealand,
Nigeria, Scotland, Somalia, South Africa,
Trinidad and Tobago, Uganda, Zambia
Sho Nepal, Tibet
Shokang Tibet
Shu Japan
Siglos Achaemenid Empire
Sik Siam (Thailand)
Silbergroschen German States, Luxembourg
Silbergulden South Germany
Sizain France
Skar Tibet
Skilling Danish West Indies, Denmark,
Norway, Sweden
Skillingrigsmont Denmark
Skot Prussia, Silesia
Sol(es) Argentina, Belgium, Bolivia, France,
Haiti, Luxembourg, Mauritius, Peru, Reunion,
Switzerland, Windward Islands
Soldo (plural **Soldi**) Italian States, Swiss
Cantons, Papal States, Yugoslavia
Solidus Argentina, Bolivia, Peru, Rome
Solot Siam
Som Kyrgyzstan
Somalo Somalia
Sosling Denmark
Sou Canada, French colonies, Guadeloupe,
Mauritius, Reunion, Spain
Souverain d'Or Austrian Netherlands
Sovereign Australia, Canada, England,
Falkland Islands, India, Isle of Man, Saudi
Arabia, South Africa, United Kingdom
Sovrano Italian States
Speciedaler Denmark, Norway
Species Ducat Denmark
Srang Tibet
Stater Greece
Stella USA
Stiver British Guiana, Ceylon, Demerara and
Essequibo, Dutch East Indies, Netherlands
Stotinka Bulgaria
Stuber German States
Stuiver Curacao, Dutch East Indies,
Netherlands, Netherlands Antilles

Styca   Northumbria
Styver   Sweden
Su   South Vietnam
Sucre   Ecuador, Galapagos
Sueldo   Bolivia, Spain
Sukus   Indonesia
Sultani   Algeria, Libya, Tunisia
Surre Altin   Ottoman Empire
Syli   Guinea
Tackoe   Gold Coast
Tael   China, Laos
Taka   Bangladesh
Tala   Samoa, Tokelau
Talar(a)   Poland
Talaro   Ethiopia
Taler   German States, Poland, Swiss Cantons
Talirion   Greece
Tallero   Ethiopia, Italian States, Ragusa
Tambac-tron   Annam
Tambala   Malawi
Tamlung   Siam
Tanga   Portuguese India
Tangka   Tibet
Tanka   Nepal
Tankah   Burma
Tarin   Naples, Sicily
Taro (plural Tari)   Italian States, Malta
Tek Altin   Ottoman Empire
Tenga   China, Bokhara, Turkestan
Ternar   Poland
Tester   England
Testern   British East Indies
Testone   Italian States
Testoon   England
Tetartemorion   Greece
Tetarteron   Byzantine Empire
Tetradrachm   Greece
Tetrobol   Greece
Thaler   Austria, Austrian States, Courland,
   Czechoslovakia, German States, Hungary,
   Liechtenstein, Poland, Roumania,
   Switzerland
Thebe   Botswana
Theler   Frankfurt
Thistle Crown   England
Thistle Merk   Scotland
Thistle Noble   Scotland
Thrymsa   Anglo-Saxon England
Tical   Cambodia, Thailand
Tien   Annam, Vietnam
Tilla   Afghanistan, Sinkiang, Turkestan
Timasha   Afghanistan
Tostao   Portugal
Toea   Papua New Guinea
Tola   India, Nepal

Tolar   Slovenia
Toman   Iran, Persia, Azerbaijan
Tornese   Italian States
Tournois   France
Trade Dollar   Great Britain, Japan, USA
Trah   Malaysia
Tremissis   Rome, Byzantine Empire, Franks,
   Lombards, Visigoths
Tressis   Rome
Triens   Rome
Trihemiobol   Greece
Triobol   Greece
Tritartemorion   Greece
Tughrik   Mongolia
Turner   Scotland
Tympf   Poland
Tyyn   Kyrgyzstan
Unghero   Italian States
Unicorn   Scotland
Unit   Scotland, French West Africa
Unite   England
Van   Vietnam
Vatu   Vanuatu
Veld Pond   South African Republic
Venezolano   Venezuela
Vereinstaler   Austria-Hungary, German States
Victoriate   Rome
Vierer   Swiss Cantons
Vintem   Portugal
Wan   Korea
Wark   Ethiopia
Warn   Korean
Wen   China
Whan   Korea
Won   South Korea
Xerafim   Portuguese India
Xu   Vietnam
Yang   Korea
Yarim   Turkey
Yen   Japan
Yirmilik   Ottoman Empire
Yuan   China
Yuzluk   Ottoman Empire
Zaire   Zaire
Zalat   Yemen Arab Republic
Zecchino   Italian States, Malta
Zelagh   Morocco
Zeri Mahbub   Egypt, Libya, Turkey
Zloty (plural Zlote or Zlotych)   Poland
Zolota   Turkey
Zolotnik   Russia
Zolotoj   Russia
Zweidritteltaler   German States
Zyfert   East Friesland

Glossary of coin terms

In this section we list all the terms commonly encountered in numismatics or in the production of coins.

Abbey Coins Medieval coins struck in the abbeys, convents and other great religious houses which were granted coinage rights. These coins were often used also by pilgrims journeying from one monastery to another.

Abschlag (German for "discount") A *restrike* from an original die.

Accolated Synonym for *conjoined* or *jugate* and signifying two or more profiles overlapping.

Acmonital Acronym from *Aciaio Monetario Italiano*, a stainless steel alloy used for Italian coins since 1939.

Adjustment Reduction of metal in a *flan* or *blank* to the specified weight prior to striking, accomplished by filing down the face. Such file marks often survived the coining process and are occasionally met with in coins, especially of the 18th century.

Ae Abbreviation for the Latin *Aes* (bronze), used for coins made of brass, bronze or other copper alloys.

Aes Grave (Latin for heavy bronze) Heavy circular coins first minted at Rome in 269 BC.

Aes Rude (Latin for rough bronze) Irregular lumps of bronze which gradually developed into ingots of uniform shape and were the precursors of coins in Rome.

Aes Signatum (Latin for signed bronze) Bronze ingots of regular size and weight, bearing marks of authority to guarantee their weight (289–269 BC).

Agonistic (Greek) Term for coins issued to commemorate, or pertaining to, sporting events.

Alliance Coinage struck by two or more states acting together and having common features of design or inscription.

Alloy Coinage metal composed of two or more metallic elements.

Altered Deliberately changed, usually unofficially, with the aim of increasing the numismatic value of a coin, medal or note. This applies particularly to dates, where a common date may be altered to a rare date by filing or re-engraving one of the digits.

Aluminium (American *Aluminum*) Silvery lightweight metal, developed commercially in the late 19th century for commemorative medals, but used for tokens and emergency money during the First World War and since 1940 widely used in subsidiary coinage.

Aluminium-bronze Alloy of aluminium and copper. Hard-wearing and gold-coloured, it is now widely used in tokens and subsidiary coinage.

Amulet Coin or medal believed to have talismanic qualities, such as warding off disease and bad luck. Many Chinese and Korean pieces come into this category. See also *Touchpiece*.

Androcephalous Heraldic term for creatures with a human head.

Anepigraphic Coins or medals without a legend.

Annealing Process of heating and cooling applied to metal to relieve stresses and prepare it for striking into coins.

Annulet Small circle often used as an ornament or spacing device in coin inscriptions.

Antimony Brittle white metal, chemical symbol *Sb*, virtually impractical as a coinage metal but used for the Chinese 10 cents of Kweichow, 1931. Alloyed with tin, copper or lead, it produces the white metal popular as a medallic medium.

Antoniniani Silver coins minted in Imperial Rome. The name derives from the Emperor Caracalla (Marcus Aurelius Antoninus) in whose reign they were first struck. The silver content was progressively reduced and by the last issue (AD 295) they were reduced to *billon*.

Ar Abbreviation for Latin *Argentum* (silver), used for coins struck in this metal.

Assay Mark Mark applied to a medal struck in precious metal by an assayer or assay office as a guarantee of the fineness of the metal.

Assignat Type of paper money used in France 1789–96, representing the land assigned to the holders.

Attribution Identification of a coin by characteristics such as issuing authority, date or reign, mint, denomination, metal, and by a standard reference.

Au Abbreviation for *aurum* (Latin for gold), denoting coins of this metal.

AU Abbreviation for "About Uncirculated", often found in catalogues and dealers' lists to describe the condition of a numismatic piece.

Autodollar Name given to the silver yuan issued by Kweichow, 1928, and having a contemporary motor car as the obverse motif.

Auxiliary Payment Certificate Form of paper money intended for use by American military personnel stationed in overseas countries. See also *Baf* and *Scrip*.

Babel Note Nickname given to the paper money of the Russian Socialist Federated Soviet Republic (1919) because it bore the slogan "workers of the world unite" in seven languages, a reference to the biblical tower of Babel.

Baf Acronym from British Armed Forces, the popular name for the vouchers which could only be exchanged for goods in service canteens from 1945 onwards.

Bag Mark Minor scratch or abrasion on an otherwise uncirculated coin, caused by coins in mint bags knocking together.

Banknote Form of paper money issued by banks and usually promising to pay the bearer on demand in coin of the realm.

Barbarous Imitation of Greek or Roman coins by the Celtic and Germanic tribes who lived beyond the frontiers of the civilised world.

Base Non-precious metals or alloys.

Bath Metal Inferior bronze alloy, named after the English city where it was used for casting cannon. Used by William Wood of Bristol for Irish and American tokens and by Amos Topping for Manx coins of 1733/4.

Beading Ornamental border found on the raised rim of a coin.

Behalfszahlungsmittel German term for auxiliary payment certificates used in occupied Europe from 1939 to 1945.

Bell Metal Alloy of copper and tin normally used for casting bells, but employed for the subsidiary coinage of the French Revolutionary period.

Billon Silver alloy containing less than 50 per cent fine silver, usually mixed with copper. In Spain this alloy was known as *vellon*.

Bi-metallic Coins struck in two separate metals or alloys. Patterns for such coins exist from the 19th century but actual coins with a centre of one metal surrounded by a ring of another did not appear till 1982 (Italy, San Marino and Vatican). Canada introduced coins with a tiny plaque inset in a second metal (1990). See also *Clad*, *Plugged* and *Sandwich*.

Bi-metallism Monetary system in which two metals are in simultaneous use and equally available as legal tender, implying a definite ratio between the two. A double standard of gold and silver, with a ratio of 16:1, existed till the mid-19th century.

Bingle American term for a trade token, more specifically the US government issue of tokens for the Matacuska, Alaska colonization project, 1935.

Birthday Coins Coins celebrating the birthday of a ruler originated in Roman Imperial times, notably the reigns of Maximianus (286–305) and Constantinus I (307–37). Birthday talers were issued by many German states, and among recent examples may be cited coins marking the 70th, 80th and 90th birthdays of Gustaf Adolf VI of Sweden, 80th and 90th birthday coins from the British Commonwealth for the Queen Mother, and coins honouring Queen Elizabeth, the Duke of Edinburgh and the Prince of Wales.

Bit Term denoting fragments of large silver coins, cut up and circulating as fractional values. Spanish dollars were frequently broken up for circulation in the American colonies and the West indies. Long bits and short bits circulated at 15 and 10 cents respectively, but the term came to be equated with the Spanish real or eighth of a peso, hence the American colloquialism "two-bit" signifying a quarter dollar.

Black Money English term for the debased silver deniers minted in France which circulated freely in England until they were banned by government decree in 1351.

Blank Piece of metal, cut or punched out of a roller bar or strip, and prepared for striking to produce coins. Alternate terms are *flan* and *planchet*.

Blundered Inscription Legend in which the lettering is jumbled or meaningless, indicating the illiteracy of the tribes who copied Greek and Roman coins.

Bonnet Piece Scottish gold coin, minted in 1539–40. The name is derived from the obverse portraying King James V in a large, flat bonnet.

Bon Pour French for "good for", inscribed on Chamber of Commerce brass tokens issued in 1920–7 during a shortage of legal tender coinage.

Bouquet Sou Canadian copper token halfpenny of 1837 deriving its name from the nosegay of heraldic flowers on the obverse.

Box Coin Small container formed by *obverse* and *reverse* of two coins, hollowed out and screwed together.

Bracteate (Latin *bractea*, a thin piece of metal) Coins struck on blanks so thin that the image applied to one side appears in reverse on the other. First minted in Erfurt and Thuringia in the 12th century, and later produced elsewhere in Germany, Switzerland and Poland till the 14th century.

Brass Alloy of copper and zinc, widely used for subsidiary coinage. The term was also formerly used for bronze Roman coins, known numismatically as first, second or third brass.

Commonwealth halfcrown "Breeches Money".

Breeches Money Derisive term given by the Royalists to the coinage of the Commonwealth, 1651, the conjoined elongated oval shields on the reverse resembling a pair of breeches.

Brockage Mis-struck coin with only one design, normal on one side and *incuse* on the other. This occurs when a coin previously struck adheres to the die and strikes the next blank to pass through the press.

Broken Bank-note Note issued by a bank which has failed, but often applied more generally to banknotes which have been demonetised.

Bronze Alloy of copper and tin, first used as a coinage metal by the Chinese c. 1000 BC. Often used synonymously with copper, though it should be noted that bronze only superseded copper as the constituent of the base metal British coins in 1860.

Bull Neck Popular term for the coins of King George III, 1816–17.

Bullet Money Pieces of silver, *globular* in shape, bearing various *countermarks* and used as coins

in Siam (Thailand) in the 18th and 19th centuries.

Bullion Precious metal in bars, ingots, strip or scrap (i.e. broken jewellery mounts, watch-cases and plate), its weight reckoned solely by weight and fineness, before being converted into coin.

Bullion Coin A coin struck in platinum, gold or silver, whose value is determined solely by the prevailing market price for the metal as a commodity. Such coins do not generally have a nominal face value, but include in their inscriptions their weight and fineness. Good examples of recent times include the Krugerrand (South Africa), the Britannia (UK), the Maple Leaf (Canada), Libertad (Mexico), the Nugget (Australia) and the Eagle (USA).

Bun Coinage British coins of 1860–94 showing Queen Victoria with her hair in a bun.

Bungtown Coppers Derisive term (from Anglo-American slang *bung*, to swindle or bribe) for halfpence of English or Irish origin, often counterfeit, which circulated in North America towards the end of the colonial period.

Carat (American *Karat*) Originally a unit of weight for precious stones, based on carob seeds (ceratia), it also denotes the fineness or purity of gold, being 1/24th part of the whole. Thus 9 carat gold is .375 fine and 22 carat, the English sovereign standard, is .916 fine. Abbreviated as ct or kt.

Cartwheel Popular term for the large and cumbersome penny and twopenny pieces of 1797 weighing one and two ounces, struck by Matthew Boulton at the Soho Mint, Birmingham.

Cased Set Set of coins in mint condition, housed in the official case issued by the mint. Formerly leather cases with blue plush or velvet lining were used, but nowadays many sets are encapsulated in plastic to facilitate handling.

Cash (from Portuguese *caixa*, Hindi *kasu*). Round piece of bronze or brass with a square hole in the centre, used as subsidiary coinage in China for almost 2000 years, till the early 12th century. In Chinese these pieces were known as *Ch'ien* or *Li* and strung together in groups of 1000 were equivalent to a silver tael.

Cast Coins Coins cast from molten metals in moulds. This technique, widespread in the case of early commemorative medals, has been used infrequently in coins, the vast majority of which are struck from *dies*. Examples of cast coins include the Chinese cash and the Manx coins of 1709.

Check A form of *token* given as a means of identification, or issued for small amounts of money or for services of a specific nature.

Cheque (American *Check*) A written order directing a bank to pay money.

Chop (Hindi, to seal). Countermark, usually consisting of a single character, applied by Chinese merchants to precious metal coins and ingots as a guarantee of their weight and fineness. Coins may be found with a wide variety of chop marks and the presence of several different marks on the same coin considerably enhances its interest and value. See also *Shroff mark*.

Christmas Coins issued as Christmas gifts date from the Middle Ages when the Venetian Doges struck *Osselle* as presents for their courtiers. In modern times, however, the custom has developed only since the late 1970s, several countries having issued attractive coins at Christmas since then.

Cistophori (Greek for chest bearing) a generic term for the coins of Pergamum with an obverse motif of a serpent crawling out of the half-opened lid. Cistophori became very popular all over Asia Minor in the 3rd and 2nd centuries BC and were struck also at mints in Ionia, Phrygia, Lydia and Mysia.

Clad Coins Coins with a core of one alloy, covered with a layer or coating of another. US half dollars from 1965 to 1970, for example, had a core of 21 per cent silver and 79 per cent copper, bonded to outer layers of 80 per cent silver and 20 per cent copper. More recently, however, coins usually have a body in a cheap alloy, with only a thin cladding of a more expensive material, such as the British 1p and 2p coins of stainless steel with a copper cladding, introduced late in 1992.

Clash Marks Mirror image traces found on a coin which has been struck from a pair of dies, themselves damaged by having been struck together without a blank between.

Clipped Coins Precious metal coins from which small amounts have been removed by clipping the edges. It was to prevent this that *graining* and *edge inscriptions* were adopted.

Cob Crude, irregularly shaped silver piece, often with little more than a vestige of die impressions, produced in the Spanish American mints in the 16th–18th centuries.

Coin Piece of metal, marked with a device, issued by government authority and intended for use as money.

Collar Retaining ring within which the *dies* for the *obverse* and *reverse* operate. When the *blank* is struck under high pressure between the dies the metal flows sideways and is formed by the collar, taking up the impression of *reeding* or *edge inscription* from it.

Commemorative Coin, medal, token or paper note issued to celebrate a current event or the anniversary of a historic event or personality.

Examples of communion tokens.

Communion Token Token, cast in lead, but later struck in pewter, brass, bronze or white metal, issued to members of a congregation to permit them to partake of the annual communion service in the Calvinist and Presbyterian churches. John Calvin himself is said to have invented the communion token in 1561 but they were actually referred to in the minutes of the Scottish General Assembly in 1560. Later they were adopted by the Reformed churches in many parts of Europe. They survived in Scotland till the early years of this century. Each parish had its own tokens, often bearing the names or initials of individual ministers, with dates, symbols and biblical texts.

Conjoined Term denoting overlapped profiles of two or more rulers (e.g. William and Mary).

Contorniate (from Italian *contorno*, edge). Late 4th and 5th century Roman bronze piece whose name alludes to the characteristic grooving on the edges.

Contribution Coins Coins struck by Bamberg, Eichstatt, Fulda and other German cities in the 1790s during the First Coalition War against the French Republic. The name alludes to the fact that the bullion used to produce the coins necessary to pay troops was raised by contribution from the Church and the public.

Convention Money Any system of coinage agreed by neighbouring countries for mutual acceptance and interchange. Examples include the Amphictyonic coins of ancient Greece, and the Austrian and Bavarian talers and gulden of 1753–1857 which were copied by other south German states and paved the way for the German Monetary union.

Copper Metallic element, chemical symbol *Cu*, widely used as a coinage medium for 2,500 years. Pure or almost pure copper was used for subsidiary coinage in many countries till the mid-19th century, but has since been superseded by copper alloys which are cheaper and more durable: *bronze* (copper and tin), *brass* (copper and zinc), *Bath metal* or *bell metal* (low-grade copper and tin), *aluminium-bronze* (copper and aluminium), *potin* (copper, tin, lead and silver) or *cupro-nickel* (copper and nickel). Copper is also alloyed with gold to give it its reddish hue, and is normally alloyed with silver in coinage metals. When the copper exceeds the silver content the alloy is known as *billon*.

Copperhead Popular term for a copper *token* about the size and weight of an American cent which circulated in the USA during the Civil War (1861–65) during a shortage of subsidiary coinage. Many different types were produced, often of a political or patriotic nature.

Coppernose Popular name for the debased silver shillings of Henry VIII. Many of them were struck in copper with little more than a silver wash which tended to wear off at the highest point of the obverse, the nose on the full-face portrait of the king.

Counter A piece resembling a coin but intended for use on a medieval accountancy board or in gambling. See also *jeton*.

Counterfeit Imitation of a coin, token or banknote intended for circulation to deceive the public and defraud the state.

Countermark Punch mark applied to a coin some time after its original issue, either to alter its nominal value, or to authorise its circulation in some other country.

Cowrie Small shell (*Cypraea moneta*) circulating as a form of primitive currency from 1000 BC (China) to the present century (East and West Africa) and also used in the islands of the Indian and Pacific Oceans.

Crockard Debased silver imitation of English pennies produced in the Netherlands and imported into England in the late 13th century. Edward I tried to prevent their import then, in 1299, allowed them to pass current as halfpennies. As they contained more than a halfpennyworth of silver this encouraged their trading in to be melted down and they disappeared from circulation within a year. Sometimes known as *pollards*. See also *lushbourne*.

Crown Gold Gold of 22 carat (.916) fineness, so called on account of its adoption in 1526 for the English gold crown. It has remained the British standard gold fineness ever since.

Cumberland Jack Popular name for a counter or medalet of sovereign size, struck unofficially in 1837 in brass. The figure of St George was replaced by the Duke of Cumberland on horseback with the inscription "To Hanover" a reference to the unpopular Duke of Cumberland, uncle of Queen Victoria, who succeeded to the

Hanoverian throne since Victoria, as a female, was debarred by Salic law from inheritance.

Cupellation (Latin *cupella*, a little cup). Process by which gold and silver were separated from lead and other impurities in their ores. A cupel is a shallow cup of bone-ash or other absorbent material which, when hot, absorbs any molten material that wets its surface. Lead melts and oxidises with impurities into the cupel, whereas gold and silver remain on the cupel. Cupellation is also used in assaying the fineness of these precious metals.

Cupro-nickel Coinage alloy of 75 per cent copper and 25 per cent nickel, now widely used as a base metal substitute for silver. A small amount of zinc is added to the alloy in modern Russian coins.

Currency Coins, tokens, paper notes and other articles intended to pass current in general circulation as money.

Current Coins and paper money still in circulation.

Cut Money Coins cut into smaller pieces to provide correspondingly smaller denominations. The cross on many medieval coins assisted the division of silver pennies into halfpence and farthings. Spanish dollars were frequently divided into *bits* which themselves became units of currency in America and the West Indies.

Darlehnskassen (German for "state loan notes"). Paper money issued during the First World War in an abortive bid to fill the shortage of coinage in circulation. These low-denomination notes failed to meet demand and were superseded by local issues of small *Notgeld* in 1916.

Debasement The reduction in the precious metal content of the coinage, widely practised since time immemorial by governments for economic reasons. British coins, for example, were debased from sterling (.925 fine) silver to .500 in 1920 and from silver to cupro-nickel in 1947.

Decimalisation A currency system in which the principal unit is subdivided into ten, a hundred, or a thousand fractions. Russia was the first country to decimalise, in 1534 when the rouble of 100 kopeks was introduced, but it was not till 1792 that France adopted the franc of 100 centimes and 1793 when the USA introduced the dollar of 100 cents. Most European countries decimalised their currency in the 19th century. Britain toyed with the idea, introducing the florin or tenth of a pound in 1849 as the first step, but did not complete the process till 1971. The last countries to decimalise were Malta and Nigeria, in 1972 and 1973 respectively.

Demidiated Heraldic term to describe the junction of two armorial devices, in which only half of each is shown.

Demonetisation The withdrawal of coins or paper money from circulation and declaring them to be worthless.

Device Heraldic term for the pattern or emblem on coins or paper notes.

Die Hardened piece of metal bearing a mirror image of the device to be struck on one side of a coin or medal.

Die Proof An impression, usually pulled on soft carton or India paper, of an *intaglio* engraving of a banknote, usually taken during the progress of the engraving to check the detail. Banknote proofs of this nature usually consist of the portrait or some detail of the design, such as the border, rather than the complete motif.

Dodecagonal Twelve-sided, a term applied to the nickel-brass threepence of Great Britain, 1937–67.

Dump Any primitive coin struck on a very thick *flan*, but more specifically applied to the circular pieces cut from the centre of Spanish dollars, countermarked with the name of the colony, a crown and the value, and circulated in New South Wales at 15 pence in 1813. See *Holey Dollar*.

Duodecimal Currency system based on units of twelve, i.e. medieval money of account (12 denarii = 1 soldo) which survived in Britain as 12 pence to the shilling as late as 1971.

Ecclesiastical Coins Coins struck by a religious authority, such as an archbishop, bishop, abbot, prior or the canons of a religious order. Such coins were common in medieval times but survived as late as the early 19th century, the bishops of Breslau (1817) and Gurk (1823) being the last prelates to exercise coinage rights. Coins were struck by authority of the Pope at Rome till 1870 but since 1929 coinage has been struck at the Italian state mint on behalf of the Vatican City State.

Edge Inscription Lettering on the edge of a coin or medal to prevent clipping. Alluding to this, the Latin motto *Decus et Tutamen* (an ornament and a safeguard) was applied to the edge of English milled coins in the reign of Charles II.

Edge Ornament An elaboration of the *graining* found on many milled coins to prevent clipping, taking the form of tiny leaves, florets, interlocking rings, pellets and zigzag patterns. In some cases the ornament appears between layers of more conventional reeding.

EF Abbreviation for Extremely Fine.

Effigy An image or representation of a person, normally the head of state, a historical personage,

or an allegorical figure, usually on the *obverse* or "heads" side of a coin or medal.

Electrotype A reproduction of a coin or medal made by an electrolytic process.

Electrum Alloy of gold and silver, sometimes called white gold, used for minting the staters of Lydia, 7th century BC, and other early European coins.

Elongated Coin An oval *medalet* created by passing a coin, such as an American cent, between rollers under pressure with the effect of squeezing it out and impressing on it a souvenir or commemorative motif.

A Mafeking siege note, an example of emergency money.

Emergency Money Any form of money used intimes of economic and political upheaval, when traditional kinds of currency are not available. Examples include the comparatively crude silver coins issued by the Royalists during the *Civil War* (1642–49), *obsidional* money, issued in time of siege, from Tyre (1122) to Mafeking (1900), the *Notgeld* issued by many German towns (1916–23), *encased money*, *fractional currency*, *guerrilla notes*, *invasion*, *liberation* and *occupation money* from the two World Wars and minor campaigns. Among the more recent examples may be cited the use of sweets and cheques in Italy (1976–77) and the issue of coupons and vouchers in many of the countries of the former Soviet Union pending the introduction of their own distinctive coins and notes.

Enamelled Coins Coins decorated by enamelling the obverse and reverse motifs in contrasting colours was an art practised by many jewellers in Birmingham and Paris in the 19th century, and revived in Europe and America in the 1970s.

Encased Money Postage and revenue stamps enclosed in small metal and mica-faced discs, circulated as small change in times of emergency.

The practice was invented by John Gault, a Boston sewing-machine salesman, during the American Civil War (1862). The face of the stamp was visible through the transparent window, while the back of the disc was embossed with firms' advertisements. This practice was revived during and after the First World War when there was again a shortage of small coins. Encased stamps have also been recorded from France, Austria, Norway, Germany and Monaco. See also *Stamp Money*.

Engrailing Technical term for the close serrations or vertical bars round the edge of a coin, applied as a security device.

Engraving The art of cutting lines or grooves in plates, blocks or dies. Numismatically this takes the form of engraving images into the face of the dies used in striking coins, a process which has now been almost completely superseded by *hubbing* and the use of *reducing machinery*. In the production of paper money, *intaglio* engraving is still commonly practised. In this process the engraver cuts the design into a steel die and the printing ink lies in the grooves. The paper is forced under great pressure into the grooves and picks up the ink, and this gives banknotes their characteristic ridged feeling to the touch. Nowadays many banknotes combine traditional intaglio engraving with multicolour lithography or photogravure to defeat the would-be counterfeiter.

Epigraphy The study of inscriptions, involving the classification and interpretation of coin legends, an invaluable adjunct to the study of a coin series, particularly the classical and medieval coins which, in the absence of dates and mintmarks, would otherwise be difficult to arrange in chronological sequence.

Erasion The removal of the title or effigy of a ruler from the coinage issued after his or her death. This process was practised in imperial Rome, and applied to the coins of Caligula, Nero and Geta, as part of the more general practice of *damnatio memoriae* (damnation of the memory) ordered by the Senate.

Error Mistakes on coins and paper money may be either caused at the design or engraving stage, or as a result of a fault in the production processes. In the first category come misspellings in legends causing, in extreme cases, *blundered inscriptions*, or anachronisms or inaccuracies in details of the design. In the second, the most glaring error is the mule caused by marrying the wrong dies. Faulty alignment of dies can cause obverse and reverse to be out of true. Although many coins are issued with obverse and reverse upside down in

relation to each other, this can also occur as an error in coins where both sides should normally be facing the same way up. Other errors caused at the production stage include striking coins in the wrong metal or with the wrong *collar* thus creating a different edge from the normal (e.g. British 10p with scalloped Hong Kong edge).

Essay (From the French *essai*, a trial piece). The term is applied to any piece struck for the purposes of examination, by parliamentary or financial bodies, prior to the authorisation of an issue of coins or paper money. The official nature of these items distinguishes them from *patterns*, which denote trial pieces often produced by mints or even private individuals bidding for coinage contracts.

Evasion Close copy or imitation of a coin, with sufficient deliberate differences in the design or inscription to avoid infringing counterfeit legislation. A good example is the imitation of Sumatran coins by European merchants, inscribed SULTANA instead of SUMATRA.

Exergue Lower segment of a coin or medal, usually divided from the rest of the *field* by a horizontal line, and often containing the date, value, ornament or identification symbols.

Exonumia Generic term for numismatic items not authorised by a government, e.g. *patterns*, *tokens*, *medalets* or *model coins*.

Face The surface of a coin, medal or token, referred to as the *obverse* or the *reverse*. The corresponding faces of a paper note are more correctly termed *verso* and *recto*, but the coin terms are often used instead.

Facing Term for the portrait, usually on the obverse, which faces to the front instead of to the side (profile).

Fantasy Piece of metal purporting to be the coinage of a country which does not exist. Recent examples include the money of Atlantis and the Hutt River Province which declared its independence of Western Australia.

FDC Abbreviation for *Fleur de Coin*, a term denoting the finest possible condition of a coin.

Fiat Money Paper notes issued by a government but not redeemable in coin or bullion.

Field Flat part of the surface of a coin or medal, between the *legend*, the *effigy* and other raised parts of the design.

Fillet Heraldic term for the ribbon or headband on the effigy of a ruler or allegorical figure.

Find Term applied to an archaeological discovery of one or more coins. A large quantity of such material is described as a *hoard*.

Flan Alternative name for *blank* or *planchet*, the piece of metal struck between dies to produce a coin or medal.

Forgery An unauthorised copy or imitation, made with the intention of deceiving collectors. Forgeries intended to pass current for real coins or notes are more properly called *counterfeits*.

Fractional Currency Emergency issue of small-denomonation notes by the USA in 1863–5, following a shortage of coins caused by the Civil War. This issue superseded the *Postage Currency* notes, but bore the inscription "Receivable for all US stamps", alluding to the most popular medium of small change at that time. Denominations ranged from 3c to 50c.

Franklinium Cupro-nickel alloy developed by the Franklin Mint of Philadelphia and used for coins, medals and gaming tokens since 1967.

Freak An *error* or *variety* of a non-recurring type, usually caused accidentally during production.

Frosting Matt surface used for the high relief areas of many proof coins and medals, for greater contrast with the mirrored surface of the field.

Funeral Money Imitations of banknotes, used in China and Latin America in funeral ceremonies.

Geat (Git) Channel through which molten metal is ducted to the mould. Cast coins and medals often show tiny protrusions known as geat marks.

Ghost Faint image of the design on one side of a coin visible on the other. Good examples were the British penny and halfpenny of George V, 1911–27, the ghosting being eliminated by the introduction of a smaller effigy in 1928.

Globular Coins struck on very thick *dumps* with convex faces. The term is applied to some Byzantine coins, and also the *bullet money* of Siam (Thailand).

Godless (or *Graceless*) Epithet applied to any coin which omits the traditional reference to the deity, e.g. the British florin of 1849 which omitted D.G. (*Dei Gratia*, "by the Grace of God").

Gold Precious metal, atomic symbol and numismatic abbreviation *Au*, from the *Latin Aurum*, used as a coinage medium from the 7th century BC till the present day. The purity of gold is reckoned in *carats* or a decimal system. Thus British gold sovereigns are 22 carat or .916 fine. Medieval coins were 23.5 carat or .995 fine, and some modern bullion coins are virtually pure gold, denoted by the inscription .999. Canadian maple leaves are now struck in "four nines" gold and bear the inscription .9999.

Goodfor Popular name for token coins and *emergency money* made of paper or card, from the inscription "Good for" or its equivalent in other languages (e.g. French *Bon pour* or Dutch *Goed voor*) followed by a monetary value. They have been recorded from Europe, Africa and America during times of economic crises or shortage of more traditional coinage.

Gothic Crown Popular name for the silver crown issued by the United Kingdom (1847–53), so-called on account of its script (more properly Old English, rather than Gothic).

Grain The weight of a single grain of wheat was taken as the smallest unit of weight in England. The troy grain was 1/5760 of a pound, while the avoirdupois grain was 1/7000 pound, the former being used in the weighing of precious metals and thus employed by numismatists in weighing coins. A grain is 1/480 troy ounce or 0.066 gram in the metric system.

Graining Term sometimes used as a synonym for the *reeding* on the edge of milled coins.

Gripped Edge Pattern of indentations found on the majority of American cents of 1797, caused by the milling process. Coins of the same date with a plain edge are rather scarcer.

Guerrilla Money Money issued in areas under the control of guerrillas and partisans during wartime range from the *veld ponds* of the Boers (1900–2) to the notes issued by the Garibaldi Brigade in Italy and the anti-fascist notes of Tito's forces in Yugoslavia. The most prolific issues were those produced in Luzon, Mindanao and Negros Occidental by the Filipino resistance during the Japanese occupation (1942–5).

Guilloche French term signifying the intricate pattern of curved lines produced by the rose engine and used as a security feature in the production of banknote, cheques, stocks and share certificates.

Gun Money Emergency coinage of Ireland (1689–91) minted from gunmetal, a type of bronze used in the casting of cannon. All denominations of James II, from the sixpence to the crown, normally struck in silver, were produced in this base metal.

Gutschein German word for voucher or coupon, denoting the paper money used aboard ships of the Imperial Navy during the First World War. The last issue was made at Scapa Flow, 1918–19, during the internment of the High Seas Fleet.

Hammered Term denoting coins produce by the traditional method of striking a *flan* laid on an anvil with a hammer. A characteristic of hammered coins is their uneven shape which tended to encourage *clipping*. This abuse was gradually eliminated by the introduction of the screw press in the 15th century and the mechanisation of coining processes in the course of the 16th and 17th centuries.

Hard Times Token Copper piece the size of the large cent, issued in the USA, 1834–44, during a shortage of coins caused by the collapse of the Bank of the United States, the panic of 1837 and the economic crisis of 1839, the landmarks in the period known as the Hard Times. Banks suspended *specie* payments and the shortage of coinage was filled by tradesmen's tokens. Many of these were more in the nature of satirical *medalets* than circulating pieces.

Hat Piece Alternative name for the *bonnet piece* of James VI of Scotland, 1591.

Hell Notes Imitation paper money used in Chinese funeral ceremonies and buried with the dead to pay for services in the next world.

Hoard Accumulation of coins concealed in times of economic or political upheaval and discovered, often centuries later. Under English common law, such hoards are subject to th law of *treasure trove* if they contain precious metal.

Hog Money Popular name for the early coinage of Bermuda, issued about 1616. The coins were minted in brass with a silver wash and circulated at various values from twopence to a shilling. They derived their name from the hog depicted on the obverse, an allusion to the pigs introduced to the island in 1515 by Juan Bermudez.

Holed Term denoting two different categories: (a) coins which have been pierced for suspension as a form of jewellery or talisman, and (b) coins which have a hole as part of their design. In the latter category come the Chinese *cash* with a square hole, and numerous issues of the 19th and 20th centuries from many countries, with the object of reducing weight and metal without sacrificing overall diameter.

Holey Dollar Spanish silver peso of 8 reales with the centre removed. The resultant ring was counter-marked "New South Wales" and dated 1813, with "Five Shillings" on the reverse, and placed into circulation during a shortage of British coin. The centre, known as a *dump*, was circulated at 15 pence.

Hub Heavy circular piece of steel on which the *die* for a coin or medal is engraved. The process of cutting the die and transferring the master die, by means of intermediary *punches*, to the die from which the coins will be struck, is known as hubbing. Soft steel is used in the preliminary process, and after the design has been transferred, the hub is hardened by chemical action.

Hybrid Alternative name for a *mule*.

Imitation Money Also known as play money or toy money, it consists of coins and notes produced for games of chance (like Monopoly), children's toy shops and post offices, as tourist souvenirs, or for political satire (e.g. the shrinking pound or dollar). See also *funeral money, hell notes, model coins* and *skit notes*.

Imprint Inscription on a paper note giving the name of the printer.

Incuse Impression which cuts into the surface of a coin or medal, as opposed to the more usual raised relief. Many of the earliest coins, especially those with a device on one side only, bear an incuse impression often in a geometric pattern. An incuse impression appears on one side of the coins, reflecting the image on the other side. Few modern coins have had an incuse design, notable examples being the American half and quarter eagle gold coins of 1908–29 designed by Bela Pratt. Incuse inscriptions on a raised rim, however, are more common, and include the British *Cartwheel* coins of 1797 and the 20p coins since 1982.

Inflation Money Coins produced as a result of inflation date back to Roman times when bronze minimi, little bigger than a pinhead, circulated as denarii. Nearer the present day inflation has had devastating effects on the coinge and banknotes of Germany (1921–3), Austria (1923), Poland (1923), Hungary (1945–6) Greece (1946) and many Latin American countries since the 1980s. Hungary holds the record for the highest value of any note ever issued — one thousand million adopengos, equivalent to 20,000,000,000,000,000,000,000,000,000 pengos.

Ingot Piece of precious metal, usually cast in a mould, and stamped with the weight and fineness. though mainly used as a convenient method of storing bullion, ingots have been used as currency in many countries, notably Russia and Japan.

Intaglio Form of *engraving* in which lines are cut into a steel die for the recess-printing of banknotes.

Intrinsic The net metallic value of a coin, as distinguished from the nominal or face value.

Iron Metal, chemical symbol Fe (from Latin *Ferrum*), used as a primitive form of currency from classical times onwards. Iron spits (obeliskoi) preceded the obol as the lowest unit of Greek coinage, a handful of six spits being worth a drachma (from *drassomai*, "I grasp"). Cast iron coins were issued in China as a substitute for copper *cash*. Many of the emergency token issues of Germany during the First World War were struck in iron. Iron coins were issued by Bulgaria in 1943. See also *Steel*.

Ithyphallic (Greek for "erect penis"). Term descriptive of coins of classical Greece showing a satyr.

Janiform Double profiles back to back, after the Roman god Janus.

Jeton (From French *jeter*, to throw). Alternative term for *counter*, and used originally on the chequerboard employed by medieval accountants. Nuremberg was the most important centre for the production of medieval jetons, often issued in lengthy portrait series. In modern parlance the term is often synonymous with *token*, though more specifically confined to pieces used in vending equipment, parking meters, laundromats, telephones and urban transport systems in many European countries. Apart from security, removing the temptation of vandals to break into the receptacles, the main advantage of such pieces is that they can be retariffed as charges increase, without any alteration in their design or composition, a method that is far cheaper than altering costly equipment to take larger coins.

Jugate (From Latin *jugum*, a yoke). Alternative to *accolated* or *conjoined* to denote overlapping profiles of rulers.

Key Date Term describing the rarest in a long-running series of coins with the dates changed at annual intervals.

Kipperzeit German term meaning the time of clipped money, denoting the period during and after the Thirty Years War (1618–48) in which debased and clipped money was in circulation.

Klippe Rectangular or square pieces of metal bearing the impression of a coin. Coins of this type were first struck in Sweden in the 16th century and were subsequently produced in many of the German states. The idea has been revived in recent years as a medium for striking commemorative pieces.

Knife Money Cast bronze pieces, with an elongated blade and a ring at one end to facilitate stringing together in bunches, were used as currency in China from the 9th century BC until the 19th century.

Kreditivsedlar (Swedish for "credit notes"). The name given to the first issue of paper money made in the western world. Paper money of this type was the brainchild of Johan Palmstruch at Riga in 1652, but nine years elapsed before it was implemented by the Stockholm Bank in Sweden. The notes were redeemable in copper *platmynt*.

Laureate Heraldic term for a laurel wreath, often framing a state emblem or shown, in the Roman fashion, as a crown on the ruler's forehead.

Leather Money Pieces of leather embossed with an official device have been used as money on several occasions, during the sieges of Faenza and Leiden and in the Isle of Man in the 15th and 16th centuries. Several towns in Austria and Germany produced leather tokens during and after the First World War.

Legal Tender Coins or paper money which are declared by law to be current money and which tradesmen and shopkeers are obliged to accept in payment for goods or services. (See *Money and the Law*).

Legend The inscription on a coin or medal.

Liberation Money Paper money prepared for use in parts of Europe and Asia, formerly under Axis occupation. Liberation notes were used in France, Belgium and the Netherlands in 1944–5, while various Japanese and Chinese notes were overprinted for use in Hong Kong when it was liberated in 1945. Indian notes overprinted for use in Burma were issued in 1945–6 when that country was freed from Japanese occupation.

Ligature (From Latin *ligatus*, bound together). Term denoting the linking of two letters in a *legend*, e.g. Æ and Œ.

Long Cross Coinage Type of coinage introduced by King Henry III in 1247, deriving its name from the reverse which bore a cross whose arms extended right to the edge to help safeguard the coins against *clipping*. This remained the style of the silver penny, its fractions and multiples, till the reign of Henry VII, and vestiges of the long cross theme can be seen in the silver coins throughout the remaining years of the Tudor period.

Love Token A coin which has been altered by smoothing one or both surfaces and engraving initials, dates, scenes, symbols of affection and messages thereon.

Lushbourne English word for base pennies of inferior silver, said to have emanated from Luxembourg, from which the name derived. These coins were first minted under John the Blind who adopted the curious spelling of his name EIWANES in the hope that illiterate English merchants might confuse it with EDWARDVS and thus be accepted as coin issued in the name of Edward III. Lushbournes were also minted by Robert of Bethune, William I of Namur and the bishops of Toul during the mid-14th century.

Lustre The sheen or bloom on the surface of an uncirculated coin resulting from the centrifugal flow of metal caused by striking.

Magnimat Trade name used by VDM (*Verein Deutscher Metallwerke*) for a high-security alloy containing copper, nickel and magnetised steel. First used for the 5 deutschemark coin of 1975, it has since been adopted for other high-value coins in Germany and other countries.

Manilla Copper, bronze or brass rings, sometimes shaped like horseshoes and sometimes open, with flattened terminals, used as currency in West Africa until recent years.

Matrix Secondary die for a coin or medal, produced from the master die by means of an intermediate punch. In this way dies can be duplicated from the original cut on the reducing machine.

Matt or Matte Finely granulated surface or overall satin finish to proof coins, a style which was briefly fashionable at the turn of the century. The Edward VII proof set of 1902 is a notable example. In more recent years many issues of the Franklin Mint have been issued in this finish.

Maundy Money Set of small silver coins, in denominations of 1, 2, 3 and 4 pence, distributed by the reigning British monarch to the poor and needy on Maundy Thursday. The custom dates back to the Middle Ages, but in its present form, of distributing pence to as many men and women as the years in the monarch's age, it dates from 1666. At first ordinary silver pennies and multiples were used but after they went out of everyday use distinctive silver coins were produced specifically for the purpose from the reign of George II (1727–60) onwards. For centuries the ceremony took place in Westminster Abbey but since 1955 other venues have been used in alternate years.

Medal (French *medaille*, Italian *medaglia*, from Latin *metallum*). A piece of metal bearing devices and legends commemorating an event or person, or given as an award. Military medals date from the 16th and 17th centuries, but were not generally awarded to all ranks till the 19th century. Commemorative medals can trace their origin back to Roman times, but in their present form they date from the Italian Renaissance when there was a fashion for large-diameter cast portrait medals.

Medalet A small medal, generally 25mm or less in diameter.

Medallion Synonym for medal, but usually confined to those with a diameter of 50mm or more.

Milling Process denoting the mechanical production of coins, as opposed to the handmade technique implied in *hammering*. It alludes to the use of watermills to drive the machinery of the screw presses and blank rollers developed in the 16th century. As the even thickness and diameter of milled coins permitted a security edge, the term milling is popularly, though erroneously, used as a synonym for *graining* or *reeding*.

Mint The place in which coins and medals are produced. Mint condition is a term sometimes used to denote pieces in an uncirculated state.

Mint Set A set of coins or medals in the package or case issued by the mint. See also *year set*.

Mintmark A device appearing on a coin to denote the place of minting. Athenian coins of classical times have been recorded with up to 40 different marks, denoting individual workshops. In the 4th century AD the Romans adopted this system to identify coins struck in provincial mints. This system was widely used in the Middle Ages and survives in France and Germany to this day. Initials and symbols are also used to identify mints, especially where the production of a coin is shared between several different mints. From 1351 onwards symbols were adopted in England to denote periods between trials of the *Pyx*, and thus assist the proper chronological sequence of coins, in an era prior to the adoption of dating. These mintmarks continued into the 17th century, but gradually died out as the use of dates became more widespread. See also *countermark* and *privy mark*.

Mionnet Scale Scale of nineteen diameters covering all sizes of coins belonging to the classical period, devised by the French numismatist, Theodore-Edme Mionnet (1770– 1842) during the compilation of his fifteen-volume catalogue of the numismatic collection in the Bibliotheque Nationale in Paris.

Mirror Finish The highly polished surface of proof coins.

Misstrike A coin or medal on which the impression has been struck off-centre.

Model Coin Tiny pieces of metal, either reproducing the designs of existing coins (used as play money by children) or, more specifically, denoting patterns produced by Joseph Moore and Hyam Hyams in their attempts to promote an improved subsidiary coinage in 19th century Britain. These small coins were struck in bronze with a brass or silver centre and were designed to reduce the size of the existing cumbersome range of pence, halfpence and farthings.

Modified Effigy Any coin in which the profile on the obverse has been subtly altered. Examples include minor changes in the Victorian Young Head and Old Head effigies and the George V profile by Sir Bertram Mackennal.

Money Order Certificate for a specified amount of money, which may be transmitted by post and encashed at a money order office or post office. This system was pioneered by Britain and the United States in the early 19th century and is now virtually worldwide. The term is now confined to certificates above a certain value, the terms *postal order* and *postal note* being used for similar certificates covering small amounts.

Mule Coin whose obverse is not matched with its official or regular reverse. Mules include the erroneous combination of dies from different reigns, but in recent years such hybrids have arisen in mints where coins for several countries are struck. Examples include the Coronation Anniversary crowns combining Ascension and Isle of Man dies and the 2 cent coins with Bahamas and New Zealand dies. *Restrikes* of rare American coins have been detected in which the dated die has been paired with the wrong reverse die, e.g. the 1860 restrike of the rare 1804 large cent.

Mute An *anepigraphic* coin, identifiable only by the devices struck on it.

Nail Mark Small indentation on ancient coins. The earliest coins of Asia Minor developed from the electrum *dumps* which merchants marked with a broken nail as their personal guarantee of value, the ancient counterpart of the *chop* marks used in China and Japan.

NCLT Coins Abbreviation for "Non Circulating Legal Tender", a term devised by modern coin catalogues to denote coins which, though declared *legal tender*, are not intended for general circulation on account of their precious metal content or superior finish.

Nicked Coin Coin bearing a tiny cut or nick in its edge. Silver coins were tested by this method, especially in the reign of Henry I (1100–35) when so many base silver pennies were in circulation. Eventually people refused to accept these nicked coins a problem which was only overcome when the state decreed that all coins should have a nick in them.

Nickel Metallic element, chemical symbol *Ni*, a hard white metal relatively resistant to tarnish, and extensively used as a cheap substitute for silver. It was first used for the American 5 cent coin in 1866, hence its popular name which has stuck ever since, although nowadays the higher denominations are minted in an alloy of copper and nickel. Although best known as a silver substitute, nickel was widely used in Jamaica (1869–1969) for halfpence and pennies and in British West Africa for the tiny 1/10th pennies (1908–57). Pure nickel is used for French francs and German marks, but usually it is alloyed with copper or zinc to produce *cupro-nickel* or nickel brass.

Notaphily Hybrid word from Latin *nota* (note) and Greek philos (love), coined about 1970 to denote the branch of numismatics devoted to the study of paper money.

Notgeld German word meaning emergency money, applied to the *tokens*, in metals, wood, leather and even ceramic materials, issued during the First World War when coinage disappeared from circulation. These tokens were soon superseded by low-denomination paper money issued by shops and businessmen in denominations from 10 to 50 pfennige and known as *kleine Notgeld* (small emergency money). These notes were prohibited in September 1922 but by that time some 50,000 varieties are thought to have been issued. Inflation raced out of control and the government permitted a second issue of local notes, known as *large Notgeld*, as the denominations were in thousands, and latterly millions, of marks. Some 3,600 types appeared in 1922 and over 60,000 in 1923 alone. These colourful mementos of the German hyperinflation ceased to circulate in 1924 when the currency was reformed.

Numismatics The study of coins, medals and other related fields, a term derived from the Latin *numisma* and Greek *nomisma* (money).

Obsidional Currency (From Latin *obsidium*, a siege). Term for *emergency money* produced by the defenders of besieged towns and cities. These usually took the form of pieces of silver plate, commandeered for the purpose, crudely marked with an official device and the value. Instances of such seige coinage have been recorded from the 12th to the 19th centuries. Paper money was issued in Venice during the Austrian siege of 1848, and by Mafeking during the Boer War.

Obverse The "heads" side of a coin or medal, generally bearing the effigy of the head of state or an allegorical figure (e.g. Liberty—Argentina, USA; Helvetia or William Tell—Switzerland; La Semeuse—France).

Off Metal Term denoting a piece struck in a metal other than the officially authorisied or issued alloy. This originally applied to *patterns* which were often struck in lead or copper instead of gold and silver as trial pieces or to test the dies; but in recent years it has applied to collectors' versions, e.g. proofs in platinum, gold or silver of coins normally issued in bronze or cupro-nickel.

Overdate One or more digits in a date altered by superimposing another figure. Alterations of this kind, by means of small hand punches, were made to dated dies so that they could be used in years other than that of the original manufacture. Coins with overdates invariably show traces of the original digit.

Overstrike Coin, token or medal produced by using a previously struck pieces as a flan. The Bank of England dollar of 1804 was overstruck on Spanish pieces of eight, and examples showing traces of the original coins are worth a good premium.

Paduan Name given to imitations of medals and bogus coins produced in Italy in the 16th century, and deriving from the city of Padua where forgeries of bronze sculpture were produced for the antique market.

Patina Oxidation forming on the surface of metallic objects. So far as coins and medals are concerned, this applies mainly to silver, brass, bronze and copper pieces which may acquire oxidation from the atmosphere, or spectacular patination from salts in the ground in which they have been buried. In extreme forms patina leads to verdigris and other forms of rust which corrode the surface, but in uncirculated coins it may be little more than a mellowing of the original *lustre*. Coins preserved in blue velvet presentation cases often acquire a subtle toning from the dyes in the material.

Pattern Piece resembling a coin or medal, prepared by the mint to the specifications or on the authorisation of the coin-issuing authority, but also applied to pieces produced by mints when tendering for coinage or medal contracts. Patterns may differ from the final coins as issued in the type of alloy used (*off metal*) but more often they differ in details of the design.

Pellet Raised circular ornament used as a spacing device between words and abbreviations in the *legend* of coins and medals. Groups of pellets were also used as ornaments in the angles of the cross on the reverse of English silver pennies.

Piece de Plaisir (French for "fancy piece"). Term given to coins struck in a superior precious metal, or to a superior finish, or on a much thicker flan than usual. See *off metal, piedfort* and *proof*.

Piedfort (Piefort) Piece struck with coinage dies on a *flan* of much more than normal thickness. This practice originated in France in the late 16th century and continues to the present day. In recent years it has been adopted by mints in Britain and other countries as a medium for collectors' pieces.

Pile Lower die incorporating the obverse motif, used in striking coins and medals. See also *trussel*.

Planchet French term used as an alternative for *blank* or *flan*.

Plaque or **Plaquette** Terms sometimes used for medals struck on a square or rectangular flan.

Plaster Cast taken from the original model for a coin or medal sculpted by an artist, and used in modern reducing machines in the manufacture of the master *die*.

Plated Coins Coins stuck in base metal but given a wash of silver or some other precious metal. This expedient was adopted in inflationary times, from the Roman Republic (91 BC) till the Tudor period. American cents of 1943 were struck in steel with a zinc coating, and more recently *clad* coins have produced similar results.

Platinum The noblest of all precious metals, platinum has a higher specific gravity than gold and a harder, brighter surface than silver. Until an industrial application was discovered in the mid-19th century, it was regarded as of little value, and was popular with counterfeiters as a cheap substitute for gold in their forgeries which, with a light gold wash, could be passed off as genuine. It was first used for circulating coins in Russia (the chief source of the metal since 1819) and 3, 6 and 12 rouble coins were mined at various times between 1828 and 1845. In recent years platinum has been a popular metal for limited-edition proof coins.

Platmynt (Swedish for "plate money"). Large copper plates bearing royal cyphers and values from half to ten dalers produced in Sweden between 1643 and 1768. They represented laudable attempts by a country rich in copper to produce a coinage in terms of its silver value, but the net result was far too cumbersome to be practical. The weight of the daler plate, for example, ranged from 766 grams to 1.1kg, and special carts had to be devised to transport them!

Plugged Coins Coins struck predominantly in one metal, but containing a small plug of another. This curious practice may be found in the farthings of Charles II (1684–85) and the halfpence or farthings of James II (1685–87), which were struck in tin, with a copper plug, to defeat forgers.

Pollard Alternative name for *crockard*.

Porcelain Money Tokens made of porcelain circulated in Thailand from the late 18th century till 1868. The Meissen pottery struck tokens in 1920–22 as a form of small *Notgeld*, using reddish-brown Bottger stoneware and white *bisque* porcelain. These ceramic tokens circulated in various towns of Saxony.

Postage Currency Small paper notes in denominations of 5, 10, 25 and 50 cents, issued by the US federal government in 1862–63, were thus inscribed and had reproductions of postage stamps engraved on them — five 5c stamps on the 25c and five 10c stamps on the 50c notes. The earliest issue even had perforations in the manner of stamps, but this unnecessary device was soon done away with. See also *stamp money*.

Postal Notes or Orders Low-value notes intended for transmission by post and encashable at post offices. Introduced by Britain in 1883, they were an extension of the earlier *money order* system, and are now issued by virtually every country.

Potin (French for pewter). Alloy of copper, tin, lead and silver used as a coinage metal by the Celtic tribes of eastern Gaul at the beginning of the Christian era.

Privy Mark   Secret mark incorporated in the design of a coin or medal to identify the minter, or even the particular die used. The term is also used more loosely to denote any small symbol or initials appearing on a coin other than a *mint mark*, and is sometimes applied to the symbols associated with the trial of the *Pyx* found on English coins.

Prize Coins   Coins of large size and value struck primarily as prizes in sporting contests. this principle dates from the late 5th century BC when Syracuse minted decadrachms as prizes in the Demareteian Games. The most notable example in modern times is the lengthy series of talers and five-franc coins issued by the Swiss cantons since 1842 as prizes in the annual shooting festivals, the last of which honoured the Lucerne contest of 1939.

Profile   A side view of the human face, widely used as a coinage effigy.

Proof   Originally a trial strike testing the *dies*, but now denoting a special collectors' version struck with dies that have been specially polished on *flans* with a mirror finish. Presses operating at a very slow speed, or multi-striking processes, are also used.

Propaganda Notes   Paper money containing a political slogan or a didactic element. During the Second World War forgeries of German and Japanese notes were produced by the Allies and additionally inscribed or overprinted with slogans such as "Co-Prosperity Sphere—What is it worth?" (a reference to the Japanese occupied areas of SE Asia). Forged dollars with anti-American propaganda were airdropped over Sicily by the Germans in 1943 and counterfeit pounds with Arabic propaganda over Egypt in 1942–43. Various anti-communist organisations liberated propaganda forgeries of paper money by balloon over Eastern Europe during the Cold War period.

Provenance Mark   Form of *privy mark* denoting the source of the metal used in coins. Examples include the plumes or roses on English coins denoting silver from Welsh or West of England mines, and the elephant or elephant and castle on gold coins denoting bullion imported by the African Company. Coins inscribed VIGO (1702–03) or LIMA (1745–46) denote bullion seized from the Spaniards by Anglo-Dutch privateers and Admiral Anson respectively. Other provenance marks on English coins include the letters EIC and SSC, denoting bullion imported by the East India Company or the South Sea Company.

Pseudo Coins   Derisory term coined in recent years to signify pieces of precious metal, often struck in *proof* versions only, aimed at the international investment market. Many of these pieces, though bearing a nominal face value, are not *legal tender* in the countries purporting to issue them and in many cases they go straight from the overseas mint where they are produced to coin dealers in America and western Europe, without ever appearing in the so-called country of origin. See also *NCLT coins*.

Punch or Puncheon   Intermediate *die* whereby working dies can be duplicated from the master die, prior to the striking of coins and medals.

Pyx   Box in which a specimen from every 15 pounds troy weight of gold and every 60 pounds of silver minted in England is kept for annual trial by weight and assay. Many of the *mintmarks* on English coins of the 14th–17th centuries were in use from one trial to the next and still exist today and can therefore be used to date them.

Reducing Machinery   Equipment designed on the pantographic principle for transferring the image from a *plaster* to a *hub* and reducing it to the size of the actual coin or medal. The image is transferred by means of a stylus operating rather like a gramophone needle, but working from the centre to the outer edge.

Reeding   Security edging on coins, consisting of close vertical ridges. As a rule, this appears all round the edge but some coins, e.g. New Zealand's 50c (1967) and the Isle of Man's £1 (1978) have segments of reeding alternating with a plain edge, to help blind and partially sighted persons to identify these coins.

Re-issue   A coin or note issued again after an extended lapse of time.

Relief   Raised parts of the *obverse* and *reverse* of coins and medals, the opposite of *incuse*.

Remainder   A note from a bank or issuing authority which has never been circulated, due to inflation, political changes or bank failure. Such notes, some-times in partial or unfinished state (e.g. missing serial numbers or signatures), are generally unloaded on to the numismatic market at a nominal sum and provide a good source of inexpensive material for the beginner.

Restrike   Coin, medal or token produced from *dies* subsequent to the original use. Usually restrikes are made long after the original and can often be identified by marks caused by damage, pitting or corrosion of the dies after they were taken out of service.

Retrograde   Term describing inscriptions running from right to left, or with the letters in a mirror image, thought to arise from unskilled die-cutters failing to realise that inscriptions have to be engraved in negative form to achieve a positive impression. Retrograde inscriptions are common on ancient Greek coins, but also found on Roman and Byzantine coins.

Reverse The side of a coin or medal regarded as of lesser importance; in colloquial parlance, the "tails" side.

Saltire Heraldic term for a cross in the shape of an X.

Sandwich Coin *blank* consisting of thin outer layers in one alloy bonded to a core in another. See *clad coins*.

Sceat (Anglo-Saxon for "treasure", or German *Schatz*). Money of account in Kent early in the 7th century as the twelfth part of a shilling or Merovingian gold tremissis. As a silver coin, it dates from about AD 680–700 and weighed about 20 grains, putting it on par with the Merovingian denier or penny. Sceats spread to other parts of England in the 8th century but tended to decline in weight and value, but from about 760 it was gradually superseded by the silver penny minted under Offa and his successors.

Scissel The clippings of metal left after a *blank* has been cut. Occasionally one of these clippings accidentally adheres to the blank during the striking process, producing characteristic crescent-shaped flaws on the finished coin.

Scrip Paper money of restricted validity or circulation, e.g. *Bafs* and other military scrip used in canteens and post exchanges.

Scyphate (Greek *scypha*, a skiff or small boat). Byzantine coin with a concave *flan*.

Sede Vacante (Latin for "Vacant See"). Coins struck at *ecclesiastical mints* between the death of a prelate and the election of his successor are often thus inscribed. This practice originated at Rome in the 13th century and spread to every part of Europe.

Seignorage or Seigneurage Royalty or percentage paid by persons bringing *bullion* to a mint for conversion into coin, but nowadays synonymous with the royalty paid by mints in respect of the precious metal versions of coins sold direct to collectors. It arises from the medieval right of the king to a small portion of the proceeds of a mint, and amounted to a tax on moneying. It has also been applied to the money accruing to the state when the coinage is re-issued in an alloy of lesser fineness, as, for example, the debased sovereigns of Henry VIII in 20 instead of 23 carat gold, the king's treasury collecting the difference.

Series Term applied to sets of medals of a thematic character, which first became fashionable in the early 18th century. Jean Dassier pioneered the medallic series in the 1720s with his set of 72 medals portraying the rulers of France till Louis XV. The idea was developed by J. Kirk, Sir

Edward Thomason, J. Mudie and A. J. Stothard in Britain, and by Moritz Fuerst and Amedee Durand in Europe. The fashion died out in the 19th century, but has been revived in America and Europe since 1964.

Serrated Having a notched or toothed edge, rather like a cogwheel. Coins of this type, struck in *electrum*, an alloy of silver and gold, are known from Carthage in the 2nd century BC, and some silver denarii of Rome in the 2nd century AD also come into this category.

Sexagesimal System Monetary system in which the principal unit is divided into 60 parts. The oldest system in the Western world was based on the gold talent of 60 minae and the mina of 60 shekels. In medieval Europe 60 groschen were worth a fine mark; in England from 1551, the silver coinage was based on the crown of 60 pence, and in the south German states till 1873 the gulden was worth 60 kreuzers.

Shin Plasters Derisory term originally applied to the Continental currency notes issued during the American War of Independence, the fractional currency of the Civil War period and also the low-denomination notes of Canada between 1870 and 1935, but often applied indiscriminately to any other low-denomination, small-format notes.

Short Cross Coinage Term for the silver coinage introduced by Henry II in 1180 and minted till 1247 at which time it was replaced by the *Long Cross* type. The termination of the arms of the cross on the reverse well within the circumference encouraged the dishonest practice of *clipping*.

Shroff Mark A *countermark* applied by Indian bankers or merchants to attest the full weight and purity of coins. See also *chop*.

Siege Money See *Obsidional Currency*

Silver Precious metal, chemical symbol *Ag*, numismatic abbreviation *Ar*, from Latin *Argentum*, widely used as a coinage metal from the 6th century BC to the present day. **Sterling silver** denotes an alloy of .925 fine silver with .075 copper. Fine silver alloys used over the past 2,500 years have ranged from .880 to .960 fine, but base silver has also been all too common. British coins from 1920 to 1946 were struck in .500 fine silver, while alloys of lesser fineness are known as *billon* or *vellon*. Silver alloyed with gold produces a metal called *electrum*, used for the earliest coinage of the western world, the staters of Lydia in the 7th century BC. Since 1970 silver as a medium for circulating coinage has virtually disappeared, yet the volume of silver coins for sale to collectors has risen considerably in recent years.

George Cruikshank's famous skit note.

Skit Note   Piece of paper masquerading as a bankntoe. It differs from a *counterfeit* in that its design parodies that of a genuine note, often for political, satirical or advertising reasons. Others were produced as April Fools' Day jokes or a form of Valentine (e.g. the Bank of Lovers). In recent years they have been produced as advertising gimmicks, or as coupons permitting a discount off the list price of goods.

Slug   Popular name for the $50 gold pieces produced by private mints in California in the mid-19th century. The term is also applied nowadays to *tokens* intended for use in gaming machines.

Spade Guinea   Name given to the guineas of George III issued between 1787 and 1799 because the shield on the reverse design resembled the shape of a spade. In Victorian times the spade guinea was extensively copied in brass for gaming counters.

Spade Money   Cast bronze pieces resembling miniature spades and other agricultural implements, used as money and derived from the actual implements which had previously been used in barter. Often referred to as *Pu* or *Boo* money.

Specie   Financial term denoting money in the form of precious metals (silver and gold), usually struck as coin, as opposed to money in the form of paper notes and bills of exchange. It occurs in the name of some European coins (e.g. *speciedaler, speciestaler* and *speciesducat*) to denote the use of fine silver or gold.

Specimen   Generally used to denote a single piece, but more specifically applying to a coin in a special finish, less than *proof* in quality but superior to the general circulating version. It also denotes paper notes intended for circulation between banks or for press publicity and distinguished from the generally issued version by zero serial numbers, punch holes or a security endorsement.

Spintriae   Metal tokens produced in Roman imperial times, with erotic motifs, thought to have been tickets of admission to brothels.

Spit   Copper or iron rod used as a primitive form of currency in the Mediterranean area. The Greek word *belos* meant a spit, dart or bolt, and from this came the word *obolos* used for a coin worth a 6th of a drachma.

Stamp Money   Both postage and revenue (fiscal) stamps have circulated as money during shortages of coins, from the American Civil War onwards. *Encased postage stamps* were used in the USA, 1861–62, before they were superseded by *Postage Currency* notes, but the same expedient was adopted by many countries during and immediately after the First World War. Stamps affixed to special cards have circulated as money in Rhodesia (now Zimbabwe) in 1900, the French colonies and Turkey during the First World War, in Spain during the Civil War (1936–39) and the Philippines during the Japanese occupation (1942–45). Stamps printed on thick card, with an inscription on the reverse signifying their parity with silver coins, were issued in Russia (1917–18) and also in Armenia, the Crimea and the Ukraine (1918–20). During the Second World War Ceylon (now Sri Lanka) and several Indian states issued small money cards with contemporary stamps printed on them.

Steel   Refined and tempered from *iron*, and used in chromed or stainless versions as a coinage metal in the 20th century. Zinc-coated steel cents were issued by the USA (1943) but in the form known as *acmonital* (nickel steel) it has been extensively used by Italy since 1939. Other alloys of nickel and steel have been used for coins of the Philippines (1944–45) and Roumania since 1963. Chrome steel was used by France for 5 centime coins in 1961–64. Copper-clad steel is now extensively used for subsidiary coins formerly struck in bronze.

Sterling   Word of uncertain origin denoting money of a standard weight and fineness, and hence the more general meaning of recognised worth. The tradi-tionally accepted derivation from the Easterlings, north German merchants who settled in London in the 13th century and produced silver pennies of uniform fineness, is unlikely as the term has been found in documents a century earlier. A more plausible explanation is from Old English *steorling* ("little coin with a star"), alluding to Viking pennies with this device, or even as a diminutive of *stater*. Sterling silver denotes silver of .925 fineness.

Stone Money   Primitive currency in the form of large stone discs, used in West Africa in the pre-colonial period, and in the Pacific island of Yap (now Micronesia) as recently as 1940.

Striation A pattern of alternate light and dark parallel marks or minute grooves on the surface of a coin or medal. In the latter case it is sometimes done for textural effect, but in coins it may result from faulty *annealing*. Deliberate ridging of the surface, however, was a distinctive feature of Japanese *koban* and *goryoban* coins of 1736–1862.

Styca Name given to the debased silver *sceats* of Northumbria in the 8th century.

Sutlers' Tokens Tokens issued by US Army canteen-keepers for use on military posts and redeemable in merchandise. They were mainly issued in the second half of the 19th century.

Tael Chinese unit of weight corresponding to the European ounce and sometimes referred to as a liang. It was a measure of silver varying between 32 and 39 grams. In the 19th century it served as *money of account*, 100 British or Mexican trade dollars being worth 72 tael. The term has also been loosely applied to the Chinese silver yuan, although this was worth only .72 tael, or 7 mace and 2 candareens (10 candareens = 1 mace; 10 mace = 1 tael).

Thrymsa Early Anglo-Saxon gold coin based on the Merovingian tremissis or third-solidus, current in Kent, London and York about AD 63–75.

Tical Unit of weight in Thailand, first appearing as coins in the form of crudely shaped *bullet money* current from the 14th till the late 19th centuries. When European-style coins were introduced in 1860 the word was retained as a denomination (32 solot = 16 atts = 8 peinung or sio = 4 songpy or sik = 2 fuang= 1 salung or quarter-tical. The currency was decimalised in 1909 (100 satangs = 1 tical), and the tical was superseded by the baht about 1950.

Tin Metallic element, chemical symbol *St* (from Latin *Stannum*). Because of its unstable nature and tendency to oxidise badly when exposed to the atmosphere, it is unsatisfactory as a coinage metal, but has been used on several occasions, notably in Malaya, Thailand and the East Indies. In was also used for British halfpence and farthings, 1672–92.

Token Any piece of money whose nominal value is greater than its intrinsic value is, strictly speaking, a token or promise. Thus most of the coins issued since 1964 can be regarded in this light, but numismatists reserve the term for a piece of limited validity and circulation, produced by tradesmen, chambers of commerce and other organisations during times of a shortage of government coinage. The term is also loosely applied to metal tickets of admission, such as *communion tokens*, or *jetons* and *counters* intended for games of chance. Tokens with a nominal value may be produced for security reasons to lessen the possibility of theft from milk bottles, vending machines, telephones, parking meters and transport facilities. Tokens exchangeable for goods have been issued by co-operative societies and used in prisons and internment camps in wartime. In addition to the traditional coinage alloys, tokens have been produced in ceramics, plastics, wood, stout card, leather and even rubber, in circular, square or polygonal shapes.

Tombac Type of brass alloy with a high copper content, used in coinage requiring a rich golden colour. It is, in fact, a modern version of the *aurichalcum* used by the Romans. It was used for the Canadian 5-cent coins of 1942–43, while 5- and 10-pfennig coins of Germany have a tombac cladding on a steel core.

Touchpiece Coin kept as a lucky charm, but more specifically the medieval gold angel of England which was worn round the neck as an antidote to scrofula, otherwise known as king's evil, from the belief that the reigning monarch possessed the power of healing by touch. The ceremony of touching for king's evil involved the suspension of an angel round the victim's neck, hence the prevalence of these coins pierced for suspension.

Trade Coins Coins widely used as a medium of international trade, often far beyond the boundaries of the country issuing them. The earliest examples were the Aiginetan turtles and Athenian tetrdrachms of the classical period. In the Middle Ages the English *sterling* was widely prized on account of its silver purity. Arab dinars and Italian florins were popular as gold coins in late-medieval times, while the British gold sovereign has been the preferred gold coin of modern times. The Maria Theresa silver thaler of Austria, with its date frozen at 1782, has been minted widely down to the present time for circulation in the Near and Middle East as a trade coin. Trade dollars were minted by Britain, the USA, the Netherlands and Japan to compete with the Spanish, and later the Mexican, peso or 8-reales coins as a trading medium in the Far East.

Transport Tokens Coin-like pieces of metal, plastic or card, issued by companies and corporations to employees and exchangeable for rides on municipal transport systems, date from the mid-19th century. In more recent times similar tokens have been used in many countries to activate turnstiles in buses, trams and rapid-transit railway systems.

Treasury Note Paper money worth 10 shillings or one pound, issued by the British Treasury on the outbreak of the First World War when *specie* payments were suspended, and continuing till 1928 when the Bank of England took over responsibility for note-issuing. They were popularly known as Bradburys, from the signature of the Treasury official, Sir John Bradbury, engraved on them.

Treasure Trove Articles of precious metal concealed in times of economic or political upheaval and discovered years (often centuries) later are deemed by law to be treasure trove (from the French word *trouve*, found). For further details see *Money and the Law*.

Trial Plate Plate of the same metal as the current coinage against which the fineness and quality of the coins being produced are compared and tested.

Troy Weight System of weights derived from the French town of Troyes whose standard pound was adopted in England in 1526. It continued in Britain till 1879 when it was abolished, with the exception of the troy ounce and its decimal parts and multiples, which were retained for gold, silver, platinum and precious stones. The troy ounce of 480 grains is used by numismatists for weighing coins.

Truncation Stylised cut at the base of a coinage effigy, sometimes containing a die number, engraver's initials or *mintmark*.

Trussel Reverse die in *hammered* coinage, the opposite of the *pile*.

Type Principal motif on a coin or medal, enabling numismatists to identify the issue.

Type Set A set of coins comprising one of each coin in a particular series, regardless of the actual date of issue.

Uncirculated Term used in grading coins to denote specimens in perfect condition, with original mint lustre. In recent years the term "Brilliant Uncirculated" has been adopted (abbreviated as B.Unc. or BU).

Uniface Coin, medal or token with a device on one side only.

Unique Extant in only one known example.

Variety Variation in, or modification of type, effigy, motif or inscription.

Vecture Term (mainly American) for a *transport token*.

Veld Pond (Dutch for "field pound"). Gold coin struck by the Boer guerrillas at Pilgrims Rest in 1902, in imitation of the British sovereign.

Vellon Spanish form of *billon*.

VF Abbreviation for Very Fine, used to describe the state of a coin or medal.

VG Abbreviation for Very Good.

Vignette Strictly speaking the pictorial element of a paper note shading off into the surrounding unprinted paper rather than having a clearly defined border or frame; but nowadays applied generally to the picture portion of a banknote, as opposed to portrait, armorial or numeral elements.

Vis-à-Vis (French for "face to face"). Term describing coins with double portraits of rulers, their profiles or busts facing each other. A good example is the English coinage of Philip and Mary, 1554–48.

Wampum Barter currency of the North American Indians, composed of shells of *Venus mercenaria* strung together to form belts or "fathoms" worth 5 shillings. Wampum were tariffed variously from three to six to the English penny in the American colonies till 1704.

White Gold Alternative term for *electrum*.

Wire Money Primitive currency of the Maldive Islands in the form of lengths of silver wire known as lari, from which the modern currency unit *laree* is derived. The term was also applied to English coins of the 18th century in which the numerals of value were exceptionally thin, resembling wire.

Wooden Coins Thin pieces of wood used as tokens are known from the 19th and 12th centuries in many parts of China and Africa, and as small *Notgeld* from Austria and Germany during the First World War. Wooden nickels are the somewhat contradictory name given to tokens of a commemorative nature, widely popular in the USA since 1930.

Year Set A set of coins issued annually by a mint. Such a set often contains specimens which were not generally released for circulation in that year.

Young Head Profile of Queen Victoria sculpted by William Wyon for the Guildhall Medal of 1837 and subsequently utilised for British coins struck from 1837 to 1860 (copper) and 1887 (silver and gold).

Zinc Metallic element, chemical symbol *Zn*, widely used, with copper, as a constituent of brass, although it was not isolated till the 18th century. Alloyed with copper to form *tombac*, it was used for Canadian 5-cent coins (1942–43) and, coated on steel, it was used for American cents (1943). Zinc was used for *emergency coinage* in Austria, Belgium, Luxembourg and Germany (1915–18) and in Germany and German-occupied countries during the Second World War. Since then alloys of copper, nickel and zinc have been used for coinage in Eastern Europe, and an alloy of zinc with titanium has been developed in the 1970s as a potential substitute for *bronze* in subsidiary coinage.

Mintmarks
of the world

The following is a list of the initials and symbols denoting mints. In many cases, notably the Royal Mint, no mintmark was used on either British coins or those struck on behalf of other countries. Conversely many countries have only used one mintmark, that of one or other of the leading private mints.

It should be noted that the mintmarks of the main private mints have been recorded on the coins of the following countries:

H (Heaton, later the Birmingham Mint): Australia, Bolivia, British Honduras, British North Borneo, British West Africa, Bulgaria, Canada, Ceylon, Chile, Colombia, Costa Rica, Cyprus, Dominican Republic, East Africa, Ecuador, Egypt, El Salvador, Finland, French Indochina, Great Britain, Greece, Guatemala, Guernsey, Haiti, Hong Kong, Iran, Israel, Italy, Jamaica, Jersey, Liberia, Malaya and British Borneo, Mauritius, Mombasa, Mozambique, Newfoundland, Nicaragua, Poland, Roumania, Sarawak, Serbia, Siam, Straits Settlements, Uruguay and Venezuela.

FM (Franklin Mint, Philadelphia): Bahamas, Belize, British Virgin Islands, Cayman Islands, Cook Islands, Guyana, Jamaica, Liberia, Malaysia, Malta, Panama, Papua New Guinea, Philippines, Solomon Islands, Trinidad and Tobago.

PM (Pobjoy Mint, Sutton, Surrey): Ascension, Bosnia, Cook Islands, Gibraltar, Isle of Man, Liberia, Macau, Niue, Philippines, St Helena, Senegal, Seychelles, Tonga and Tristan da Cunha.

ALBANIA
L	London
R	Rome
V	Valona

ARGENTINA
BA	Buenos Aires
Bs	Buenos Aires
B.AS	Buenos Aires
JPP	Jose Policarpo Patino
M	Mendoza
PNP	Pedro Nolasco Pizarro
PP	Pedro Nolasco Pizarro
PTS	Potosi
R	Rioja
RA	Rioja
SE	Santiago del Estero
SoEo	Santiago del Estero
TN	Tucuman

AUSTRALIA
A	Perth
D	Denver
H	Heaton (1912–16)
I	Bombay (1942–43)
I	Calcutta (1916–18)
M	Melbourne
P	Perth
PL	Royal Mint, London
S	Sydney
S	San Francisco (1942–43)
Dot before and after PENNY and I on obverse	Bombay (1942–43)
Dot before and after HALFPENNY and I on obverse	Bombay (1942–43)
Dot before and after PENNY	Bombay (1942–43)
Dot after HALFPENNY	Perth
Dot before SHILLING	Perth (1946)
Dot above scroll on reverse	Sydney (1920)
Dot below scroll on reverse	Melbourne (1919–20)
Dot between designer's initials KG	Perth (1940–41)
Dot after AUSTRALIA	Perth (1952–53)

AUSTRIA
A	Vienna (1765–1872)
AH–AG	Carlsburg, Transylvania (1765–76)
AH–GS	Carlsburg (1776–80)
A–S	Hall, Tyrol (1765–74)
AS–IE	Vienna (1745)
AW	Vienna (1764, 1768)
B	Kremnitz (1765–1857)
B–L	Nagybanya (1765–71)

B–V	Nagybanya (1772–80)
C	Carlsburg (1762–64)
C	Prague (1766–1855)
C–A	Carlsburg (1746–66)
C–A	Vienna (1774–80)
CG–AK	Graz (1767–72)
CG–AR	Graz (1767)
C–K	Vienna (1765–73)
CM	Kremnitz (1779)
CVG–AK	Graz (1767–72)
CVG–AR	Graz (1767)
D	Graz (1765–72), Salzburg (1800–09)
E	Carlsburg (1765–1867)
EC–SK	Vienna (1766)
EvM–D	Kremnitz (1765–74)
EvS–AS	Prague (1765–73)
EvS–IK	Prague (1774–80)
F	Hall (1765–1807)
FH	Hall
G	Graz (1761–63)
G	Gunzburg (1764–79)
G	Nagybanya (1766–1851)
G–K	Graz (1767–72)
G–R	Graz (1746–67)
GTK	Vienna (1761)
H	Hall (1760–80)
H	Gunzburg (1765–1805)
H–A	Hall (1746–65)
H–G	Carlsburg (1765–77)
H–S	Carlsburg (1777–80)
IB–FL	Nagybanya (1765–71)
IB–IV	Nagybanya (1772–80)
IC–FA	Vienna (1774–80)
IC–IA	Vienna (1780)
IC–SK	Vienna (1765–73)
I–K	Graz (1765-67)
I–K	Vienna (1767)
IZV	Vienna (1763–65)
K	Kremnitz (1760–63)
K–B	Kremnitz (1619–1765)
K–D	Kremnitz (1765)
K–M	Kremnitz (1763–65)
M	Milan (1780–1859)
N	Nagybanya (1780)
N–B	Nagybanya (1630–1777, 1849)
O	Oravicza (1783–1816)
P	Prague (1760–63)
P–R	Prague (1746–67)
PS–IK	Prague (1774–80)
S	Hall (1765–80), Schmollnitz (1763–1816)
S–C	Gunzburg (1765–74)
SC–G	Gunzburg (1765)
S–F	Gunzburg (1775–80)
S–G	Gunzburg (1764–65)
S–IE	Vienna (1745)
SK–PD	Kremnitz (1774–80)
TS	Gunzburg (1762–88)

V	Venice (1805–66)
VC–S	Hall (1774–80)
VS–K	Prague (1774–80)
VS–S	Prague (1765–73)
W	Vienna (1748–63)
W–I	Vienna (1746–71)

BAHAMAS

FM	Franklin Mint
JP	John Pinches

BELGIUM

A	Vienna
B	Kremnitz
C	Prague
E	Carlsburg
F	Hall
G	Nagybanya
H	Gunzburg
hand	Antwerp
lion	Bruges

BELIZE (British Honduras)

FM	Franklin Mint
H	Heaton (1912–16)

BOLIVIA

H	Heaton (1892–1953)
P, PTR, PTS	Potosi

BRAZIL

A	Berlin (1913)
B	Bahia (1714–1831)
C	Cuiaba (1823–33)
G	Goias (1823–33)
M	Minas Gerais (1823–28)
P	Pernambuco
R	Rio de Janeiro (1703–1834)
RS	Rio de Janeiro (1869)
SP	Sao Paulo (1825–32)

BRITISH NORTH BORNEO (Sabah)

H	Heaton (1882–1941)

BRITISH WEST AFRICA

G	JR Gaunt, Birmingham
H	Heaton, Birmingham (1911–57)
K	King's Norton
KN	King's Norton
SA	Pretoria

BULGARIA

A	Berlin
BP	Budapest
Heaton	Heaton, Birmingham (1881–1923)
KB	Kormoczbanya
cornucopia	Paris
thunderbolt	Poissy

CANADA
C   Ottawa
H   Heaton (1871–1907)
maple leaf Ottawa (on coins struck after the year
         inscribed on them)

CENTRAL AMERICAN REPUBLIC
CR   San Jose (Costa Rica)
G   Guatemala
NG   Guatemala
T   Tegucigalpa (Honduras)

CEYLON
H   Heaton (1912)

CHILE
A   Agustin de Infante y Prado (1768–72)
AJ   The above and Jose Maria de Bobadilla
         (1800–01)
D   Domingo Eizaguirre
DA   Domingo Eizaguirre and Agustin de
         Infante (1772–99)
BFF   Francisco Rodriguez Brochero
FJJF   Brochero and Jose Maria de Bobadilla
         (1803–17)
H   Heaton (1851)
J   Jose Larraneta (1749–67)
So   Santiago
VA   Val Distra

COLOMBIA
A   Paris
B   Bogota
BA   Bogota
B.B   Bogota
H   Heaton (1912)
M   Medellin
NR   Nuevo Reino
NoRo   Nuevo Reino
P   Popayan
PN, Pn   Popayan
SM   Santa Marta

COSTA RICA
CR   San Jose (1825–1947)
HBM   Heaton (1889–93)
S   San Domingo
SD   San Domingo

COURLAND
ICS   Justin Carl Schroder
IFS   Johan Friedrich Schmickert

CYPRUS
H   Heaton (1881–2)

DENMARK
FF   Altona
KM   Copenhagen Altona (1842)
crown Copenhagen
heart Copenhagen
orb   Altona (1839–48)
Other letters are the initials of mintmasters and
moneyers

DOMINICAN REPUBLIC
HH   Heaton (1888–1919)

EAST AFRICA
A   Ackroyd & Best, Morley
H   Heaton (1910–64)
I   Bombay
K   Kynoch (IMI)
KN   King's Norton
SA   Pretoria

ECUADOR
BIRM^{MH} Heaton (1915)
BIRMING-
   HAM   Heaton (1899–1900, 1928)
D   Denver
H   Heaton (1890, 1909, 1924–5)
HEATON
  BIRMING-
   HAM   Heaton (1872–95)
HF   Le Locle
LIMA   Lima
Mo   Mexico
PHILA   Philadelphia
QUITO   Quito
SANTIAGO Santiago de Chile

EGYPT
H   Heaton (1904–37)

EL SALVADOR
CAM   Central American Mint, San Salvador
H   Heaton (1889–1913)
Mo   Mexico
S   San Francisco

FIJI
S   San Francisco

FINLAND
H   Heaton (1921)
heart Copenhagen (1922). Since then coins
         have been struck at Helsinki without a
         mintmark.
Initials of mintmasters:
S   August Soldan (1864–85)
L   Johan Lihr (1885–1912)
S   Isaac Sundell (1915–47)

L	V. U. Liuhto (1948)		AGP	Cleve, Rhineland (1742–43)
H	Uolevi Helle (1948–58)		AK	Dusseldorf, Julich-Berg (1749–66)
S	Allan Soiniemi (1958–75)		ALS	Berlin (1749)
SH	Soiniemi & Heikki Halvaoja (1967–71)		B	Bayreuth, Franconia (1796–1804)
K	Timo Koivuranta (1977, 1979)		B	Breslau, Silesia (1750–1826)
KN	Koivuranta and Antti Neuvonen (1978)		B	Brunswick, Brunswick (1850–60)
KT	Koivuranta and Erja Tielinen (1982)		B	Brunswick, Westphalia (1809–13)
KM	Koivuranta and Pertti Makinen (1983)		B	Dresden, Saxony (1861–72)
N	Reino Nevalainen (1983)		B	Hannover, Brunswick (1860–71)
			B	Hannover, East Friesland (1823–25)

FRANCE

A	Paris (1768)		B	Hannover, Hannover (1821–66)
AA	Metz (1775–98)		B	Hannover, Germany (1866-78)
B	Rouen (1786–1857)		B	Regensburg, Regensburg (1809)
B	Beaumont le Roger (1943–58)		B	Vienna, Germany (1938–45)
BB	Strasbourg (1743–1870)		BH	Frankfurt (1808)
C	Castelsarrasin (1914, 1942–46)		B–H	Regensburg, Rhenish Confederation
CC	Genoa (1805)			(1802–12)
CL	Genoa (1813–14)		C	Cassel, Westphalia (1810–13)
D	Lyons (1771–1857)		C	Clausthal, Brunswick
G	Geneva (1796–1805)		C	Clausthal, Westphalia (1810–11)
H	La Rochelle (1770–1837)		C	Dresden, Saxony (1779–1804)
L	Limoges (1766–1837)		C	Frankfurt, Germany (1866–79)
K	Bordeaux (1759–1878)		CHI	Berlin (1749–63)
L	Bayonne (1761–1837)		CLS	Dusseldorf, Julich-Berg (1767–70)
M	Toulouse (1766–1837)		D	Aurich, East Friesland (1750–1806)
MA	Marseilles (1787–1857)		D	Dusseldorf, Rhineland (1816–48)
N	Montpellier (1766–93)		D	Munich, Germany (1872)
O	Riom		E	Dresden, Germany (1872–87)
P	Dijon		E	Koenigberg, East Prussia (1750–98)
Q	Perpignan (1777–1837)		E	Muldenhutte, Germany (1887–1953)
R	Royal Mint, London (1815)		EC	Leipzig, Saxony (1753–63)
R	Orleans (1780–92)		EGN	Berlin (1725–49)
T	Nantes (1739–1835)		F	Dresden, Saxony (1845–58)
U	Turin (1814)		F	Magdeburg, Lower Saxony (1740–1806)
V	Troyes		F	Cassel, Hesse-Cassel (1803–07)
W	Lille (1759–1857)		F	Stuttgart, Germany (1872)
X	Amiens (1740)		FW	Dresden, Saxony (1734–63)
&	Aix en Provence (1775)		G	Dresden, Saxony (1833–44, 1850–54)
9	Rennes		G	Glatz, Silesia (1807–09)
cow	Pau (1746–93)		G	Karlsruhe, Germany (1872)
flag	Utrecht (1811–14)		G	Stettin, Pomerania (1750–1806)
crowned R	Rome (1811–14)		GK	Cleve (1740–55)
thunderbolt	Poissy (1922-24)		GN	Bamberg, Bamberg
star	Madrid (1916)		H	Darmstadt, Germany (1872–82)

In addition, French coins include symbols denoting the privy marks of Engravers General (Chief Engravers since 1880) and Mint Directors.

GERMANY

The first name gives the location of the mint, and the second the name of the country or state issuing the coins.

			H	Dresden, Saxony (1804–12)
			HK	Rostock, Rostock (1862–64)
			I	Hamburg, Germany (1872)
			IDB	Dresden, Prussian occupation (1756–59)
			IEC	Dresden, Saxony (1779–1804)
			IF	Leipzig, Saxony (1763–65)
			IGG	Leipzig, Saxony (1716–34, 1813–32)
A	Amberg, Bavaria (1763–94)		J	Hamburg, Germany (1873)
A	Berlin (1850)		J	Paris, Westphalia (1808–09)
A	Clausthal, Hannover (1832–49)		L	Leipzig, Saxony (1761–62)
AE	Breslau, Silesia (1743–51)		MC	Brunswick, Brunswick (1813–14, 1820)
			PM	Dusseldorf, Julich-Berg (1771–83)
			PR	Dusseldorf, Julich-Berg (1783–1804)

S	Dresden, Saxony (1813–32)
S	Hannover, Hannover (1839–44)
S	Schwabach, Franconia (1792–94)
SGH	Dresden, Saxony (1804–12)
ST	Strickling, Blomberg (1820–40)

GREAT BRITAIN

A	Ashby (1645)
B	Nicolas Briot (1631–39)
B	Bridgnorth (1646)
B	Bristol (1696)
Br	Bristol (1643–45)
C	Chester (1696)
CARL	Carlisle (1644–45)
CC	Corfe Castle (1644)
CHST	Chester (1644)
CR	Chester (1644)
E	Southwark (1547–49)
E	Exeter (1696)
E	Edinburgh (1707–13)
E*	Edinburgh (1707–09)
H	Heaton, Birmingham (1874–1919)
HC	Hartlebury Castle (1646)
K	London (1547–49)
KN	King's Norton
N	Norwich (1696)
OX	Oxford (1644–45)
OXON	Oxford (1644)
PC	Pontefract (1648–49)
SC	Scarborough (1644–45)
SOHO	Birmingham (1797–1806)
T	Canterbury (1549)
TC	Bristol (1549)
WS	Bristol (1547–49)
Y	Southwark (1551)
boar	Shrewsbury (1643–44)
book	Aberystwyth (1638–42)
bow	Durham House (1548–49)
castle	Exeter (1644–45)
crown	Aberystwyth Furnace (1648–49)
plume	Shrewsbury (1642)
plume	Oxford (1642–46)
plume	Bristol (1643–46)

Other symbols and marks on the hammered coins of Great Britain are usually referred to as Initial Marks. Complete listings of these marks appear in a number of specialist publications.

GREECE

A	Paris
B	Vienna
BB	Strasbourg
H	Heaton (1921)
K	Bordeaux
KN	King's Norton
owl	Aegina (1828–32)
owl	Athens (1838-55)
thunderbolt	Poissy

GUATEMALA

CG	Guatemala City (1733-76)
G	Guatemala City (1776)
H	Heaton (1894–1901)
NG	Nueva Guatemala (1777)

GUERNSEY

H	Heaton (1855–1949)

HAITI

A	Paris
HEATON	Heaton (1863)

HONDURAS

A	Paris (1869–71)
T	Tegucigalpa (1825–62)

HONG KONG

H	Heaton (1872–1971)
KN	King's Norton

HUNGARY

A	Vienna
B	Kremnitz
BP	Budapest
CA	Vienna
G	Nagybanya
GN	Nagybanya
GYF	Carlsburg
HA	Hall
K	Kremnitz
KB	Kremnitz
NB	Nagybanya
S	Schmollnitz
WI	Vienna

INDIA

B	Bombay (1835-1947)
C	Calcutta (1835-1947)
I	Bombay (1918)
L	Lahore (1943-45)
M	Madras (1869)
P	Pretoria (1943-44)
diamond	Bombay
dot in diamond	Hyderabad
split diamond	Hyderabad
star	Hyderabad

IRAN

H	Heaton (1928–29)

IRAQ

I	Bombay

ISRAEL

H	Heaton (1951–52)
star of David	Jerusalem

ITALY AND STATES

B	Bologna
B/I	Birmingham (1893–4)
FIRENZE	Florence
H	Heaton (1866–67)
KB	Berlin
M	Milan
N	Naples
OM	Strasbourg
R	Rome
T	Turin
V	Venice
ZV	Venice
anchor	Genoa
eagle head	Turin

JAMAICA

C	Ottawa
FM	Franklin Mint
H	Heaton (1882–1916)

JERSEY

H	Heaton (1877)

KENYA

C/M	Calcutta
H	Heaton (1911–64)

LIBERIA

B	Berne
FM	Franklin Mint
H	Heaton (1896–1906)
PM	Pobjoy Mint

LIECHTENSTEIN

A	Vienna
B	Berne
M	Munich

LUXEMBOURG

A	Paris
H	Gunzburg
anchor	Paris
angel	Brussels
caduceus	Utrecht
double eagle	Brussels
sword	Utrecht

MALAYSIA

B	Bombay
FM	Franklin Mint
H	Heaton (1955–61)
I	Calcutta (1941)
I	Bombay (1945)
KN	King's Norton
W	James Watt, Birmingham

MAURITIUS

H	Heaton (1877–90)
SA	Pretoria

MEXICO

A, As	Alamos
C, CN	Culiacan
CA, CH	Chihuahua
Ce	Real del Catorce
D, Do	Durango
Eo	Tlalpam
GA	Guadalajara
GC	Guadelupe y Calvo
Go	Guanajuato
Ho	Hermosillo
M, Mo	Mexico City
Mo	Morelos
MX	Mexico City
O, OA, OKA	Oaxaca
Pi	San Luis Potosi
SLPi	San Luis Potosi
TC	Tierra Caliente
Z, Zs	Zacatecas

MONACO

A	Paris
M	Monte Carlo
clasped hands	Cabanis
thunderbolt	Poissy

MOZAMBIQUE

H	Heaton (1894)
R	Rio

NETHERLANDS AND COLONIES
Austrian Netherlands (1700-93)

H	Amsterdam
S	Utrecht
W	Vienna
hand	Antwerp
head	Brussels
lion	Bruges

Kingdom of the Netherlands

B	Brussels (1821–30)
D	Denver (1943–45)
P	Philadelphia (1941–45)
S	Utrecht (1816–36)
S	San Francisco (1944–45)
Sa	Surabaya
caduceus	Utrecht

NICARAGUA

H	Heaton (1880–1916)
NR	Leon de Nicaragua

NORWAY

hammers	Kongsberg

PANAMA
CHI   Valcambi
FM   Franklin Mint

PERU
AREQ, AREQUIPA Arequipa
AYACUCHO   Ayacucho
CUZCO, Co   Cuzco
L, LM, LR   Lima
LIMAE   Lima
PASCO   Pasco
Paz, Po   Pasco
P   Lima (1568-70)
P   Philadelphia
S   San Francisco

PHILIPPINES
BSP   Bangko Sentral Pilipinas
D   Denver (1944–45)
FM   Franklin Mint
M, MA   Manila
PM   Pobjoy Mint
S   San Francisco (1903–47)
5 point star   Manila

POLAND
AP   Warsaw (1772–74)
CI   Cracow (1765–68)
EB   Warsaw (1774–92)
EC   Leipzig (1758–63)
FF   Stuttgart (1916–17)
FH   Warsaw (1815–27)
FS   Warsaw (1765–68)
FWoF   Dresden (1734–64)
G   Cracow (1765–72)
H   Heaton (1924)
IB   Warsaw (1811–27)
IGS   Dresden (1716–34)
IP   Warsaw (1834–43)
IS   Warsaw (1768–74)
JGG   Leipzig (1750–53)
JS   Warsaw (1810–11)
KG   Warsaw (1829–34)
MV, MW   Warsaw
arrow   Warsaw (1925–39)
Dot after
date   Royal Mint (1925)
8 torches Paris (1924)

ROUMANIA
B   Bucharest (1879–85)
C   Bucharest (1886)
H   Heaton (1867–1930)
HUGUENIN   Le Locle
J   Hamburg
KN   King's Norton
V   Vienna

W   Watt, Birmingham
thunderbolt Poissy

RUSSIA
AM   Annensk (1762–96)
BM   Warsaw (1825–55)
bM   St Petersburg (1796)
C–M   Sestroretsk (1762–96)
CM   Souzan (1825–55)
E–M   Ekaterinburg (1762–1810)
KM   Kolpina (1810)
K–M   Kolyvan (1762–1810)
MM, M–M Moscow (1730–96)
MMD   Moscow (1730–96)
MW   Warsaw (1842–54)
NM   Izhorsk (1811–21)
SP   St Petersburg (1798–1800)
SPB   St Petersburg (1724–1915)
SPM   St Petersburg (1825–55)
T–M   Feodosia (1762–96)

SAN MARINO
M   Milan
R   Rome
SIAM
(Thailand)   H Heaton (1898)

SOUTH AFRICA
SA   Pretoria

SPAIN
B   Burgos
B, BA   Barcelona
Bo   Bilbao
C   Catalonia
C   Cuenca
C   Reus
CA   Zaragoza
G   Granada
GNA   Gerona
LD   Lerida
J, JA   Jubia
M, MD   Madrid
P   Palma de Majorca
PpP, PL, PA Pamplona
S, S/L   Seville
Sr   Santander
T, To, Tole Toledo
TOR:SA   Tortosa
V, VA, VAL   Valencia
crowned C   Cadiz
crowned M   Madrid
aqueduct   Segovia
crowned shield Tarragona
pomegranate   Granada
quartered shield Palma
scallop   Coruna

SPAIN *continued*

stars:

3 points	Segovia
4 points	Jubia
5 points	Manila
6 points	Madrid
7 points	Seville (1833)
8 points	Barcelona (1838)
wavy lines	Valladolid

SURINAM

P	Philadelphia
S	Sydney
caduceus	Utrecht

SWITZERLAND

A	Paris
AB	Strasbourg
B	Berne
B	Brussels (1874)
BA	Basle
BB	Strasbourg
S	Solothurn

URUGUAY

H	Heaton (1869)

UNITED STATES OF AMERICA

C	Charlotte, North Carolina
Cc	Carson City, Nevada
D	Dahlonega, Georgia (1838–61)
D	Denver, Colorado (1906)
O	New Orleans
P	Philadelphia
S	San Francisco
W	West Point

VENEZUELA

A	Paris
H	Heaton (1852)
HEATON	Heaton (1852–63)

YUGOSLAVIA (including former Serbia)

A	Paris	
H	Heaton (1883–84)	
KOBHNUA, A.D.		Kovnica
V	Vienna	
thunderbolt	Poissy	

The Royal Mint on Tower Hill, London, c. 1810, built under the direction of Sir Richard Smirke.

Coin
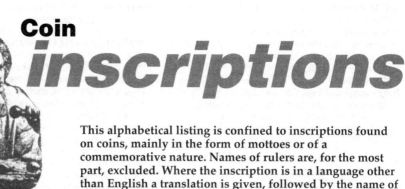
inscriptions

This alphabetical listing is confined to inscriptions found on coins, mainly in the form of mottoes or of a commemorative nature. Names of rulers are, for the most part, excluded. Where the inscription is in a language other than English a translation is given, followed by the name of the issuing country or authority in parentheses.

A Deo et Caesare   From God and the Emperor (Frankfurt).

A Domino Factum est Istud et est Mirabile in Oculis Nostris   This is the Lord's doing and it is marvellous in our eyes (England, Mary).

A Solo Iehova Sapientia   From God alone comes true wisdom (Wittgenstein).

Ab Inimicis Meis Libera Me Deus   Free me from enemies (Burgundy).

Ad Legem Conventionis   According to the law of the Convention (Furstenberg).

Ad Normam Conventionis   According to the standard of the Convention (Prussia).

Ad Palmam Pressa Laeturo Resurgo   Pressed to the palm I rise more joyfully (Wittgenstein).

Ad Usam Luxemburgi CC Vallati   For the use of the besieged Luxembourgers (Luxembourg siege coins).

Adiuva Nos Deus Salutaris Noster   Help us, O God, our Saviour (Lorraine).

Adventus Optimi Principis   The coming of the noblest prince (Papacy).

Aes Usibus Aptius Auro   Bronze in its uses is more suitable than gold (Brazil).

Aeternum Meditans Decus   An ornament intended for all time (Alencon).

Aliis Inserviendo Consumor   I spend my life devoted to others (Brunswick-Wolfenbuttel).

Alles Mit Bedacht   All with reflection (Brunswick).

Amor Populi Praesidium Regis   The love of the people is the king's protection (England, Charles I).

Ang Fra Dom Hib & Aquit   (King) of England and France, Lord of Ireland and Aquitaine (England, Edward III).

Anno Regni Primo   In the first year of the reign (Britain, edge inscription on crowns).

Apres les Tenebres la Lumiere   After the shadows, the light (Geneva).

Archangelus Michael   Archangel Michael (Italy, Grimoald IV).

Ardua ad Gloriam Via   Struggles are the way to glory (Waldeck).

Arte Mea Bis Iustus Moneta Lud Iust   By my art I am twice the just coin of King Louis (France, 1641).

Aspera Oblectant   Wild places delight (Nassau-Weilburg).

Aspice Pisas Sup Omnes Specio   Behold the coin of Pisa, superior to all (Pisa).

Audiatur Altera Pars   Let the other part be heard (Stavelot).

Auf Gott Trawe Ich   In God I trust (Brunswick).

Ausen Gefaesen der Kirchen und Burger   From the vessels of the Church and citizens (Frankfurt siege, 1796).

Auspicio Regis et Senatus Angliae   By authority of the king and parliament of England (East India Company).

Auxilio fortissimo Dei   With the strongest help of God (Mecklenburg).

Auxilium de Sanctio   Aid from the sanctuary (Papacy).

Auxilium Meum a Dno Qui Fecit Celum e Terram   My help comes from God who made heaven and earth (Portugal).

Basilea   Basle.

Beata Tranquillatis   Blessed tranquillity (Rome, Licinius II).

Beatus Qui Speravit in dom   Blessed is he who has hoped in the Lord (Mansfeld).

Benedic Haereditati Tuae   Blessings on your inheritance (Savoy).

Benedicta Sit Sancta Trinitas   Blessed be the Holy Trinity (Albon).

Benedictio Domini Divites Facit The blessing of the Lord makes the rich (Teschen).

Benedictus Qui Venit in Nomine Domini Blessed is he who comes in the name of the Lord (Flanders).

Beschaw das Ziel Sage Nicht Viel Consider the matter but say little (Quedlinburg).

Besser Land und Lud Verloren als ein Falscher Aid Geschworn Better to lose land and wealth than swear a false oath (Hesse).

Bey Gott ist Rath und That With God is counsel and deed (Mansfeld).

Britanniarum Regina Queen of the Britains (Britain, Victoria).

Britt Omn Rex King of all the Britains (i.e. Britain and the overseas dominions) (Britain, 1902–52).

Cal et Car Com de Fugger in Zin et Norn Sen & Adm Fam Cajetan and Carl, Counts of Fugger in Zinnenberg and Nordendorf, Lords and Administrators of the Family (Empire, Fugger).

Candide et Constanter Sincerely and steadfastly (Hesse-Cassel).

Candide sed Provide Clearly but cautiously (Osterwitz).

Candore et Amore With sincerity and love (Fulda).

Candore et Constantia With sincerity and constancy (Bavaria).

Capit Cath Ecclesia Monasteriensis Chapter of the Cathedral Church of Munster (Munster).

Capit Eccle Metropolit Colon Chapter of the Metropolitan Church of Cologne (Cologne).

Capitulum Regnans Sede Vacante Chapter governing, the See being vacant (Eichstadt).

Carola Magna Ducissa Feliciter Regnante Grand Duchess Charlotte, happily reigning (Luxembourg).

Carolus a Carolo Charles (I) to Charles (II) (England).

Cedunt Prementi Fata The fates yield to him who presses (Ploen, Hese-Cassel).

Charitate et Candore With charity and sincerity (East Frisia).

Charta Magna Bavariae The Great Charter of Bavaria (Bavaria).

Christo Auspice Regno I reign under the auspices of Christ (England, Charles I).

Christus Spes Una Salutis Christ is our one hope of salvation (Cleve).

Chur Mainz Electoral Principality of Mainz (Mainz).

Circumeundo Servat et Ornat It serves and decorates by going around (Sweden).

Civibus Quorum Pietas Coniuratione Die III Mai MDCCXCI Obrutam et Deletam

Libertate Polona Tueri Conabatur Respublica Resurgens To the citizens whose piety the resurgent commonwealth tried to protect Poland overturned and deprived of liberty by the conspiracy of the third day of May 1791 (Poland).

Civitas Lucemborgiensis Millesimum Ovans Expletannum Completing the celebration of a thousand years of the city of Luxembourg (Luxembourg).

Civium Industria Floret Civitas By the industry of its people the state flourishes (Festival of Britain crown, 1951).

Cluniaco Cenobio Petrus et Paulus Peter and Paul from the Abbey of Cluny (Cluny).

Comes Provincie Fili Regis Francie Court of Provence and son of the King of France (Provence).

Communitas et Senatus Bonon City and senate of Bologna (Bologna).

Concordia Fratrum The harmony of the brothers (Iever).

Concordia Patriae Nutrix Peace, the nurse of the fatherland (Waldeck).

Concordia Res Parvae Crescunt Little things increase through harmony (Batavian Republic).

Concordia Res Parvae Crescunt, Discordia Dilabuntur By harmony little things increase, by discord they fall apart (Lowenstein-Wertheim-Virneburg).

Concordia Stabili With lasting peace (Hildesheim).

Confidens Dno Non Movetur He who trusts in God is unmoved (Spanish Netherlands).

Confidentia in Deo et Vigilantia Trust in God and vigilance (Prussian Asiatic Company).

Confoederato Helvetica Swiss Confederation (Switzerland)

Conjuncto Felix Fortunate in his connections (Solms).

Conservator Urbis Suae Saviour of his city (Rome, 4th century).

Consilio et Aequitate With deliberation and justice (Fulda).

Consilio et Virtutis With deliberation and valour (Hesse-Cassel).

Constanter et Sincere Steadfastly and sincerely (Lautern).

Crescite et Multiplicamini Increase and multiply (Maryland).

Cristiana Religio Christian religion (Germany, 11th century).

Crux Benedicat May the cross bless you (Oldenburg).

Cuius Cruore Sanati Sumus By His sacrifice are we healed (Reggio).

Cultores Sui Deus Protegit   God protects His
followers (England, Charles I).

Cum Deo et Die   With God and the day
(Wurttemberg).

Cum Deo et Jure   With God and the law
(Wurtt-berg).

Cum Deo et Labore   With God and work
(Wittgenstein).

**Cum His Qui Orderant Pacem Eram
Pacificus**   With those who order peace I was
peaceful (Zug).

Curie Bonthon to so Doulo   Protect his servant,
o Lord (Byzantine Empire).

Custos Regni Deus   God is the guardian of the
kingdom (Naples and Sicily).

Da Gloriam Deo et Eius Genitrici Marie   Give
glory to God and His mother Mary
(Wurttemberg).

Da Mihi Virtutem Contra Hostes Tuos   Give
me valour against mine enemies
(Netherlands, Charles V).

Dat Wort is Fleis Gworden   The word is made
flesh (Muster).

**Date Caesaris Caesari et Quae Sunt Dei
Deo**   Render unto Caesar the things that are
Caesar's and unto God the things that are
God's (Stralsund).

De Oficina . . .   From the mint of . . . (France,
medieval).

**Decreto Reipublicae Nexu Confoederationis
Iunctae Die V Xbris MDCCXCII Stanislao
Augusto Regnante**   By decree of the state in
conjunction with the joint federation on the
fifth day of December 1792, Stanislaus
Augustus ruling (Poland).

Decus et Tutamen   An ornament and a
safeguard (Britain, pound).

Deducet Nos Mirabiliter Dextera Tua   Thy
right hand will guide us miraculously
(Savoy).

Denarium Terrae Mariae   Penny of Maryland
(Maryland).

Deo Conservatori Pacis   To God, preserver of
peace (Brandenburg-Ansbach).

**Deo OM Auspice Suaviter et Fortiter sed Luste
nec Sibi sed Suis**   Under the auspices of
God, greatest and best, pleasantly and bravely
but justly, not for himself but for his people
(Speyer).

Deo Patriae et Subditio   For God, fatherland
and neighbourhood (Mainz).

Der Recht Glaubt In Ewig Lebt   Who believes
in right will live in eternity (Linange-
Westerburg).

**Der Rhein ist Deutschlands Strom Nicht
Deutschlands Grenze**   The Rhine is
Germany's River not Germany's Frontier.

Deum Solum Adorabis   You will venerate God
alone (Hesse).

Deus Constituit Regna   God establishes
kingdoms (Ni jmegen).

Deus Dat Qui Vult   God gives to him who
wishes (Hanau-Munzenberg).

Deus et Dominus   God and Lord (Rome, 3rd
century).

Deus in Adiutorium Meum Intende   God
stretch out in my assistance (France).

Deus Providebit   God will provide
(Lowenstein-Wertheim-Virneburg).

Deus Refugium Meum   God is my refuge
(Cleve).

Deus Solatium Meum   God is my comfort
(Sweden).

Dextera Domini Exaltavit Me   The right hand
of God has raised me up (Modena, Spain).

Dextra Dei Exalta Me   The right hand of God
exalts me (Denmark).

Dieu et Mon Droit   God and my right (Britain,
George IV).

Dilexit Dns Andream   The Lord delights in St
Andrew (Holstein).

Dilexit Dominus Decorem Iustitiae   The Lord
is pleased with the beauty of justice
(Unterwalden).

Dirige Deus Gressus Meos   O God, direct my
steps (Tuscany, Britain, Una £5).

Discerne Causam Meam   Distinguish my cause
(Savoy).

**Divina Benedictiae et Caesarea
Iustitia**   Sacrifice of blessings and imperial
justice (Coblenz).

Dn Ihs Chs Rex Regnantium   Lord Jesus Christ,
King of Kings (Rome, Justinian II).

Dns Ptetor Ms Z Lib'ator Ms   The Lord is my
protector and liberator (Scotland, David II).

Dominabitur Gentium et Ipse   He himself will
also be lord of the nations (Austrian
Netherlands).

Domine Conserva Nos in Pace   O Lord
preserve us in peace (Basle, Mulhausen).

Domine Elegisti Lilium Tibi   O Lord Thou hast
chosen the lily for Thyself (France, Louis XIV).

Domine ne in Furore Tuo Arguas Me   O Lord,
rebuke me not in Thine anger (England,
Edward III).

Domine Probasti Me et Congnovisti Me   O
Lord Thou hast tested me and recognised me
(Mantua).

Domini est Regnum   The Kingdom is the
Lord's (Austrian Netherlands).

Dominus Deus Omnipotens Rex   Lord God,
almighty King (Viking coins).

Dominus Mihi Adiutor   The Lord is my helper
(Spanish Netherlands).

Dominus Providebit   The Lord will provide (Berne).

Dominus Spes Populi Sui   The Lord is the hope of his people (Lucerne).

Donum Dei ex Fodinis Vilmariens   A gift of God from the Vilmar mines (Coblenz).

Duce Deo Fide et Justicia   By faith and justice lead us to God (Ragusa).

Dum Praemor Amplior   I increase while I die prematurely (Savoy).

Dum Spiro Spero   While I live, I hope (Pontefract siege coins).

Dum Totum Compleat Orbem   Until it fills the world (France, Henri II).

Dura Pati Virtus   Valour endures hardships (Saxe-Lauenburg).

Durae Necessitatis   Through force of necessity (Bommel siege, 1599).

Durum Telum Necessitas   Hardship is a weapon of necessity (Minden).

Dux et Gubernatores Reip Genu   Duke and governors of the republic of Genoa (Genoa).

E Pluribus Unum   One out of more (USA).

Eccl S. Barbarae Patronae Fodin Kuttenbergensium Duo Flor Arg Puri   The church of St Barbara, patron of the Kuttenberg mines, two florins of pure silver (Hungary).

Een en Ondelbaer Sterk   One and indivisible (Batavian Republic).

Eendracht Mag Macht   Unity makes strength (Belgium, South African Republic).

Einigkeit Recht und Freiheit   Union, right and freedom (Germany).

Electorus Saxoniae Administrator   Elector and administrator of Saxony (Saxony).

Elimosina   Alms (France, Pepin).

Ep Fris & Ratisb Ad Prum Pp Coad Aug   Bishop of Freising and Regensburg, administrator of Pruem, prince-provost, co-adjutant bishop of Augsburg (Trier).

Equa Libertas Deo Gratia Frat Pax in Virtute Tua et in Domino Confido   I believe in equal liberty by the grace of God, brotherly love in Thy valour and in the Lord (Burgundy).

Equitas Iudicia Tua Dom   Equity and Thy judgments O Lord (Gelderland).

Espoir Me Conforte   Hope comforts me (Mansfeld).

Espreuve Faicto Par Lexpres Commandement du Roy   Proof made by the express commandment of the King (France, piedforts).

Et in Minimis Integer   Faithful even in the smallest things (Olmutz).

Ex Auro Argentes Resurgit   From gold it arises, silver again (Sicily).

Ex Auro Sinico   From Chinese gold (Denmark).

Ex Flammis Orior   I arise from the flames (Hohenlohe-Neuenstein-Ohringen).

Ex Fodinis Bipontio Seelbergensibus   From the Seelberg mines of Zweibrucken (Pfalz-Birkenfeld).

Ex Metallo Novo   From new metal (Spain).

Ex Uno Omnis Nostra Salus   From one is all our salvation (Eichstadt, Mulhouse).

Ex Vasis Argent Cleri Mogunt Pro Aris et Focis   From the silver vessels of the clergy of Mainz for altars and for hearths (Mainz).

Ex Visceribus Fodinse Bieber   From the bowels of the Bieber mine (Hanau-Munzenberg).

Exaltabitur in Gloria   He shall be exalted in glory (England, quarter nobles).

Exemplum Probati Numismatis   An example of a proof coin (France, Louis XIII piedforts).

Exemtae Eccle Passau Episc et SRI Princ   Prince Bishop of the freed church of Passau, prince of the Holy Roman Empire (Passau).

Expectate Veni   Come, o expected one (Roman Britain, Carausius).

Extremum Subidium Campen   Kampen under extreme siege (Kampen, 1578).

Exurgat Deus et Dissipentur Inimici Eius   Let God arise and let His enemies be scattered (England, James I).

Faciam Eos in Gentem Unam   I will make them one nation (England, unites and laurels).

Faith and Truth I will Bear unto You   (UK £5, 1993).

Fata Consiliis Potiora   The fates are more powerful than councils (Hesse-Cassel).

Fata Viam Invenient   The fates will find a way (Gelderland).

Fecit Potentiam in Brachio Suo   He put power in your forearm (Lorraine).

Fecunditas   Fertility (Naples and Sicily).

Fel Temp Reparatio   The restoration of lucky times (Rome, AD 348).

Felicitas Perpetua   Everlasting good fortune (Rome, Constantius II).

Felix coniunctio   Happy Union (Brandenburg-Ansbach).

Fiat Misericordia Tua Dne   Let Thy mercy be O Lord (Gelderland).

Fiat Voluntas Domini Perpetuo   Let the goodwill of the Lord last for ever (Fulda).

Fidei Defensor   Defender of the Faith (Britain).

Fidelitate et Fortitudine   With fidelity and fortitude (Batthanyi).

Fideliter et Constanter   Faithfully and steadfastly (Saxe-Coburg-Gotha).

Fidem Servando Patriam Tuendo   By keeping faith and protecting the fatherland (Savoy).

Filius Augustorum   Son of emperors (Rome, 4th century).

Fisci Iudaici Calumnia Sublata   The false accusation of the Jewish tax lifted (Rome, Nerva).

Florent Concordia Regna   Through harmony kingdoms flourish (England, Charles I and II).

Fortitudo et Laus Mea Dominu   Fortitude and my praise in the Lord (Sardinia).

Free Trade to Africa by Act of Parliment *(Sic)* (Gold Coast).

Friedt Ernehrt Unfriedt Verzehrt   Peace nourishes, unrest wastes (Brunswick).

Fulgent Sic Littora Rheni   Thus shine the banks of the Rhine (Mannheim).

Fundator Pacis   Founder of peace (Rome, Severus).

Gaudium Populi Romani   The joy of the Roman people (Rome, 4th century).

Gen C Mar VI Dim Col USC & RAMAI Cons & S Conf M   General field marshal, colonel of the only dragoon regiment, present privy councillor of both their sacred imperial and royal apostolic majesties, and state conference minister (Batthanyi).

Gerecht und Beharrlich   Just and steadfast (Bavaria).

Germ Hun Boh Rex AAD Loth Ven Sal   King of Germany, Hungary and Bohemia, Archduke of Austria, Duke of Lorraine, Venice and Salzburg (Austria).

Germ Jero Rex Loth Bar Mag Het Dux   King of Germany, Jerusalem, Lorraine and Bar, Grand Duke of Tuscany (Austrian Netherlands).

Germania Voti Compos   Germany sharing the vows (Brandenburg-Ansbach).

Gloria ex Amore Patriae   Glory from love of country (Denmark).

Gloria in Excelsis Deo   Glory to God in the highest (France, Sweden).

Gloria Novi Saeculi   The glory of a new century (Rome, Gratian).

God With Us   (England, Commonwealth).

Godt Met Ons   God with us (Oudewater).

Gottes Freundt der Pfaffen Feindt   God's friend, the Pope's enemy (Brunswick, Christian).

Gratia Dei Sum Id Quod Sum   By the grace of God, I am what I am (Navarre).

Gratia Di Rex   By the grace of God, king (France, 8th century).

Gratitudo Concivibus Exemplum Posteritati   Gratitude to fellow Citizens, an example to posterity (Poland).

Gud och Folket   God and the people (Sweden).

Hac Nitimur Hanc Tuemur   With this we strive, this we shall defend (Batavian Republic).

Hac Sub Tutela   Under this protection (Eichstadt).

Haec Sunt Munera Minerae S Antony Eremitae   These are the rewards of the mine of St Antony the hermit (Hildesheim).

Hanc Deus Dedit   God has given this (Pontefract siege coins).

Hanc Tuemur Hac Nitimur   This we defend, by this we strive (Batavian Republic).

Has Nisi Periturus Mihi Adimat Nemo   Let no one remove these (Letters) from me under penalty of death (Commonwealth, edge inscription).

Henricus Rosas Regna Jacobus   Henry (united) the roses, James the kingdoms (England and Scotland, James VI and I).

Herculeo Vincta Nodo   Bound by a Herculean fetter (Savoy).

Herr Nach Deinem Willen   O Lord Thy will be done (Palatinate, Erbach).

Herre Gott Verleich Uns Gnade   Lord God grant us grace (Brunswick).

Hic Est Qui Multum Orat Pro Populo   Here is he who prays a lot for the people (Paderborn).

Hir Steid te Biscop   Here is represented the bishop (Gittelde).

His Ventis Vela Levantur   By these winds the sails are raised up (Hesse-Cassel).

Hispaniarum Infans   Infante of Spain and its dominions (Spain).

Hispaniarum et Ind Rex   King of Spain and the Indies.

Hispaniarum Rex   King of Spain (Spain).

Hoc Signo Victor Eris   With this sign you will be victor (Rome, Vetranio).

Honeste et Decenter   Honestly and decently (Nassau-Idstein).

Honi Soit Qui Mal y Pense   Evil to him who evil thinks (Britain, George III).

Honni Soit Qui Mal y Pense   (Hesse-Cassel).

Hospitalis et S Sepul Hierusal   Hospital and Holy Sepulchre of Jerusalem (Malta).

Hun Boh Gal Rex AA Lo Wi et in Fr Dux   King of Hungary, Bohemia and Galicia, Archduke of Austria, Dalmatia, Lodomeria, Wurzburg and Duke in Franconia (Austria).

Hung Boh Lomb et Ven Gal Lod III Rex Aa   King of Hungary, Bohemia, Lombardo-Venezia, Galicia, Lodomeria and Illyria, Archduke of Austria (Austria).

Ich Dien   I serve (Aberystwyth 2d, UK 2p).

Ich Getrawe Got in Aller Noth   I trust in God in all my needs (Hesse-Marburg).

Ich Habe Nur Ein Vaterland und das Heisst Deutschland   I have only one fatherland and that is called Germany (Germany).

Ielithes Penniae   Penny of Gittelde (Gittelde, 11th century).

Iesus Autem Transiens Per Medium Illorum Ibat But Jesus, passing through the midst of them, went His way (England, Scotland, Anglo-Gallic).

Iesus Rex Noster et Deus Noster Jesus is our king and our God (Florence).

Ihs Xs Rex Regnantium Jesus Christ, King of Kings (Byzantine Empire).

Ihsus Xristus Basileu Baslie Jesus Christ, King of Kings (Byzantine Empire).

Imago Sanch Regis Illustris Castelle Legionis e Toleto The image of Sancho the illustrious king of Castile, Leon and Toledo.

In Casus Per Vigil Omnes In all seasons through vigil (Wertheim).

In Deo Meo Transgrediar Murum In my God I shall pass through walls (Teschen).

In Deo Spes Mea In God is my hope (Gelderland).

In Domino Fiducia Nostra In the Lord is our trust (Iever).

In Equitate Tua Vivificasti Me In thy equity Thou hast vivified me (Gelderland).

In God We Trust (USA).

In Hoc Signo Vinces In this sign shalt thou conquer (Portugal).

In Honore Sci Mavrici Marti In honour of the martyr St Maurice (St Maurice, 8th century).

In Manibus Domini sortes Meae In the hands of the Lord are my fates (Mainz siege, 1688–9).

In Memor Vindicatae Libere ac Relig In memory of the establishment of freedom and religion (Sweden).

In Memoriam Conjunctionis Utriusque Burgraviatus Norice In memory of the union of both burgraviates in peace (Brandenburg-Ansbach).

In Memorian Connub Feliciaes Inter Princ Her Frider Carol et Dub Sax August Louis Frider Rodas D 28 Nov 1780 Celebrati In memory of the most happy marriage between the hereditary prince Friedrich Karl and the Duchess of Saxony Augusta Louisa Frederika, celebrated on 28 Nov 1780 (Schwarzburg-Rudolstadt).

In Memorian Felicisssimi Matrimonii In memory of the most happy marriage (Wied).

In Memoriam Pacis Teschinensis Commemorating the Treaty of Teschen (Brandenburg-Ansbach).

In Nomine Domini Amen In the name of the Lord amen (Zaltbommel).

In Omnem Terram Sonus Eorum In to all the land their shall go sound (Chateau Renault, Papal States).

In Silencio et Spe Fortitudo Mea In silence and hope is my fortitude (Brandenburg-Kustrin).

In Spe et Silentio Fortitudo Mea In hope and silence is my fortitude (Vianen).

In Te Domine Confido In you O Lord I place my trust (Hesse).

In Te Domine Speravi In You, O Lord, I have hoped (Gurk).

In Terra Pax Peace in the land (Papacy).

In Via Virtuti Nulla Via There is no way for virtue on the way. (Veldenz).

Ind Imp, Indiae Imperator, Imperatrix Emperor (Empress) of India (Britain).

India Tibi Cessit India has yielded to thee (Portuguese India).

Infestus Infestis Hostile to the troublesome (Savoy).

Inimicos Eius Induam Confusione As for his enemies, I shall clothe them in shame (Sardinia, England, Edward VI).

Insignia Capituli Brixensis The badge of the chapter of Brixen (Brixen).

Isti Sunt Patres Tui Verique Pastores These are your fathers and true shepherds (Papacy).

Iudicium Melius Posteritatis Erit Posterity's judgment will be better (Paderborn).

Iure et Tempore By right and time (Groningen).

Iusques a Sa Plenitude As far as your plenitude (France, Henri II).

Iuste et Constanter Justly and constantly (Paderborn).

Iustirt Adjusted (Hesse-Cassel).

Iustitia et Concordia Justice and harmony (Zurich).

Iustitia et Mansuetudine By justice and mildness (Bavaria, Cologne).

Iustitia Regnorum Fundamentum Justice is the foundation of kingdoms (Austria).

Iustitia Thronum Firmat Justice strengthens the throne (England, Charles I).

Iustus Non Derelinquitur The just person is not deserted (Brandenburg-Calenberg).

Iustus Ut Palma Florebit The just will flourish like the palm (Portugal).

L Mun Planco Rauracorum Illustratori Vetustissimo To L Municius Plancus the most ancient and celebrated of the Rauraci (Basle).

Landgr in Cleggov Com in Sulz Dux Crum Landgrave of Klettgau, count of Sulz, duke of Krumlau (Schwarzburg-Sonderhausen).

Latina Emeri Munita Latin money of Merida (Suevi).

Lege et Fide By law and faith (Austria).

Lex Tua Veritas Thy law is the truth (Tuscany).

Liberta Eguaglianza Freedom and equality (Venice)

Coin inscriptions

Libertad en la Ley Freedom within the law (Mexico).
Libertas Carior Auro Freedom is dearer than gold (St Gall).
Libertas Vita Carior Freedom is dearer than life (Kulenberg).
Libertas Xpo Firmata Freedom strengthened by Christ (Genoa).
Liberte, Egalite, Fraternite Liberty, equality, fraternity (France).
Lucerna Pedibus Meis Verbum Est Thy word is a lamp unto mine feet (England, Edward VI).
Lumen ad Revelationem Gentium Light to enlighten the nations (Papacy).
L'Union Fait la Force The union makes strength (Belgium)
Macula Non Est in Te There is no sin in Thee (Essen).
Magnus ab Integro Saeculorum Nascitur Ordo The great order of the centuries is born anew (Bavaria).
Mandavit Dominus Palatie hanc Monetam Fiert The lord of the Palatine ordained this coin to be made (Balath).
Manibus Ne Laedar Avaris Lest I be injured by greedy hands (Sweden).
Mar Bran Sac Rom Imp Arcam et Elec Sup Dux Siles Margrave of Brandenburg, archchamberlain of the Holy Roman Empire and elector, senior duke of Silesia (Prussia).
Maria Mater Domini Xpi Mary mother of Christ the Lord (Teutonic Knights).
Maria Unxit Pedes Xpisti Mary washes the feet of Christ (France, Rene d'Anjou).
Mater Castrorum Mother of fortresses (Rome, Marcus Aurelius).
Matrimonio Conjuncti Joined in wedlock (Austria).
Me Coniunctio Servat Dum Scinditur Frangor The relationship serves me while I am being torn to pieces (Lowenstein-Wertheim).
Mediolani Dux Duke of Milan (Milan).
Mediolani et Man Duke of Mantua and Milan (Milan).
Memor Ero Tui Iustina Virgo I shall remember you, o maiden Justina (Venice).
Merces Laborum Wages of work (Wurzburg).
Mirabilia Fecit He wrought marvels (Viking coinage).
Misericordia Di Rex King by the mercy of God (France, Louis II).
Mo Arg Ord Foe Belg D Gel & CZ Silver coin of the order of the Belgian Federation, duchy of Guelder-land, county of Zutphen (Guelderland).

Moneta Abbatis Coin of the abbey (German ecclesiastical coins, 13th–14th centuries).
Moneta Argentiae Ord Foed Belgii Holl Silver coin of the federated union of Belgium and Holland (Batavian Republic).
Mo No Arg Con Foe Belg Pro Hol New silver coin of the Belgian Federation, province of Holland (Holland).
Mo No Arg Pro Confoe Belg Trai Holl New silver coin of the confederated Belgian provinces, Utrecht and Holland (Batavian Republic).
Mon Lib Reip Bremens Coin of the free state of Bremen (Bremen).
Mon Nova Arg Duc Curl Ad Norma Tal Alb New silver coin of the duchy of Courland, according to the standard of the Albert thaler (Courland).
Mon Nov Castri Imp New coin of the Imperial free city of . . . (Friedberg).
Moneta Bipont Coin of Zweibrucken (Pfalz-Birkenfeld-Zweibrucken).
Monet Capit Cathedr Fuld Sede Vacante Coin of the cathedral chapter of Fulda, the see being vacant (Fulda).
Moneta in Obsidione Tornacensi Cusa Coin struck during the siege of Tournai (Tournai, 1709).
Moneta Livosesthonica Coin of Livonia (Estonia).
Moneta Nov Arg Regis Daniae New silver coin of the king of Denmark (Denmark).
Moneta Nova Ad Norman Conventionis New coin according to the Convention standard (Orsini-Rosenberg).
Moneta Nova Domini Imperatoris New coin of the lord emperor (Brunswick, 13th century).
Moneta Nova Lubecensis New coin of Lubeck.
Moneta Nova Reipublicae Halae Suevicae New coin of the republic of Hall in Swabia.
Moneta Reipublicae Ratisbonensis Coin of the republic of Regensburg.
Nach Alt Reichs Schrot und Korn According to the old empire's grits and grain (Hesse).
Nach dem Conventions Fusse According to the Convention's basis (German Conventionsthalers).
Nach dem Frankf Schlus According to the Frankfurt standard (Solms).
Nach dem Schlus der V Staend According to the standard of the union (Hesse).
Navigare Necesse Est It is necessary to navigate (Germany).
Nec Aspera Terrent Nor do difficulties terrify (Brunswick).
Nec Cito Nec Temere Neither hastily nor rashlly (Cambrai).

Nec Numina Desunt   Nor is the divine will absent (Savoy).

Nec Temere Nec Timide   Neither rashly nor timidly (Danzig, Lippe).

Necessitas Legem Non Habet   Necessity has no law (Magdeburg).

Nemo Me Impune Lacessit   No one touches me with impunity (UK, Scottish pound edge inscription).

Nihil Restat Reliqui   No relic remains (Ypres).

Nil Ultra Aras   Nothing beyond the rocks (Franque-mont).

No Nobis Dne Sed Noi Tuo Da Gloriam   Not to us, o Lord but to Thy name be glory given (France, Francis I).

Nobilissimum Dom Ac Com in Lipp & St   Most noble lord and count in Lippe and Sternberg (Schaumburg-Lippe).

Nomen Domini Turris Fortissima   The name of the Lord is the strongest tower (Frankfurt).

Non Aes Sed Fides   Not bronze but trust (Malta).

Non Est Mortale Quod Opto   What I desire is not mortal. (Mecklenburg).

Non Mihi Sed Populo   Not to me but to the people (Bavaria).

Non Relinquam Vos Orphanos   I shall not leave you as orphans (Papacy).

Non Surrexit Major   None greater has arisen (Genoa, Malta).

Nullum Simulatum Diuturnum Tandem   Nothing that is feigned lasts long (Wittgenstein).

Nummorum Famulus   The servant of the coinage (England, tin halfpence and farthings).

Nunquam Retrorsum   Never backwards (Brunswick-Wolfenbuttel).

O Crux Ave Spes Unica   Hail, o Cross, our only hope (England half-angels, France, Rene d'Anjou).

O Maria Ora Pro Me   O Mary pray for me (Bavaria).

Ob Cives Servatos   On account of the rescued citizens (Rome, Augustus).

Oculi Domini Super Iustos   The eyes of the Lord look down on the just (Neuchatel).

Omnia Auxiliante Maria   Mary helping everything (Schwyz).

Omnia Cum Deo   Everything with God (Reuss-Greiz).

Omnia cum Deo et Nihil Sine Eo   Everthing with God and nothing without Him (Erbach).

Omnis Potestas a Deo Est   All power comes from God (Sweden).

Opp & Carn Dux Comm Rittb SCM Cons Int & Compi Mareschal   Duke of Troppau and

Carniola, count of Rietberg, privy councillor of his sacred imperial majesty, field marshal (Liechtenstein).

Opp & Carn . . . Aur Velleris Eques   Duke of Troppau . . . knight of the Golden Fleece (Liechtenstein).

Opportune   Conveniently (Savoy).

Optimus Princeps   Best prince (Rome, Trajan).

Opulentia Salerno   Wealthy Salerno (Siculo-Norman kingdom).

Pace et Iustitia   With peace and justice (Spanish Netherlands).

Pacator Orbis   Pacifier of the world (Rome, Aurelian).

Palma Sub Pondere Crescit   The palm grows under its weight (Waldeck).

Pater Noster   Our Father (Flanders, 14th century).

Pater Patriae   Farther of his country (Rome, Caligula).

Patria Si Dreptul Meu   The country and my right (Roumania).

Patrimon Henr Frid Sorte Divisum   The heritage of Heinrich Friedrich divided by lot (Hohenlohe-Langenberg).

Patrimonia Beati Petri   The inheritance of the blessed Peter (Papacy).

Patrona Franconiae   Patron of Franconia (Wurzburg).

Pax Aeterna   Eternal peace (Rome, Marcus Aurelius).

Pax et Abundantia   Peace and plenty (Burgundy, Gelderland).

Pax Missa Per Orbem   Peace sent throughout the world (England, Anne).

Pax Petrus   Peace Peter (Trier, 10th century).

Pax Praevalet Armis   May peace prevail by force of arms (Mainz).

Pax Quaeritur Bello   Peace is sought by war (Commonwealth, Cromwell).

Pecunia Totum Circumit Orbem   Money goes round the whole world (Brazil).

Per Aspera Ad Astra   Through difficulties to the stars (Mecklenburg-Schwerin).

Per Angusta ad Augusta   Through precarious times to the majestic (Solms-Roedelheim, a pun on the name of the ruler Johan August).

Per Crucem Tuam Salva Nos Christe Redemptor   By Thy cross save us, O Christ our Redeemer (England, angels).

Per Crucem Tuam Salva Nos Xpe Redemt   By Thy cross save us, O Christ our Redeemer (Portugal, 15th century).

Perdam Babillonis Nomen   May the name of Babylon perish (Naples).

Perennitati Iustissimi Regis   For the duration of the most just king (France, Louis XIII).

Perennitati Principis Galliae Restitutionis For the duration of the restoration of the prince of the Gauls (France, Henri IV).

Perfer et Obdura Bruxella Carry on and stick it out, Brussels (Brussels siege, 1579–80).

Perpetuus in Nemet Vivar Hereditary count in Nemt-Ujvar (Batthanyi).

Pietate et Constantia By piety and constancy (Fulda).

Pietate et Iustitia By piety and justice (Denmark).

Plebei Urbanae Frumento Constituto Free distribu-tion of grain to the urban working-class established (Rome, Nerva).

Pleidio Wyf Im Gwlad True am I to my country (UK, Welsh pound edge inscription).

Plus Ultra Beyond (the Pillars of Hercules) (Spanish America).

Point du Couronne sans Peine Point of the crown without penalty (Coburg).

Pons Civit Castellana The bridge of the town of Castellana (Papacy).

Populus et Senatus Bonon The people and senate of Bologna (Bologna).

Post Mortem Patris Pro Filio For the son after his father's death (Pontefract siege coins).

Post Tenebras Lux After darkness light (Geneva).

Post Tenebras Spero Lucem After darkness I hope for light (Geneva).

Posui Deum Adiutorem Meum I have made God my helper (England, Ireland, 1351–1603).

Praesidium et Decus Protection and ornament (Bologna).

Prima Sedes Galliarum First see of the Gauls (Lyon).

Primitiae Fodin Kuttenb ab Aerari Iterum Susceptarum First results dug from the Kuttenberg mines in a renewed undertaking (Austria).

Princps Iuventutis Prince of youth (Roman Empire).

Pro Defensione Urbis et Patriae For the defence of city and country (France, Louis XIV).

Pro Deo et Patria For God and the fatherland (Fulda).

Pro Deo et Populo For God and the people (Bavaria).

Pro Ecclesia et Pro Patria For the church and the fatherland (Constance).

Pro Fausio PP Reitur VS For happy returns of the princes of the Two Sicilies (Naples and Sicily).

Pro Lege et Grege For law and the flock (Fulda).

Pro maximo Dei Gloria et Bono Publico For the greatest glory of God and the good of the people (Wurttemberg).

Pro Patria For the fatherland (Wurzburg).

Propitio Deo Secura Ago With God's favour I lead a secure life. (Saxe-Lauenburg).

Protector Literis Literae Nummis Corona et Salus A protection to the letters (on the face of the coin), the letters (on the edge) are a garland and a safeguard to the coinage (Commonwealth, Cromwell broad).

Protege Virgo Pisas Protect Pisa, O Virgin (Pisa).

Provide et Constanter Wisely and firmly (Wurttem-berg).

Providentia et Pactis Through foresight and pacts (Brandenburg-Ansbach).

Providentia Optimi Principis With the foresight of the best prince (Naples and Sicily).

Proxima Fisica Finis Nearest to natural end (Orciano).

Proxima Soli Nearest to the sun (Modena).

Pulcra Virtutis Imago The beautiful image of virtue (Genoa).

Pupillum et Viduam Suscipiat May he support the orphan and the widow (Savoy).

Quae Deus Conjunxit Nemo Separet What God hath joined let no man put asunder (England, James I).

Quem Quadragesies et Semel Patriae Natum Esse Gratulamur Whom we congratulate for the forty-first time for being born for the fatherland (Lippe-Detmold).

Qui Dat Pauperi Non Indigebit Who gives to the poor will never be in need (Munster).

Quid Non Cogit Necessitas To what does Necessity not drive. (Ypres).

Quin Matrimonii Lustrum Celebrant They celebrate their silver wedding (Austria, 1879).

Quocunque Gesseris (Jeceris) Stabit Whichever way you throw it it will stand (Isle of Man).

Quod Deus Vult Hoc Semper Fit What God wishes always occurs. (Saxe-Weimar).

Reconduntur non Retonduntur They are laid up in store, not thundered back (Savoy).

Recta Tueri Defend the right (Austria).

Recte Constanter et Fortiter Rightly, constantly and bravely (Bavaria).

Recte Faciendo Neminem Timeas May you fear no one in doing right. (Solms-Laubach).

Rector Orbis Ruler of the world (Rome, Didius Julianus).

Rectus et Immotus Right and immovable (Hesse).

Redde Cuique Quod Suum Est Render to each that which is his own (England, Henry VIII).

Redeunt antiqui Gaudia Moris There return the joys of ancient custom (Regensburg).

Reg Pr Pol et Lith Saxon Dux Royal prince of Poland and Lithuania and duke of Saxony (Trier).

Regia Boruss Societas Asiat Embdae Royal Prussian Asiatic Society of Emden (Prussia).

Regier Mich Her Nach Deinen Wort Govern me here according to Thy word (Palatinate).

Regnans Capitulum Ecclesiae Cathedralis Ratisbonensis Sede Vacante Administering the chapter of the cathedral church at Regensburg, the see being vacant (Regensburg).

Regni Utr Sic et Hier Of the kingdom of the Two Sicilies and of Jerusalem (Naples and Sicily).

Religio Protestantium Leges Angliae Libertas Parliamenti The religion of the Protestants, the laws of England and the freedom of Parliament (England, Royalists, 1642).

Relinquo Vos Liberos ab Utroque Homine I leave you as children of each man (San Marino).

Restauracao da Independencia Restoration of inde-pendence (Portugal, 1990).

Restitutor Exercitus Restorer of the army (Rome, Aurelian).

Restitutor Galliarum Restorer of the Gauls (Rome, Gallienus).

Restitutor Generis Humani Restorer of mankind (Rome, Valerian).

Restitutor Libertatis Restorer of freedom (Rome, Constantine).

Restitutor Orbis Restorer of the world (Rome, Valerian).

Restitutor Orientis Restorer of the east (Rome, Valerian).

Restitutor Saeculi Restorer of the century (Rome, Valerian).

Restitutor Urbis Restorer of the city (Rome, Severus).

Rosa Americana Utile Dulci The American rose, useful and sweet (American colonies).

Rosa Sine Spina A rose without a thorn (England, Tudor coins).

Rutilans Rosa Sine Spina A dazzling rose without a thorn (England, Tudor gold coins).

S Annae Fundgruben Ausb Tha in N Oe Mining thaler of the St Anne mine in Lower Austria (Austria).

S Ap S Leg Nat Germ Primas Legate of the Holy Apostolic See, born Primate of Germany (Salzburg).

S Carolus Magnus Fundator Charlemagne founder (Munster).

S. Gertrudis Virgo Prudens Niviella St Gertrude the wise virgin of Nivelles (Nivelles).

SI Aul Reg Her & P Ge H Post Mag General hereditary postmaster, supreme of the imperial court of the hereditary kingdom and provinces (Paar).

S. Ian Bapt F. Zachari St John the Baptist, son of Zachary (Florence).

S. Kilianus Cum Sociis Francorum Apostoli St Kilian and his companions, apostles to the Franks (Wurzburg).

S. Lambertus Patronus Leodiensis St Lambert, patron of Liege (Liege).

Sac Nupt Celeb Berol For the holy matrimony celebrated at Berlin (Brandenburg-Ansbach).

Sac Rom Imp Holy Roman Empire (German states).

Sac Rom Imp Provisor Iterum Administrator of the Holy Roman Empire for the second time (Saxony).

Salus Generis Humani Safety of mankind (Rome, Vindex).

Salus Patriae Safety of the fatherland (Italy).

Salus Populi The safety of the people (Spain).

Salus Provinciarum Safety of the provinces (Rome, Postumus).

Salus Publica Salus Mea Public safety is my safety (Sweden).

Salus Reipublicae The safety of the republic (Rome, Theodosius II).

Salus Reipublicae Suprema Lex The safety of the republic is the supreme law (Poland).

Salvam Fac Rempublicam Tuam Make your state safe (San Marino).

Sanctus Iohannes Innoce St John the harmless (Gandersheim).

Sans Changer Without changing (Isle of Man).

Sans Eclat Without pomp (Bouchain siege, 1711).

Sapiente Diffidentia Wise distrust (Teschen).

Scutum Fidei Proteget Eum / Eam The shield of faith shall protect him / her (England, Edward VI and Elizabeth I).

Secundum Voluntatem Tuam Domine Your favourable will o Lord (Hesse).

Securitati Publicae For the public safety (Brandenburg-Ansbach).

Sede Vacante The see being vacant (Papal states, Vatican and ecclesiastical coinage).

Sena Vetus Alpha et W Principum et Finis Old Siena alpha and omega, the beginning and the end (Siena).

Senatus Populus QR Senate and people of Rome (Rome, 1188).

Si Deus Nobiscum Quis Contra Nos If God is with us who can oppose us (Hesse).

Si Deus Pro Nobis Quis Contra Nos If God is for us who can oppose us (Roemhild).

Sieh Deine Seeligkeit Steht Fest Ins Vaters Liebe Behold thy salvation stands surely in thy Father's love (Gotha).

Signis Receptis When the standards had been recovered (Rome, Augustus).

Signum Crucis The sign of the cross (Groningen).

Sincere et Constanter Truthfully and steadfastly (Hesse-Darmstadt).

Sit Nomen Domini Benedictum Blessed be the name of the Lord (Burgundy, Strasbourg).

St T X Adiuto Reg Iste Domba Let it be to you, o Christ, the assistant to the king of Dombes (Dombes).

Sit Tibi Xpe Dat q'tu Regis Iste Ducat May this duchy which Thou rulest be given to Thee, O Christ (Venice, ducat).

Sit Unio Haec Perennis May this union last for ever (Hohenlohe-Langenberg).

Sola Bona Quae Honesta The only good things are those which are honest (Brunswick).

Sola Facta Deum Sequor Through deeds alone I strive to follow God (Milan).

Soli Deo Honor et Gloria To God alone be honour and glory (Nassau).

Soli Reduci To him, the only one restored (Naples and Sicily).

Solius Virtutis Flos Perpetuus The flower of Virtue alone is perpetual (Strasbourg).

Spes Confisa Deo Nunquam Confusa Recedit Hope entrusted in God never retreats in a disorderly fashion (Lippe).

Spes Nr Deus God is our hope (Oudenarde siege, 1582).

Spes Rei Publicae The hope of the republic (Rome, Valens).

Strena ex Argyrocopeo Vallis S Christoph A New Year's gift from the silver-bearing valley of St Christopher (Wurttemberg, 1625).

Sub His Secura Spes Clupeus Omnibus in Te Sperantibus Under these hope is safe, a shield for all who reside hope in Thee (Bavaria).

Sub Pondere Under weight (Fulda).

Sub Protectione Caesarea Under imperial protection (Soragna).

Sub Tuum Praesidium Confug We flee to Thy protection (Salzburg).

Sub Umbra Alarum Tuarum Under the shadow of Thy wings (Iever, Scotland, James V).

Subditorum Salus Felicitas Summa The safety of the subjects is the highest happiness (Lubeck).

Sufficit Mihi Gratia Tua Domine Sufficient to me is Thy grace, o Lord (Ploen).

Supra Firmam Petram Upon a firm rock (Papacy).

Susceptor Noster Deus God is our defence (Tuscany).

Sydera Favent Industriae The stars favour industry (Furstenberg).

Sylvarum Culturae Praemium Prize for the culture of the forest (Brandenburg-Ansbach).

Tali Dicata Signo Mens Fluctuari Nequit Consecrated by such a sign the mind cannot waver (England, Henry VIII George noble).

Tandem Bona Caus Triumphat A good cause eventually triumphs (Dillenburg).

Tandem Fortuna Obstetrice With good luck ultimately as the midwife (Wittgenstein).

Te Stante Virebo With you at my side I shall be strong (Moravia).

Tene Mensuram et Respice Finem Hold the measure and look to the end (Burgundy).

Tert Ducat Secular Tercentenary of the duchy (Wurttemberg).

Thu Recht Schev Niemand Go with right and fear no one (Saxe-Lauenburg).

Tibi Laus et Gloria To Thee be praise and glory (Venice).

Timor Domini Fons Vitae The fear of the Lord is a fountain of life (England, Edward VI shillings).

Tout Avec Dieu Everything with God (Brunswick, 1626).

Traiectum ad Mosam The crossing of the Maas (Maastricht).

Transvolat Nubila Virtus Marriageable virtue soon flies past (Grueyeres).

Travail, Famille, Patrie Work, family, country (Vichy France).

Triumphator Gent Barb Victor over the barbarian people (Byzantine Empire, Arcadius).

Tueatur Unita Deus May God guard these united (Kingdoms) (England, James I; Britain, 1847).

Turck Blegert Wien Vienna besieged by the Turks (Vienna, 1531).

Tut Mar Gab Pr Vid de Lobk Nat Pr Sab Car et Aug Pr de Lobk Regency of Maria Gabriela, widow of the prince of Lobkowitz, born princess of Savoy-Carignan, and August prince of Lobkowitz (Lobkowitz).

Tutela Italiae The guardianship of Italy (Rome, Nerva).

Ubi Vult Spirat He breathes where he will (Papacy).

Ubique Pax Peace everywhere (Rome, Gallienus).

Union et Force Union and strength (France).

Urbe Obsessa The city under siege (Maastricht).

Urbem Virgo Tuam Serva   Protects thy city o virgin (Mary) (Strasbourg).

USC & RAM Cons Int Gen C Mar & Nob Praet H Turmae Capit   Privy councillor of both their holy imperial and royal apostolic majesties, general field marshal and captain of the noble praetorian Hungarian squadrons (Eszterhazy).

Vculis Aulae Argenteis Patriae Indigenti Ministravit Auxilia   With the silver vessels of the court aid was brought to the needy fatherland (Eichstadt, 1796).

Vehiculatione Italiae Remissa   Postal tax of Italy remitted (Rome, Nerva).

Veni Luumen Cordium   Come light of hearts (Vatican).

Veni Sancte Spiritus   Come Holy Ghost (Vatican).

Verbum Domini Manet in Aeternum   The word of the Lord abides forever (Hesse-Darmstadt, Veldenz).

Veritas Lex Tua   The truth is your law (Salzburg).

Veritas Temporis Filia   Truth is the daughter of time (England and Ireland, Mary Tudor).

Veritate et Labore   By truth and work (Wittgenstein).

Veritate et Iustitia   By truth and justice (German states).

Victoria Principum   The victory of princes (Ostrogoths).

Videant Pauperes et Laetentur   Let the poor see and rejoice (Tuscany).

Virgo Maria Protege Civitatem Savonae   Virgin Mary Protect the city of Savona (Savona).

Viribus Unitis   With united strength (Austria).

Virtute et Fidelitate   By virtue and faithfulness (Hesse-Cassel).

Virtute et Prudentia   With virtue and prudence (Auersperg).

Virtute Viam Dimetiar   I shall mark the way with valour (Waldeck).

Virtutis Gloria Merces   Glory is the reward of valour (Holstein-Gottorp).

Vis Unita Concordia Fratrum Fortior   United power is the stronger harmony of brothers (Mansfeld).

Visitavit Nos Oriens ex Alto   He has visited us arising on high (Luneburg).

Vivit Post Funera   He lives after death (Bremen).

Von Gottes Gn Iohan Bischof Zu Strasburg Landtgraf in Elsass   By God's grace John, Bishop of Strasbourg, Landgrave in Alsace (Strasbourg).

Vota Optata Romae Fel   Vows taken for the luck of Rome (Rome, Maxentius).

Vox de Throno   A voice from the throne (Papacy).

Was Got Beschert Bleibet Unerwert   What God hath endowed leave undisturbed

Wider macht und List Mein Fels Gott Ist   Against might and trickery God is my rock (Hesse-Cassel).

Xpc Vincit Xpc Regnat   Christ conquers, Christ reigns (Scotland, Spain).

Xpc Vivet Xpc Regnat Xpc Impat   Christ lives, Christ reigns, Christ commands (Cambrai).

Xpe Resurescit   Christ lives again (Venice).

Xpistiana Religio   Christian religion (Carolingian Empire).

Xps Ihs Elegit me Regem Populo   Jesus Christ chose me as king to the people (Norway).

Zelator Fidei Usque ad Montem   An upholder of the faith through and through (Portugal).

Zum Besten des Vaterlands   To the best of the fatherland (Bamberg).

Care
of coins

There is no point in going to a great deal of trouble and expense in selecting the best coins you can afford, only to let them deteriorate in value by neglect and mishandling. Unless you give some thought to the proper care of your coins, your collection is unlikely to make a profit for you if and when you come to sell it. Housing your coins is the biggest problem of all, so it is important to give a lot of attention to this.

Storage

The ideal, but admittedly the most expensive, method is the coin cabinet, constructed of air-dried mahogany, walnut or rosewood (*never* oak, cedar or any highly resinous timber likely to cause chemical tarnish). These cabinets have banks of shallow drawers containing trays made of the same wood, with half-drilled holes of various sizes to accommodate the different denominations of coins. Such cabinets are handsome pieces of furniture but, being largely handmade, tend to be rather expensive. Occasionally good specimens can be picked up in secondhand furniture shops, or at the dispersal of house contents by auction, but the best bet is still to purchase a new cabinet, tailored to your own requirements.

Peter Nichols of 3 Norman Road, St Leonards-on-Sea, East Sussex TN37 6NH (telephone 01424 436682) is a specialist manufacturer of display and storage systems who has also been producing coin and medal cabinets to suit every need for more than a quarter of a century. He can produce a cabinet to fit into a wall safe or some other form of security box. He can match existing work, and thus replicate cabinets which you may already be using, or even produce designs to suit your specific requirements. The only proviso is that the cabinets are made in only one timber—Brazilian mahogany, for reason of chemical balance. A nice touch is that all the products in the Nichols repertoire take their names from Elizabethan mint-marks.

Nichols also offers a custom drilling service for coin trays, either all of the same diameter or in mixed sizes, depending on what you require. Drilling templates are also available on request. Apart from coin cabinets, Peter Nichols manufactures *medal* cabinets in two basic types, the seven-tray Pheon and the fourteen-tray Crozier.

The cases for these cabinets are similar in all respects to the coin cabinets, but medal trays are twice the thickness of coin trays. Each tray is made up from solid mahogany mouldings, base and polished mahogany front edges and trimmed with two turned brass knobs. The base of each tray is trimmed with a red felt pad.

Nichols produces a wide range of cabinets from

The 4-tray Martlet—the smallest in an extensive range from Peter Nichols.

The Crozier—a cabinet for the connoisseur.

The Mini-Porter, smallest of Abafil's plush Diplomat range.

the seven-tray Pheon all the way up to the massive 40-tray specials designed for the British Museum. All cabinets are fitted with double doors. Nichols also produces the glass-topped Crown display case and the Sceptre display case, fitted with a glazed lid and containing a single tray. The Orb range of display cases are intended for wall mounting and are ideal for a display of campaign medals and decorations.

Prices start at around £30 for a four-tray Martlet coin cabinet and go all the way to the Coronet thirty-tray version at about £300. They are not cheap, but you have the satisfaction of acquiring exquisite examples of the cabinetmaker's craft which would be an elegant addition to any lounge or study.

An excellent compromise is provided by firms such as Abafil of Italy and Lindner of Germany who manufacture coin trays in durable, felt-lined materials with shallow compartments to suit the various sizes of coins. These trays interlock so that they build up into a cabinet of the desired size, and there are also versions designed as carrying cases, which are ideal for transporting coins.

Collectors Gallery of Castle Hall, Castle Gate, Shrewsbury, SY1 2AD (telephone: 01743 272140, fax: 01743 366041) is the UK agent and distributor for the Abafil series manufactured in Milan. These cases are of stout wooden construction covered with simulated leather and lined with red plush. The Diplomat range is designed primarily for secure transportation, but the Mini-diplomat, at around £40, makes a good static cabinet, and can take up to three standard trays holding a maximum of 241 coins, while the Custom case holds 14 de luxe or 20 standard trays and will house up to 1,500 coins. Even cheaper is the Mignon case holding up to 105 coins, ideally suited for carrying in a briefcase or travel bag.

Lindner Publications of 13 Fore Street, Hayle, Cornwall TR27 4DX (telephone 01726 751914) are well-known for their wide range of philatelic and

numismatic accessories, but these include a full array of coin boxes, capsules, carrying cases and trays. The basic Lindner coin box is, in fact, a shallow tray available in a standard version or a smoked glass version. These trays have a crystal clear frame, red felt inserts and holes for various diameters of coins and medals. A novel feature of these trays is the rounded insert which facilitates the removal of coins from their spaces with the minimum of handling. These boxes are designed in such a manner that they interlock and can be built up into banks of trays, each fitted with a draw-handle and sliding in and out easily. Various types of chemically inert plastic capsules and envelopes have been designed for use in combination with plain shallow trays, without holes drilled. Lindner also manufacture a range of luxury cases lined in velvet and Atlas silk with padded covers and gold embossing on the spines, producing a most tasteful and elegant appearance.

Safe Albums of 16 Falcon Business Park, Hogwood Lane, Finchampstead, Berkshire RG11 4QW (telephone 01734 328976) are the UK agents for the German Stapel-Element, a drawer-stacking system with clear plasticiser-free trays that fit into standard bookshelves. The sliding coin compartments, lined with blue velvet, can be angled for display to best advantage. Stackable drawers cost around £12 each, and can be built up to any height desired. A wide range of drawer sizes is available, with compartments suitable for the smallest coins right up to four-compartment trays designed for very large artefacts such as card-cases or cigarette cases. The Mobel-Element cabinet is a superb specialised cabinet constructed of the finest timber with a steel frame and steel grip bars which can be securely locked. It thus combines elegance with security and is the ideal medium for the most valuable coins and medals.

There are also various storage systems, such as Coindex, which operate on the principle of narrow

Adding on to the stacking Lindner range is easy.

drawers in which the coins are stored in envelopes of chemically-inert plastic. A strip across the top holds a little slip giving a brief description, catalogue number and the price of each coin.

Kwikseal of the USA produce cards with a plastic window: these cards are especially suitable for slabbing coins. The traditional method used by many collectors was to house coins in small, air-dried manila envelopes that could be stored upright in narrow wooden or stout card boxes—knife-boxes were highly regarded as being the right width and depth. The Sydney Museum in Australia, for example, keeps its coins in manila envelopes stored in plastic lunch-boxes which seemed to do the job pretty well!

Albums can be carried around easily

Safe's cabinet combines elegance with security.

Coin Albums

When coin collecting became a popular hobby in the 1960s, several firms marketed ranges of coin albums. They had clear plastic sleeves divided into tiny compartments of various sizes and had the merit of being cheap and taking up little room on a bookshelf.

They had several drawbacks, however, not the least being the tendency of the pages to sag with the weight of the coins, or even, in extreme cases, to pull away from the pegs or rings holding them on to the spine. They required very careful handling as the coins could easily fall out of the top row as the pages were turned. The more expensive albums had little flaps that folded over the top of the coin to overcome this problem.

Arguably the worst aspect of these albums was the use of polyvinyl chloride (PVC) in the construction of the sleeves. Collectors soon discovered to their horror that this reacted chemically with their coins, especially those made of silver, causing a rather disgusting yellow slime to adhere to the coins' surface. I shudder to think how many fine collections were ruined as a result,

or of the countless coins that required highly expert treatment in a bid to restore them to as near the original condition as possible.

Fortunately the lesson has been learned and the coin albums now on the market are quite safe. Lindner offer a wide range of albums designed to house coins, medals or banknotes. The old problem about sagging pages is overcome by the use of a multi-ring binding welded to a very stout spine, while the sleeves contain neither Styrol nor PVC and will not affect any metals at all. In addition to pages with pockets of uniform size, the Karat range of albums operates on a slide principle which enables the user to insert vertical strips of different sizes on the same page, so that the coins of one country or series, or perhaps a thematic display of coins from different countries, can be displayed side by side.

Safe Albums offer a wide range of albums in the Coinholder System and Coin-Combi ranges. These, too, offer the choice of fixed pages with uniform-sized pockets, or interchangeable sliding inserts for different sizes side by side.

Cleaning Coins

This is like matrimony—it should not be embarked on lightly. Indeed, the advice given by the magazine *Punch* in regard to marriage is equally sound in this case—don't do it! It is far better to have a dirty coin than an irretrievably damaged one. Every dealer has horror stories of handling coins that previous owners have cleaned, to their detriment. The worst example I ever saw was a display of coins found by a metal detectorist who "improved" his finds by abrading them in the kind of rotary drum used by lapidarists to polish gemstones. If you really must remove the dirt and grease from coins, it is advisable to practise on coins of little value.

Warm water containing a mild household detergent or washing-up liquid will work wonders in removing surface dirt and grease from most coins, but silver is best washed in a weak solution of ammonia and warm water—one part ammonia to ten parts water. Gold coins can be cleaned with diluted citric acid, such as lemon juice. Copper or bronze coins present more of a problem, but patches of verdigris can usually be removed by careful washing in a 20 per cent solution of sodium sesquicarbonate. Wartime coins made of tin, zinc, iron or steel can be cleaned in a 5 per cent solution of caustic soda containing some aluminium or zinc foil or filings, but they must be rinsed afterwards in clean water and carefully dried. Cotton buds are ideal for gently prising dirt out of coin legends and crevices in the designs. Soft brushes (with animal bristles—*never* nylon or other artificial bristles)

designed for cleaning silver are most suitable for gently cleaning coins.

Coins recovered from the soil or the sea bed present special problems, due to chemical reaction between the metals and the salts in the earth or sea water. In such cases, the best advice is to take them to the nearest museum and let the professional experts decide on what can or should be done.

Both Lindner and Safe Albums offer a range of coin-cleaning kits and materials suitable for gold, silver, copper and other base alloys respectively. Safe (living up to their name) also provide a stern warning that rubber gloves should be worn and care taken to avoid breathing fumes or getting splashes of liquid in your eyes or on your skin. Obviously, the whole business of cleaning is a matter that should not be entered into without the utmost care and forethought.

POLISHING: A WARNING

If cleaning should only be approached with the greatest trepidation, polishing is definitely *out!* Beginners sometimes fall into the appalling error of thinking that a smart rub with Brasso or Duraglit might improve the appearance of their coins. Short of actually punching a hole through it, I cannot imagine a more destructive act. Polishing a coin may improve its superficial appearance for a few days, but such abrasive action will destroy the patina and reduce the fineness of the high points of the surface. Even if a coin is only polished once, it will never be quite the same again, and an expert can tell this a mile off.

Celtic
coinage of Britain

Celtic coins were the first coins made in Britain. They were issued for a century and a half before the Roman invasion, and possibly a little later in some areas. They were issued by 11 tribal groups or administrative authorities situated southeast of a line from the Humber to the Severn. In this short article Celtic specialist CHRIS RUDD introduces this increasingly popular area.

The earliest coins were uninscribed and often abstract in design. Later ones carried the names of local leaders and tribal centres, and in the southeast became increasingly Roman in style, sometimes copying classical images quite closely.

Most Celtic coins were struck between two dies on flans of gold, silver, billion and bronze. Some were cast in strip moulds in tin-rich bronze alloy called "potin".

Because the Celts wrote no books and left no written records of their activities, little is known about the people and places behind their coins. Who made them? When? Where? And why? These are questions that are still largely unanswered, except in the very vaguest terms. Celtic cataloguers talk about gold quarters, silver units and silver minims. But the truth is we don't even know what the Celts themselves called their coins.

British Celtic coins are among the most fascinating ever fashioned and perhaps the least familiar to the average collector because of their rarity. Like the Celts themselves, Celtic coin designs are wild, free flowing, flamboyant and full of fun. Yes, Celtic moneyers had a great sense of humour!

Celtic coins bear a vast variety of gods and goddesses, armed warriors, chariot wheels, hidden faces, decapitated heads, suns, moons, stars, thunderbolts, floral motifs, magic signs and phallic symbols. Plus a menagerie of antelopes, bears, boars, bulls, cocks, crabs, cranes, dogs, dolphins, ducks, eagles, hares, all kinds of horses (some with wings, some with human heads, many with three tails, a few breathing fire), goats, lions, lizards, owls, rams, rats, ravens, snakes, stags, starfish, worms and wolves. Not to mention dragons, griffins, hippocamps, sphinxes and ram-horned serpents.

Ask any metal detectorist how many Celtic coins he or she has found and you will immediately realise they are rarer than Roman coins in this country—at least a thousand times rarer on average. This is because far fewer Celtic coins were minted, in smaller runs, over a much shorter time span. Though some may have been made as early as 80 BC, the majority of British Celtic coins were struck from 54 BC to AD 43; barely 100 years of production, and most of that seems to have been sporadic.

However, the greater rarity of Celtic coins doesn't mean they are necessarily more costly than other ancient coins: in fact, they are often cheaper. You see, in the coin market, demand determines price. The more collectors that want a coin, the higher its price.

A recent survey revealed "worldwide there may be no more than 150 regular private collectors

Method that may have been used for striking Celtic coins (drawing by Simon Pressey).

103

of Celtic coins, buying on average one or more coins per month". Whereas there are literally thousands of people collecting the other major series of ancient and medieval coins. That is why Celtic coins are still comparatively less costly than Greek, Anglo-Saxon and English hammered coins. The Celtic market is smaller, though expanding. For example a very fine Celtic gold stater typically costs half the price of a Greek gold stater or an English gold noble of comparable quality and

rarity. The price differential can be even more dramatic at major international auctions. But the disparity is diminishing as more and more collectors are beginning to appreciate the hitherto unrecognised beauty, scarcity and good value of British Celtic coins. So now could be a good time to start collecting Celtic coins, before their prices begin climbing more steeply.

Thirty years ago collecting British Celtic coins was a rich man's hobby and understanding them

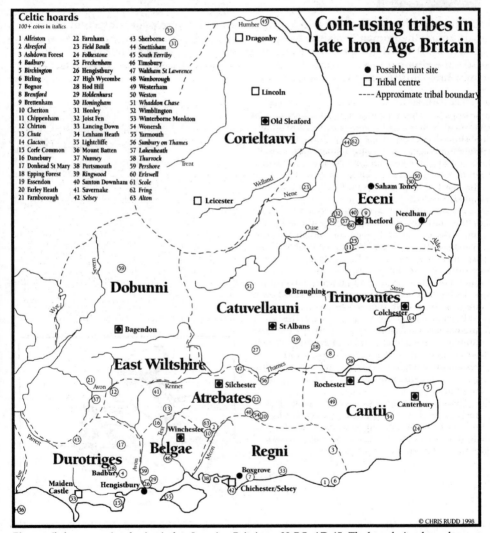

Eleven tribal groups minted coins in late Iron Age Britain, c. 80 BC–AD 45. The boundaries shown here are guesstimates, not actual, and often follow rivers, many of which are still known by their Celtic names.

Silver unit attributed to King Prasutagus of the Eceni, whose death resulted in the revolt of Queen Boudica, AD 60 (drawn four times actual size by Susan White).

was the lonely pursuit of a few scholarly numismatists. Today, thanks to the popularity of metal detecting, Celtic coins are more plentiful and almost everyone can afford to collect them. Most ancient coin dealers sell Celtic coins, some for as little as £20 each, and you will always find a few trays of them at every coin fair.

British Celtic coins are also easier to study today, thanks to the publication of some excellent books on the subject. The Celtic collector's bible is *Celtic Coinage of Britain* by Robert D. Van Arsdell (Spink, 1989)—well researched, well written, well illustrated, always quoted in dealers' catalogues, often controversial when dates are discussed and hopefully soon to be republished in a revised edition. For the dedicated Celtic devotee *British Iron Age Coins in the British Museum* by Richard Hobbs (British Museum Press, 1996) is an invaluable companion volume to Van Arsdell— more cautious, less speculative.

By far the best introductory book is *Celtic Coinage in Britain* by Dr Philip de Jersey (Shire Archaeology, 1996) who manages the Celtic Coin Index, a photographic record of over 23,000 British coins at the Institute of Archaeology, Oxford. In plain language Dr Philip de Jersey explains how Celtic coins and the images they carry can reveal information on the political, economic and social life of the Celts. *Celtic Coinage in Britain* contains clear twice-size photos of over a hundred Celtic

coins, some of them rarely seen before. It gives the names, addresses and phone numbers of the museums in England, Scotland and Wales with the best and most accessible collections of Celtic coins.

In short, if you want to know more about British Celtic coins, *Celtic Coinage in Britain* is where you start reading and keep reading. This is the best little book ever written about British Celtic coins and outstanding value for money at £4.99.

How should you start collecting British Celtic coins? First, get a few of the commoner uninscribed types from each of the 11 tribal areas, aiming for the highest grade you can comfortably afford. Then you may wish to get an inscribed coin of each of the main rulers. You would also be well advised to acquire some Gaulish coins at the same time, because many British coins were influenced by Gallic prototypes.

How much do British Celtic coins cost? Very little, considering how scarce they are. Types with legends usually cost more than those without and top quality bronze is frequently more pricey than top quality silver (which may surprise you) because silver is commoner and generally survives better after two-thousand years underground.

Chris Rudd is a well-known dealer who specialises in Celtic coins.

Collecting

Ancient coins

Ancient coins differ from most other series which are collected in Britain in that every piece has spent the major part of the last two thousand years in the ground. As JOHN CUMMINGS, dealer in ancient coins and antiquities explains here, the effect that burial has had on the surface of the coin determines more than anything else the value of a particular piece. With more modern coins, the only things which affect price are rarity and grade. There may be a premium for coins exhibiting particularly fine tone, or with outstanding pedigrees, but an 1887 crown in "extremely fine" condition has virtually the same value as every other piece with the same grade and of the same date. With ancient coins the story is very different.

A large number of different criteria affect the price of an ancient coin. Factors affecting prices can be broken down into several categories:

Condition

The most important factor by far in determining price. Ancient coins were struck by hand and can exhibit striking faults. Value suffers if the coin is struck with the designs off-centre, is weakly struck, or if the flan is irregular in shape. Many of the Celtic tribes issued coins of varying fineness and those made from low quality gold or silver are worth less than similar specimens where the metal quality is better. Conversely, coins on exceptional flans, particularly well struck, or with fine patinas command a premium.

Many ancient coins have suffered during their stay in the ground. It must be borne in mind that the prices given in the price guide are for uncorroded, undamaged examples. A Roman denarius should be graded using the same criteria as those used for grading modern coins. The surfaces must be good, and the coin intact. The fact that the coin is 2,000 years old is irrelevant as far as grading is concerned. Coins which are not perfectly preserved are not without value but the value for a given grade decreases with the degree of fault.

Rarity

As with all other series, rare coins usually command higher prices than common ones

although this is not written in stone. A unique variety of a small fourth century Roman bronze coin, even in perfect condition, can be worth much less than a more worn and common piece from an earlier part of the empire. In the Celtic series, there is an almost infinite variety of minor types and a unique variety of an uninscribed type will rarely outbid an inscribed issue of a known king.

Historical and local significance

Types which have historical or local interest can command a price far above their scarcity value. Denarii of the emperor Tiberius are believed to have been referred to in the New Testament and command a far higher price than a less interesting piece of similar rarity. Similarly, pieces which have British reverse types such as the "VICT BRIT" reverse of the third century AD are more expensive than their scarcity would indicate. The 12 Caesars are ever popular especially in the American market and this affects prices throughout the world. In the Celtic series, coins of Cunobelin or Boudicca are far more popular than pieces which have no historical interest but which are far scarcer.

Reverse types

All Roman emperors who survived for a reasonable time issued coins with many different reverse types. The most common of these usually show various Roman gods. When a coin has an unusual reverse it always enhances the value.

Particularly popular are architectural scenes, animals, references to Judaism, and legionary types.

Artistic merit

Most Celtic tribes issued several distinct series which generally speaking, improved in style up to the time of the Roman invasion. Later issues which exhibit fine "Celtic" style are usually more popular than the more stylised, earlier types.

Typical of the former would be the beautiful gold staters of Tasciovanus and Cunobelin. The Roman coinage is blessed with a large number of bust varieties and these can have a startling effect on price. A common coin with the bust left instead of right can be worth several times the price of a normal example. The coinage of Hadrian has a large number of bust varieties some of which are extremely artistic and these can command a premium.

The coinage used in Britain from the time of the invasion in AD43 was the same as that introduced throughout the Empire by the emperor Augustus around 20 BC. The simple divisions of 2 asses equal to one dupondius, 2 dupondii equal to 1 sestertius, 4 sestertii equal to one denarius and 25 denarii equal to one aureus continued in use until the reformation of the coinage by Caracalla in AD 214.

Aureus (gold)

Denarius (silver)

Sestertius (bronze)

Dupondius (copper)

As (copper)

107

Introducing

Hammered coinage

The hammered currency of medieval Britain is among some of the most interesting coinage in the world. The turbulent history of these islands is reflected in the fascinating changes in size, design, fineness and workmanship, culminating in the many strange examples that emanated from the strife of the Civil War.

The Norman Conquest of England in 1066 and succeeding years had far-reaching effects on all aspects of life. Surprisingly, however, it had little impact on the coinage. William the Conqueror was anxious to emphasise the continuity of his reign, so far as the ordinary people were concerned, and therefore he retained the fabric, size and general design pattern of the silver penny. Almost 70 mints were in operation during this reign, but by the middle of the 12th century the number was reduced to 55 and under Henry II (1154–89) it fell to 30 and latterly to only eleven. By the early 14th century the production of coins had been centralised on London and Canterbury, together with the ecclesiastical mints at York and Canterbury. The silver penny was the principal denomination throughout the Norman period, pieces cut along the lines of the cross on the reverse continuing to serve as halfpence and farthings.

Eight types of penny were struck under William I and five under his son William Rufus, both profiles (left and right) and facing portraits being used in both reigns allied to crosses of various types. Fifteen types were minted under Henry I (1100–35), portraiture having now degenerated to crude caricature, the lines engraved on the coinage dies being built up by means of various punches. Halfpence modelled on the same pattern were also struck, but very sparingly and are very rare.

On Henry's death the succession was contested by his daughter Matilda and his nephew Stephen of Blois. Civil war broke out in 1138 and continued till 1153. Stephen controlled London and its mint, but Matilda and her supporters occupied the West Country and struck their own coins at Bristol. Several of the powerful barons struck their own coins, and there were distinct regional variants of the regal coinage. Of particular interest are the coins struck

Silver pennies of, from left to right, William I, William Rufus, Henry I and Stephen.

from obverse dies with Stephen's portrait erased or defaced, believed to date from 1148 when the usurper was under papal interdict.

Peace was restored in 1153 when it was agreed that Matilda's son Henry should succeed Stephen. On the latter's death the following year, Henry II ascended the throne. Coins of Stephen's last type continued to be minted till 1158, but Henry then took the opportunity to overhaul the coinage which had become irregular and sub-standard during the civil war. The new "Cross Crosslet" coins, usually known as the Tealby coinage (from the hoard of over 5,000 pennies found at Tealby, Lincolnshire in 1807), were produced at 30 mints, but when the recoinage was completed this number was reduced to a dozen. The design of Henry's coins remained virtually the same throughout more than two decades, apart from minor variants. Then, in 1180, a new type, known as the Short Cross coinage, was introduced. This was a vast improvement over the poorly struck Cross Crosslet coins and continued without alteration, not only to the end of the reign of Henry II in 1189, but throughout the reigns of his sons Richard (1189–99) and John (1199–1216) and the first half of the reign of his grandson Henry III (1216–46). Throughout that 66 year period, however, there were minor variations in portraits and lettering which enable numismatists to attribute the HENRICUS coins to specific reigns and periods.

"Tealby" type penny, left, and "Short Cross" penny of Henry II.

The style and workmanship of the Short Cross coinage deteriorated in the reign of Henry III. By the 1220s coin production was confined to the regal mints at London and Canterbury, the sole exception being the ecclesiastical mint maintained by the Abbot of Bury St Edmunds.

Halfpence and farthings were briefly struck in 1221–30, though halfpence are now extremely rare and so far only a solitary farthing has been discovered.

By the middle of this reign the coinage was in a deplorable state, being poorly struck, badly worn and often ruthlessly clipped. In 1247 Henry ordered a new coinage and in this the arms of the cross on the reverse were extended to the rim as a safeguard against clipping. This established a pattern of facing portrait and long cross on obverse and reverse respectively that was to continue till the beginning of the 16th century. Several provincial mints were re-activated to assist with the recoinage but they were all closed down again by 1250, only the regal mints at London and Canterbury and the ecclesiastical mints at Durham and Bury St Edmunds remaining active.

"Long Cross" pennies of Henry III, left, and Edward I.

In 1257 Henry tentatively introduced a gold penny (worth 20 silver pence and twice the weight of a silver penny). The coin was undervalued and soon disappeared from circulation.

The Long Cross coinage of Henry III continued under Edward I till 1279 when the king introduced a new coinage in his own name. The penny continued the style of its predecessors, though much better designed and executed; but new denominations were now added. Henceforward halfpence and farthings became a regular issue and, at the same time, a fourpenny coin known as the groat (from French *gros*) was briefly introduced (minting ceased in 1282 and was not revived till 1351). Due to the centralisation of coin production the name of the moneyer was now generally dropped, although it lingered on a few years at Bury St Edmunds. The provincial mints were again revived in 1299–1302 to recoin the lightweight foreign imitations of pennies which had flooded in from the Continent.

The coinage of Edward II (1307–27) differed only in minor respects from that of his father, and a similar pattern prevailed in the first years of Edward III. In 1335 halfpence and farthings below the sterling fineness were struck. More importantly, further attempts were made to introduce gold coins. In 1344 the florin or double

Pre-Treaty Noble of Edward III which contained reference to France in the legend.

leopard of six shillings was introduced, along with its half and quarter. This coinage was not successful and was soon replaced by a heavier series based on the noble of 80 pence (6s. 8d.), half a mark or one third of a pound. The noble originally weighed 138.5 grains but it was successively reduced to120 grains, at which weight it continued from 1351. During this reign the protracted conflict with France known as the Hundred Years' War erupted. Edward III, through his mother, claimed the French throne and inscribed this title on his coins. By the Treaty of Bretigny (1361) Edward temporarily gave up his claim and the reference to France

Noble of Edward IV, issued before he was forced to abandon the throne of England.

was dropped from the coins, but when war was renewed in 1369 the title was resumed, and remained on many English coins until the end of the 18th century. The silver coinage followed the pattern of the previous reign, but in 1351 the groat was re-introduced and with it came the twopence or half-groat. Another innovation was the use of mintmarks at the beginning of the inscriptions. Seven types of cross and one crown were employed from 1334 onwards and their sequence enables numismatists to date coins fairly accurately.

The full range of gold (noble, half-noble and quarter-noble) and silver (groat, half-groat, penny, halfpenny and farthing) continued under Richard II (1377–99). Little attempt was made to alter the facing portrait on the silver coins, by now little more than a stylised caricature anyway.

Noble of Henry IV which was reduced in weight due to the shortage of gold.

Under Henry IV (1399–1413) the pattern of previous reigns prevailed, but in 1412 the weights of the coinage were reduced due to a shortage of bullion. The noble was reduced to 108 grains and its sub-divisions lightened proportionately. The penny was reduced by 3 grains, and its multiples and sub-divisions correspondingly reduced. One interesting change was the reduction of the fleur de lis of France from four to three in the heraldic shield on the reverse of the noble; this change corresponded with the alteration in the arms used in France itself. The Calais mint, opened by Edward III in 1363, was closed in 1411. There was no change in the designs used for the coins of Henry V (1413–22) but greater use was now made of mintmarks to distinguish the various periods of production. Coins were by now produced mainly at London, although the episcopal mints at Durham and York were permitted to strike pennies.

The supply of gold dwindled early in the reign of Henry VI and few nobles were struck after 1426. The Calais mint was re-opened in 1424 and struck a large amount of gold before closing finally in 1440. A regal mint briefly operated at York in 1423–24. Mintmarks were now much more widely used and tended to correspond more closely to the annual trials of the Pyx. The series of civil upheavals known as the Wars of the Roses erupted in this period.

In 1461 Henry VI was deposed by the Yorkist Earl of March after he defeated the Lancastrians at Mortimer's Cross. The Yorkists advanced on London where the victor was crowned Edward IV. At first he continued the gold series of his predecessor, issuing nobles and quarter-nobles, but in 1464 the weight of the penny was reduced

Groat of Richard III (1483–85).

to 12 grains and the value of the noble was raised to 100 pence (8s. 4d.).The ryal or rose-noble of 120 grains, together with its half and quarter, was introduced in 1465 and tariffed at ten shillings or half a pound. The need for a coin worth a third of a pound, however, led to the issue of the angel of 80 grains, worth 6s. 8d., but this was initially unsucessful and very few examples are now extant. The angel derived its name from the figure of the Archangel Michael on the obverse; a cross surmounting a shield appeared on the reverse.

In 1470 Edward was forced to flee to Holland and Henry VI was briefly restored. During this brief period (to April 1471) the ryal was discontinued but a substantial issue of angels and half-angels was made both at London and Bristol. Silver coins were struck at York as well as London and Bristol, the issues of the provincial mints being identified by the initials B or E (Eboracum, Latin for York). Edward defeated

the Lancastrians at Tewkesbury and deposed the luckless Henry once more. In his second reign Edward struck only angels and half-angels as well as silver from the groat to halfpenny. In addition to the three existing mints, silver coins were struck at Canterbury, Durham and the archiepiscopal mint at York. Mintmarks were now much more frequent and varied. Coins with a mark of a halved sun and rose are usually assigned to the reign of Edward IV, but they were probably also struck in the nominal reign of Edward V, the twelve-year-old prince held in the Tower of London under the protection of his uncle Richard, Duke of Gloucester. Coins with this mark on the reverse had an obverse mark of a boar's head, Richard's personal emblem. The brief reign of Richard III (1483–5) came to an end with his defeat at Bosworth and the relatively scarce coins of this period followed the pattern of the previous reigns, distinguished by the sequence of mint marks and the inscription RICAD or RICARD.

In the early years of Henry VII's reign the coinage likewise followed the previous patterns, but in 1489 the first of several radical changes was effected, with the introduction of the gold sovereign of 20 shillings showing a full-length portrait of the monarch seated on an elaborate throne. For reverse, this coin depicted a Tudor rose surmounted by a heraldic shield. A similar reverse appeared on the ryal of 10 shillings, but the angel and angelet retained previous motifs. The silver coins at first adhered to the medieval pattern, with the stylised facing portrait and long cross, but at the beginning of the 16th century a large silver coin, the testoon or shilling of 12 pence, was introduced and adopted a realistic profile of the king, allied to a reverse showing a cross surmounted by the royal arms.

First coinage Angel of Henry VIII which retained the traditional 23½ carat fineness.

The same design was also used for the later issue of groat and half groat.

This established a pattern which was to continue till the reign of Charles I. In the reign of Henry VIII, however, the coinage was subject to considerable debasement. This led to the eventual introduction of 22 carat (.916 fine) gold for the crown while the traditional 23 ½ carat gold was retained for the angel and ryal. This dual system continued until the angel was discontinued at the outset of the Civil War in 1642; latterly it had been associated with the ceremony of touching for "King's Evil" or scrofula, a ritual used by the early Stuart monarchs to bolster their belief in the divine right of kings.

Under the Tudors and Stuarts the range and complexity of the gold coinage increased, but it was not until the reign of Edward VI that the silver series was expanded. In 1551 he introduced the silver crown of five shillings, the first English coin to bear a clear date on the obverse. Under Mary dates were extended to the shilling and sixpence.

The mixture of dated and undated coins continued under Elizabeth I, a reign remarkable for the range of denominations—nine gold and eight silver. The latter included the sixpence, threepence, threehalfpence and threefarthings, distinguished by the rose which appeared behind the Queen's head.

The coinage of James I was even more complex, reflecting the king's attempts to unite his dominions. The first issue bore the legend ANG: SCO (England and Scotland), but from 1604 this was altered to MAG: BRIT (Great Britain). This period witnessed new denominations, such as the rose-ryal and spur-ryal, the unite, the Britain crown and the thistle crown, and finally the laurel of 20 shillings and its sub-divisions.

In the reign of Elizabeth experiments began with milled coinage under Eloi Mestrell. These continued sporadically in the 17th century, culminating in the beautiful coins struck by Nicholas Briot (1631–39). A branch mint was established at Aberystwyth in 1637 to refine and coin silver from the Welsh mines. Relations between King and Parliament deteriorated in the reign of Charles I and led to the Civil War (1642). Parliament controlled London but continued to strike coins in the King's name. The Royalists struck coins, both in pre-war and new types, at Shrewsbury, Oxford, Bristol, Worcester, Exeter, Chester, Hereford and other Royalist strongholds, while curious siege pieces were pressed into service at Newark, Pontefract and Scarborough.

After the execution of Charles I in 1649 the Commonwealth was proclaimed under Oliver Cromwell. Gold and silver coins were now inscribed in English instead of Latin. Patterns portraying Cromwell and a crowned shield restored Latin in 1656. Plans for milled coinage were already being considered before the Restoration of the monarchy in 1660. Hammered coinage appeared initially, resuming the style of coins under Charles I, but in 1662 the hand-hammering of coins was abandoned in favour of coins struck on the mill and screw press. The hammered coins of 1660–62 were undated and bore a crown mintmark, the last vestiges of medievalism in British coinage.

The magnificent Rose-Ryal of James I.

COIN
grading

CONDITION is the secret to the value of virtually anything, whether it be antiques, jewellery, horses or second-hand cars—and coins are *certainly* no exception. When collecting coins it is vital to understand the recognised standard British system of grading, i.e. accurately assessing a coin's condition or state of wear. Grading is an art which can only be learned by experience and so often it remains one person's opinion against another's, therefore it is important for the beginner or inexperienced collector to seek assistance from a reputable dealer or knowledgeable numismatist when making major purchases.

The standard grades as used in this Price Guide are as follows:

UNC **Uncirculated**
A coin that has never been in circulation, although it may show signs of contact with other coins during the minting process.

EF **Extremely Fine**
A coin in this grade may appear uncirculated to the naked eye but on closer examination will show signs of minor friction on the highest surface.

VF **Very Fine**
A coin that has had very little use, but shows signs of wear on the high surfaces.

F **Fine**
A coin that has been in circulation and shows general signs of wear, but with all legends and date clearly visible.

Other grades used in the normal grading system are:

BU **Brilliant Uncirculated**
As the name implies, a coin retaining its mint lustre.

Fair A coin extensively worn but still quite recognisable and legends readable.

Poor A coin very worn and only just recognisable.

Other abbreviations used in the Price Guide are:

Obv **Obverse**

Rev **Reverse**

Other abbreviations, mintmarks, etc. can be identified under the appropriate section of this Yearbook.

Coins illustrated in the following listings are indicated with an asterisk (*)

A SIMPLIFIED PRICE GUIDE
TO
ANCIENT COINS USED IN BRITAIN

PART I
CELTIC

The prices given in this section are those that you would expect to pay from a reputable dealer and not the prices at which you could expect to sell coins.

The list below contains most of the commonly available types: a full comprehensive guide is beyond the scope of this book. Prices are for coins with good surfaces which are not weakly struck or struck from worn dies. Examples which are struck from worn or damaged dies can be worth considerably less. Particularly attractive examples of bronze Celtic coins command a very high premium. Where a price is given for an issue of which there are many varieties, the price is for the most common type.

The illustrations are representative examples only and are indicated by an asterisk (*) in the listings.

	F	VF	EF
UNINSCRIBED COINAGE			
GOLD STATERS			
Gallo-Belgic A	£600	£1,350	£5,000
Gallo-Belgic E (Ambiani)	£135	£250	£400
Chute type	£145	£265	£375
Cheriton type			
normally rather "brassy" metal	£200	£345	£675
Corieltauvi (various types)	£150	£300	£500
Norfolk "wolf" type			
fine gold	£200	£400	£735
brassy gold	£125	£250	£420
very debased	£75	£150	£350
*Whaddon Chase types	£150	£275	£550
Wonersh type	£200	£400	£700
Iceni (various types)	£250	£450	£800
Remic type	£200	£350	£550
Dobunni	£250	£450	£800
GOLD QUARTER STATERS			
North Thames types	£155	£245	£375
North Kent types	£155	£235	£365
Iceni	£145	£200	£320
Sussex types	£100	£175	£300
Dobunni	£150	£250	£500
SILVER COINAGE			
North Thames types	£85	£150	£300
South Thames types	£85	£150	£300
Durotriges full stater			
fine silver	£50	£145	£265
*base silver	£35	£75	£180

Uninscribed Whaddon Chase type gold stater

Uninscribed Durotriges base silver stater

	F	VF	EF
Durotriges small silver	£30	£75	£150
Dobunni	£40	£90	£200

(Note—Most examples are base in appearance. Prices for examples
with fine surfaces are appreciably higher)

	F	VF	EF
Corieltauvi	£40	£100	£200
Eceni ("crescent" types)	£30	£65	£125
Eceni ("Norfolk god" types)	£50	£100	£250
Armorican Billon staters	£60	£130	£350

POTIN COINAGE

	F	VF	EF
Thames & South	£30	£45	£100
Kent & N. Thames	£50	£90	£160

BRONZE COINAGE

	F	VF	EF
Durotriges debased stater	£25	£45	£85
*Durotriges cast bronzes	£60	£120	£200
North Thames types. Various issues from:	£40	£90	£400

Durotriges cast bronze

INSCRIBED CELTIC COINAGE

ATTREBATES & REGNI

	F	VF	EF
*Commios			
stater	£550	£1,250	£2,650
Tincomarus			
stater	£420	£850	£1,850
quarter stater	£145	£250	£435
silver unit	£75	£140	£275
silver quarter unit	£155	£285	£525
Eppillus			
quarter stater	£145	£235	£425
silver unit	£75	£145	£300
bronze			Rare
Verica			
stater	£255	£550	£1,000
quarter stater	£155	£275	£420
silver unit	£55	£100	£220
Epatticus			
stater	£1,000	£2,000	£4,000
*silver unit	£50	£100	£265
silver quarter unit	£55	£110	£275
Caratacos			
silver unit	£165	£320	£465
silver quarter unit	£110	£220	£310

Commios stater

CANTII

	F	VF	EF
Dubnovellaunos			
stater	£280	£565	£900
silver unit	£130	£210	£500
bronze unit	£55	£150	£350
Vosenos			
stater	£1,000	£2,500	£4,500
quarter stater	£265	£565	£1,100
silver unit	£135	£285	£650
bronze unit	£110	£215	£550
Eppillus			
stater	£1,000	£2,000	£4,000
quarter stater	£145	£255	£500
silver unit	£65	£145	£350
bronze unit	£55	£125	£450
Amminus			
silver unit	£155	£320	£650
silver quarter unit	£110	£215	£450
bronze unit	£80	£155	£500

Epatticus silver unit

	F	VF	EF
DUROTRIGES			
Crab			
silver	£155	£320	£650
silver quarter unit	£100	£250	£400
TRINOVANTES			
Addedomaros			
stater	£265	£500	£800
quarter stater	£155	£320	£550
Diras			
stater		Rare	
Dubnovellaunos			
stater	£255	£455	£775
quarter stater	£155	£310	£550
*bronze unit	£55	£130	£450

Dubnovellaunos bronze unit

	F	VF	EF
CATUVELLAUNI			
Tasciovanus			
*stater	£225	£425	£1,000
quarter stater	£130	£235	£450
silver unit	£80	£165	£375
bronze unit	£55	£135	£350
bronze half unit	£55	£135	£275
Andoco			
stater	£510	£1,250	£2,750
quarter stater	£210	£420	£755
silver unit	£155	£400	£750
bronze	£85	£215	£355
Cunobelin			
*stater	£200	£455	£1,000
quarter stater	£145	£265	£420
silver unit	£85	£165	£360
bronze unit	£65	£145	£320

	F	VF	EF
DOBUNNI			
Anted			
stater	£310	£650	£1,250
silver unit	£55	£120	£300
Eisu			
stater	£450	£750	£1,500
silver unit	£55	£125	£320
Inam			
stater		Rare	
Catti			
stater	£255	£520	£1,000
Comux			
stater	£800	£1,650	£3,150
Corio			
stater	£265	£525	£1,000
quarter stater	£200	£355	£625
Boduoc			
stater	£1,000	£2,000	£3,500
silver unit	£200	£500	£850

Tasciovanos stater

	F	VF	EF
ECENI			
Duro			
silver unit	£110	£265	£550
Anted			
stater	£425	£1,000	£2,500
silver unit	£35	£65	£185
silver half unit	£45	£95	£165
Ecen			
silver unit	£35	£65	£185
silver half unit	£45	£95	£185

Cunobelin stater

117

	F	VF	EF
Saemu			
silver unit	£60	£125	£285
Aesu			
silver unit	£60	£125	£285
Prasutagus			
silver unit	£420	£1,000	£1,850
Iat Iso			
silver unit	£155	£420	£1,150
Ale Sca			
silver unit	£355	£765	£1,550
CORIELTAUVI			
Aun Ast			
stater	£255	£565	£1,000
silver unit	£85	£185	£315
silver half unit	£85	£160	£300
Esup Asu			
stater	£330	£675	£1,250
silver unit	£155	£310	£550
Vep Corf			
stater	£410	£1,000	£2,150
*silver unit	£80	£185	£300
silver half unit	£100	£215	£450
Dumno Tigir Seno			
stater	£755	£1,850	£3,150
silver unit	£100	£185	£500
Volisios Dumnocoveros			
*stater	£310	£725	£1,550
silver unit	£100	£185	£475
silver half unit	£100	£185	£450
Volisios Dumnovellaunos			
stater	£300	£675	£1,250
silver half unit	£150	£335	£655
Volisios Cartivel			
silver half unit	£300	£620	£1,150

Vep Corf silver unit

Volisios Dumnocoveros stater

Illustrations by courtesy of Chris Rudd.

A SIMPLIFIED PRICE GUIDE
TO
ANCIENT COINS USED IN BRITAIN

PART II
ROMAN BRITAIN

In certain cases, especially with large bronze coins, the price for coins in extremely fine condition are _much_ higher than the price for the same coin in very fine condition as early bronze coins are seldom found in hoards and perfect undamaged examples are rarely available.

The illustrations provided are a representative guide to assist with identification only and are indicated by an asterisk (*) in the listings.

	F	VF	EF
Julius Caesar			
aureus	£900	£2,500	£4,000
denarius ("elephant" type)	£100	£250	£400
denarius (with portrait)	£275	£850	£2,500
Mark Anthony			
denarius ("Galley" type)	£55	£120	£350
denarius (with portrait)	£145	£375	£1,850
Augustus			
aureus	£655	£1,850	£3,500
denarius (Caius & Lucius Caesars)	£55	£145	£375
*other types	£65	£185	£650
as	£65	£150	£500
Livia			
Ae as	£95	£285	£850
Tiberius			
aureus	£455	£1,350	£2,600
*denarius	£85	£175	£450
Drusus			
as	£65	£150	£450
Germanicus			
*as	£65	£150	£450
Caligula			
denarius	£350	£675	£1,850
*as	£85	£255	£850
Claudius			
aureus ("DE BRITANN" type)	£950	£2,250	£5,500
denarius similar	£350	£1,000	£2,200
sestertius	£120	£450	£1,650
as	£55	£120	£300
Nero			
aureus	£500	£1,350	£2,850
sestertius	£195	£355	£2,200
as	£55	£145	£550

Augustus

Germanicus

Caligula

	F	VF	EF
Galba			
denarius	£95	£355	£1,000
*sestertius	£185	£425	£3,250
as	£75	£175	£700
Otho			
denarius	£225	£520	£1,850
Vitellius			
denarius	£125	£320	£950
sestertius	£265	£755	£4,250
as	£115	£315	£1,800
Vespasian			
aureus	£655	£1,850	£2,850
sestertius	£110	£285	£655
as	£50	£155	£455
Titus			
aureus	£650	£1,750	£2,850
denarius	£55	£155	£325
as	£65	£185	£425
Domitian			
aureus	£650	£1,550	£3,350
denarius	£45	£65	£210
*sestertius	£90	£325	£1,900
as	£55	£110	£455
Nerva			
aureus	£655	£1,850	£3,850
denarius	£65	£150	£385
as	£65	£175	£585
Trajan			
aureus	£520	£1,365	£2,850
denarius	£45	£75	£190
sestertius	£45	£195	£565
as	£40	£85	£365
Hadrian			
aureus	£565	£1,365	£2,850
denarius	£50	£80	£200
as	£55	£125	£330
Sabina			
denarius	£40	£80	£300
*sestertius	£80	£220	£825
as	£48	£155	£385
Aelius			
denarius	£65	£145	£380
sestertius	£110	£265	£1,000
as	£50	£155	£615
Antoninus Pius			
denarius	£22	£55	£155
sestertius	£48	£115	£475
as	£38	£65	£285
Faustina Senior			
denarius	£30	£60	£155
sestertius	£38	£115	£565
as	£30	£75	£285
Marcus Aurelius			
*denarius	£28	£55	£155
sestertius	£50	£135	£565
as	£32	£70	£265
Faustina Junior			
*denarius	£28	£55	£150
sestertius	£40	£115	£535
as	£25	£65	£265
Lucius Verus			
denarius	£28	£70	£185
sestertius	£50	£155	£750
as	£45	£135	£365

Galba

Domitian

Sabina

Marcus Aurelius

Faustina Junior

	F	VF	EF	

Lucilla

denarius	£35	£80	£255
sestertius	£42	£140	£565
as	£32	£70	£275

Commodus

Commodus

denarius	£28	£60	£155
*sestertius	£42	£155	£675
as	£34	£78	£325

Crispina

denarius	£38	£85	£255

Pertinax

*denarius	£215	£625	£1,650

Didius Julianus

denarius	£455	£1,000	£2,150

Clodius Albinus

denarius	£65	£185	£420
sestertius	£85	£315	£1,300

Pertinax

Septimius Severus

denarius	£22	£42	£100
denarius (VICT BRIT)	£48	£100	£195
sestertius	£70	£225	£650
as	£55	£135	£350

Julia Domna

denarius	£22	£50	£90
sestertius	£80	£265	£900
as	£48	£135	£465

Caracalla

Caracalla

*denarius	£28	£50	£100
denarius (VICT BRIT)	£48	£95	£200
sestertius	£85	£215	£750
as	£46	£95	£375

Plautilla

denarius	£48	£95	£225

Geta

denarius	£26	£50	£115
denarius (VICT BRIT)	£55	£125	£235
sestertius	£65	£215	£650
as	£55	£135	£375

Macrinus

denarius	£58	£135	£285
*sestertius	£110	£285	£850

Macrinus

Diadumenian

*denarius	£125	£250	£475

Elagabalus

antoninianus	£50	£120	£225
denarius	£28	£52	£125

Julia Paula

denarius	£60	£145	£285

Aquilla Severa

denarius	£145	£265	£550

Diadumenian

Julia Soaemias

denarius	£28	£65	£135

Julia Maesa

denarius	£28	£55	£100

Severus Alexander

*denarius	£25	£55	£100
sestertius	£32	£65	£245
as	£28	£55	£175

Orblana

denarius	£115	£230	£550

Julia Mamaea

denarius	£25	£50	£145

Severus Alexander

	F	VF	EF
Maximinus I			
denarius	£28	£50	£100
*sestertius	£42	£80	£300
as	£42	£80	£250
Maximus			
denarius	£135	£265	£475
sestertius	£75	£150	£420
Balbinus			
denarius	£125	£255	£475
Papienus			
denarius	£125	£255	£475
Gordian III			
antoninianus	£18	£25	£55
denarius	£22	£40	£85
sestertius	£22	£60	£150
Philip I			
antoninianus	£18	£28	£55
*sestertius	£22	£75	£185
Otacilla Severa			
antoniniaus	£18	£28	£55
sestertius	£35	£80	£265
Philip II			
antoninianus	£18	£28	£65
Trajan Decius			
antoninianus	£18	£28	£65
Herennius Etruscus			
antoninianus	£22	£55	£135
Hostilian			
antoninianus	£50	£115	£265
Trebonianus Gallus			
antoninianus	£18	£28	£65
Volusian			
antoninianus	£20	£32	£80
Aemillan			
*antoninianus	£55	£135	£255
Valerian I			
antoninianus	£18	£28	£60
Gallienus			
*silver antoninianus	£15	£28	£48
Ae antoninianus	£10	£18	£32
Salonina			
Ae antoninianus	£10	£18	£32
Valerian II			
billon antoninianus	£18	£32	£100
Saloninus			
antoninianus	£18	£38	£125
Macrianus			
billon antoninianus	£38	£85	£175
Quietus			
billon antoninianus	£38	£85	£175
Postumus			
silver antoninianus	£12	£22	£50
*Ae antoninianus	£8	£15	£28
Laelianus			
antoninianus	£155	£285	£500
Marius			
antoninianus	£42	£90	£185
Victorinus			
Ae antoninianus	£8	£18	£32
Claudius II Gothicus			
Ae antoninianus	£8	£18	£32
Tetricus I			
Ae antoninianus	£8	£18	£32

Maximinus

Philip I

Aemillian

Gallienus

Postumus

	F	VF	EF
Tetricus II			
Ae antoninianus	£8	£18	£40
Quintillus			
*Ae antoninianus	£10	£20	£65
Aurelian			
Ae antoninianus	£8	£18	£45
Severina			
*Ae antoninianus	£12	£25	£65
Tacitus			
Ae antoninianus	£10	£22	£60
Florian			
Ae antoninianus	£42	£85	£165
Probus			
Ae antoninianus	£8	£15	£38
Carus			
Ae antoninlanus	£12	£25	£70
Numerian			
Ae antoninianus	£12	£25	£70
Carinus			
Ae antoninianus	£12	£25	£70
Diocletian			
Ae follis (London mint)	£18	£38	£80
Ae follis (other mints)	£12	£25	£60
Maximianus			
Ae follis (London mint)	£18	£38	£80
*Ae follis (other mints)	£12	£25	£60
Carausius			
denarius	£255	£765	£1,550
antoninianus	£28	£68	£200
Allectus			
antoninianus	£28	£78	£265
quinarius	£22	£62	£185
Constantius I.			
Ae follis (London mint)	£22	£58	£115
Ae follis (other mints)	£12	£25	£50
Galerius			
Ae follis (London mint)	£18	£38	£80
Ae follis (other mints)	£12	£25	£48
Galeria Valeria			
follis	£32	£70	£185
Severus II			
Ae follis (London mint)	£65	£130	£265
*Ae follis (other mints)	£32	£80	£185
Maximinus II			
Ae follis (London mint)	£22	£50	£100
*Ae follis (other mints)	£12	£25	£50
Maxentius			
follis	£8	£20	£45
Licinius I			
follis	£8	£18	£40
Ae 3	£5	£12	£35
Licinius II			
Ae 3	£7	£18	£45
Constantine I			
follis (London mint)	£12	£28	£55
follis (other mints)	£6	£16	£38
Ae 3	£5	£15	£35
Fausta			
Ae 3 (London mint)	£100	£180	£315
Ae 3 (other mints)	£15	£50	£100
Helena			
*Ae 3 (London mint)	£115	£185	£340
Ae 3 (other mints)	£18	£50	£100

Quintillus

Severina

Maximianus

Severus II

Maximinus II

Helena

	F	VF	EF
Theodora			
Ae 4	£10	£18	£50
Crispus			
*Ae 3	£8	£15	£45
Deimatius			
Ae 3/4	£12	£25	£68
Hanniballianus			
Ae 4	£125	£250	£435
Constantine II			
Ae 3	£8	£15	£40
Ae 4	£5	£12	£25
Constans			
*centenionalis	£12	£22	£60
Ae 4	£5	£10	£20
Constantius II			
*siliqua	£28	£55	£125
centenionalis	£10	£18	£48
Ae 4	£5	£10	£20
Magnentius			
double centenionalis	£32	£65	£155
centenionalis	£15	£25	£75
Decentius			
double centenionalis	£42	£85	£200
centenionalis	£18	£35	£115
Constantius Gallus			
centenionalis	£10	£25	£60
Julian II			
*siliqua	£22	£52	£115
Ae 1	£60	£145	£355
Ae 3 (helmeted bust)	£15	£42	£100
Jovian			
Ae 1	£48	£115	£265
Ae 3	£15	£42	£100
Valentinian I			
gold solidus	£155	£285	£555
siliqua	£25	£55	£130
Ae 3	£8	£18	£48
Valens			
gold solidus	£155	£300	£565
*siliqua	£25	£60	£135
Ae 3	£8	£18	£45
Gratian			
*siliqua	£25	£60	£135
Ae 3	£8	£18	£45
Valentinian II			
siliqua	£25	£65	£140
Ae 2	£12	£28	£65
Ae 4	£8	£15	£30
Theodosius I			
siliqua	£25	£65	£135
Magnus Maximus			
solidus	£755	£1,850	£4,250
siliqua	£40	£100	£180
*Ae 2	£20	£75	£135

Crispus

Constans

Constantius II

Julian II

Valens

Gratian

Magnus Maximus

Ae=bronze; Ae 1, 2, 3, 4=bronze coins in descending order of size.

Illustrations by courtesy of Classical Numismatic Group/Seaby Coins.

A SIMPLIFIED PRICE GUIDE
TO
ENGLISH HAMMERED COINS 1066–1663

PART I
1066–1485

INTRODUCTION

In this section we give an approximate price guide that one could expect to pay for the more commonly-located hammered coins in gold and silver. Although coins were struck in England for up to 1,000 years before the Norman Conquest, 1066–1663 provides a useful historical period with which most new collectors can associate.

PRICING

The prices given in the following pages are intended to be used as a "Pocket book guide" to the values of the *most common* coins within any denomination of any one reign. The price quoted is what a collector may expect to pay for such a piece in the condition indicated. For more detailed information we recommend the reader to one of the many specialist publications.

GRADING

The prices quoted are for three different grades of condition: Fine (F), Very Fine (VF) and Extremely Fine (EF). A "Fine" coin is assumed to be a fairly worn, circulated, piece but with all or most of the main features and lettering still clear. "Very Fine" is a middle grade with a small amount of wear and most details fairly clear. For this edition we have included the prices for coins in Extremely Fine condition where appropriate, although very few hammered coins actually turn up in this grade (i.e. nearly mint state with hardly any wear). In some instances the prices quoted are theoretically based and are only included to provide a guide. It is important to note that on all hammered coins the very nature of striking, i.e. individually, by hand, means hammered coinage is rarely a straight grade and when listed by a dealer the overall condition will often be qualified by terms such as: *weak in parts, struck off-centre, cracked or chipped flan, double struck*, etc. When applicable the price should be adjusted accordingly.

HISTORY

Below the heading for each monarch we have given a few historical notes as and when they apply to significant changes in the coinage.

WILLIAM I
(1066–87)

The Norman Conquest had very little immediate effect on the coinage of England. The Anglo-Saxon standard of minting silver pennies was very high and the practise of the moneyer putting his name and mint town on the reverse continued as before,except with William's portrait of course. It is worth noting here that non-realistic, stylised portraits were used until the reign of Henry VII.

There are eight major types of William I penny of which the last, the PAXS type, is by far the commonest.

	F	VF	EF
William I, Penny	£90	£180	£350

WILLIAM II
(1087–1100)

Very little change from his father's reign except that five new types were issued, most of which were much more crudely designed than previous, all are scarce.

	F	VF	EF
William II, Penny	£275	£600	—

HENRY I
(1100–35)

There are fifteen different types of penny for this reign of which the last two are the most common. Most issues are of a very poor standard both in workmanship and metal, the prices reflect a poor quality of issue.

	F	VF	EF
Henry I, Penny	£110	£250	—

STEPHEN
(1135–54)

This is historically a very complicated time for the coinage, mainly due to civil war and a consequential lack of central control in the country which resulted in very poor quality and deliberately damaged pieces. Coins were struck not only in the name of Stephen and his main rival claimant Matilda but also by their supporters. The commonest issue is the "Watford" type; so named, as are many issues, after the area in which a hoard was found.

	F	VF	EF
Stephen, Penny	£115	£275	—

HENRY II
(1154–89)

There were two distinct issues struck during this reign. The first, Cross and Crosslets or "Tealby" coinage (named after Tealby in Lincolnshire), continued to be very poorly made and lasted 20 years. However, in 1180 the new and superior "Short Cross" issue commenced, being issued from only twelve major towns.

	F	VF	EF
Henry II, Penny, Tealby	£50	£130	—
Henry II, Penny, Short Cross	£35	£80	£200

RICHARD I
(1189–1199)

There were no major changes during this reign, in fact pennies continued to be struck with his father Henry's name throughout the reign. The coins struck under Richard tend to be rather crude in style.

	F	VF	EF
Richard I, Penny	£40	£100	£275

JOHN
(1199–1216)

As with his brother before him, there were no major changes during the reign of King John, and pennies with his father's name were struck throughout the reign, although they tended to be somewhat neater in style than those struck during the reign of Richard I.

	F	VF	EF
John, Penny	£30	£65	£135

HENRY III
(1216–72)

The coinage during Henry III's reign continued as before with the short cross issue. However, in 1247 a new long cross design was introduced to prevent clipping. This design was to last in one form or another for many centuries.

	F	VF	EF
Henry III, Penny, Short Cross	£15	£35	£100
Henry III, Penny, Long Cross	£15	£30	£70

EDWARD I
(1272–1307)

After a few years of issuing similar pieces to his father, in 1279 Edward I ordered a major re-coinage. This consisted of well-made pennies, halfpennies and farthings in relatively large quantities, and for a brief period a groat (four pence) was produced. The pennies are amongst the most common of all hammered coins.

	F	VF	EF
Edward I (and Edward II)			
Groat (often damaged)	£900	£2,850	—
Penny	£15	£25	£55
Halfpenny	£20	£45	£135
Farthing	£15	£30	£100

Edward I halfpenny

EDWARD II
(1307–1327)

The coinage of Edward II differs in only a very few minor details from that of Edward I and are of similar value.

EDWARD III
(1327–77)

This was a long reign which saw major changes in the coinage, the most significant being the introduction of a gold coinage (based on the Noble, valued at 6s 8d, and its fractions) and a regular issue of a large silver groat (and half groat). The mints were limited to a few episcopal cities but coins of English type were also struck in the newly-acquired Calais.

	F	VF	EF
Gold			
Noble	£300	£600	£1,250
Half Noble	£200	£400	£800
Quarter Noble	£140	£280	£525
Silver			
Groat	£40	£90	£250
Half Groat	£20	£45	£140
Penny	£15	£35	£110
Half Penny	£15	£35	£90
Farthing	£30	£60	£140

Gold Noble

RICHARD II
(1377–1399)

The denominations continued during this reign much as before. However, coins are quite rare mainly due to the lack of bullion gold and silver going into the mints, mainly because of an inbalance with European weights and fineness.

	F	VF	EF
Gold			
Noble	£500	£1,000	£2,250
Half Noble	£575	£1,200	—
Quarter Noble	£250	£500	£850
Silver			
Groat	£200	£550	—
Half Groat	£150	£375	—
Penny	£40	£135	—
Half Penny	£25	£70	—
Farthing	£110	£225	—

Groat

HENRY IV
(1399–1413)

Because of the continuing problems with the scarcity of gold and silver the coinage was reduced in weight in 1412, towards the end of the reign. All coins of this reign are quite scarce.

	F	VF
Gold		
Noble	£900	£1,850
Half Noble	£2,300	£5,000
Quarter Noble	£385	£800
Silver		
Groat	£1,250	£3,500
Half Groat	£450	£900
Penny	£175	£550
Half Penny	£140	£275
Farthing	£425	£950

Noble

HENRY V
(1413–22)

Monetary reform introduced towards the end of his father's reign in 1412 improved the supply of bullion and hence coins of Henry V are far more common. All of the main denominations continued as before.

	F	VF	EF
Gold			
Noble	£340	£675	£1,400
Half Noble	£375	£750	—
Quarter Noble	£200	£400	£775
Silver			
Groat	£75	£175	—
Half Groat	£65	£165	—
Penny	£25	£75	—
Half Penny	£20	£50	—
Farthing	£110	£275	—

Half Groat

HENRY VI
(1422–61 and again 1470–71)

Although there were no new denominations during these reigns (see Edward IV below), Henry's first reign saw eleven different issues, each for a few years and distinguished by privy marks, i.e. crosses, pellets, annulets, etc.

HENRY VI *continued*

Gold	F	VF	EF
First reign—			
Noble	£325	£650	£1,200
Half Noble	£225	£450	£900
Quarter Noble	£160	£300	£550
2nd reign—			
Angel	£650	£1,350	£2,750
Half Angel	£1,500	£3,250	—

Silver	F	VF	EF
Groat	£30	£60	£140
Half Groat	£25	£45	£110
Penny	£20	£45	£100
Half Penny	£15	£35	£90
Farthing	£90	£225	—

Groat

EDWARD IV
(1461–70 and again 1471–83)

The significant changes during these reigns were the replacement of the noble by the rose Ryal (and revalued at 10s) and the introduction of the angel at the old noble value. We also start to see mint-marks or initial marks appearing, usually at the top of the coin, they were used to denote the period of issue for dating purposes and often lasted for 2–3 years.

Gold	F	VF	EF
Ryal	£325	£650	£1,150
Half Ryal	£280	£550	£950
Quarter Ryal	£200	£425	£700
Angel	£265	£525	£1,100
Half Angel	£250	£525	£1,000

Silver	F	VF	EF
Groat	£35	£75	£200
Half Groat	£30	£65	£185
Penny	£20	£60	£150
Half Penny	£25	£65	—
Farthing	£300	£600	—

Gold Ryal

RICHARD III
(1483–85)

The close of the Yorkist Plantagenet and the beginning of the Medieval period come together at this time. There are no new significant numismatic changes but most coins of Richard whilst not really rare, continue to be very popular and priced quite high.

Gold	F	VF	EF
Angel	£950	£2,000	—
Half Angel	£2,250	£5,000	—

Silver	F	VF	EF
Groat	£285	£575	£1,250
Half Groat	£475	£900	—
Penny	£135	£350	—
Half Penny	£120	£285	—
Farthing	£725	£1,850	—

Groat

PART II: 1485–1663

Among the more significant features of the post-Renaissance period as it affected coinage is the introduction of realistic portraiture during the reign of Henry VII. We also have a much wider and varied number of new and revised denominations, for example eleven different gold denominations of Henry VIII and the same number of silver for Elizabeth I. Here we only mention the introduction or changes in the main denominations, giving a value for all of them, once again listing the commonest type.

HENRY VII
(1485–1509)

The gold sovereign of 20 shillings makes its first appearance in 1489 as does the testoon (later shilling) in about 1500. The silver penny was re-designed to a rather crude likeness of the sovereign.

	F	VF	EF
Gold			
Sovereign	£6,500	£14,000	—
Ryal	£6,500	£17,000	—
Angel	£250	£500	£900
Half Angel	£190	£425	£825
Silver			
Testoon 1/-	£4,750	£9,500	—
Groat	£45	£120	£350
Half Groat	£25	£60	£200
Penny	£25	£65	£150
Half Penny	£20	£60	—
Farthing	£125	£300	—

Profile Groat

Sovereign-style penny

HENRY VIII
(1509–47)

After a long initial period of very little change in the coinage, in 1526 there were many, with an attempt to bring the gold/silver ratio in line with the continental currencies. Some gold coins only lasted a short time and are very rare. The crown (in gold) makes its first appearance. Towards the end of the reign we see large issues of debased silver coins (with a high copper content) bearing the well-known facing portrait of the ageing King. These tend to turn up in poor condition.

Gold	F	VF	EF
Sovereign	£1,600	£3,600	—
Half Sovereign	£275	£600	—
Angel	£250	£525	£950
Half Angel	£200	£450	£850
Quarter Angel	£240	£480	—
George Noble	£2,750	£6,000	—
Half George Noble	Rare	Rare	—
Crown of the rose	Rare	Rare	—
Crown of the double rose	£240	£500	£900
Half Crown of the double rose	£225	£450	—
Silver			
Testoon 1/-	£500	£1,400	—
Groat	£50	£120	£325
Half Groat	£25	£70	£185
Penny	£25	£70	£140
Half Penny	£20	£55	—
Farthing	£250	£600	—

Facing Groat

Crown of the double rose

EDWARD VI
(1547–53)

Some of the coins struck in the first few years of this short reign could really be called Henry VIII posthumous issues as there is continuity in both name and style from his father's last issue. However, overlapping this period are portrait issues of the boy King, particularly shillings (usually poor quality coins). This period also sees the first dated English coin (shown in Roman numerals). In 1551 however, a new coinage was introduced with a restored silver quality from the Crown (dated 1551) down to the new sixpence and threepence.

	F	VF	EF
Gold			
Sovereign (30s)	£1,850	£3,800	—
Half Sovereign	£450	£1,000	—
Crown	£650	£1,400	—
Half Crown	£600	£1,300	—
Angel	£3,250	£7,500	—
Half Angel	—	—	—
Sovereign (20s)	£1,000	£2,400	—
Silver			
Crown	£325	£700	—
Half Crown	£240	£575	—
Shilling	£60	£175	£500
Sixpence	£70	£220	—
Groat	£425	£1,100	—
Threepence	£140	£400	—
Half Groat	£185	£500	—
Penny	£45	£115	—
Half Penny	£150	£375	—
Farthing	£600	—	—

Base Shilling, obverse

Fine Shilling

MARY
(1553–54)

The early coins of Mary's sole reign are limited and continue to use the same denominations as Edward, except that the gold Ryal was reintroduced.

	F	VF
Gold		
Sovereign (30s)	£2,000	£4,400
Ryal	£7,000	—
Angel	£600	£1,250
Half Angel	£1,700	£3,800
Silver		
Groat	£70	£225
Half Groat	£500	£1,400
Penny	£300	£850

Groat

PHILIP & MARY
(1554–58)

After a very short reign alone, Mary married Philip of Spain and they technically ruled jointly (although not for very long in practise) until her death. After her marriage we see both her and Philip on the shillings and sixpences.

	F	VF
Gold		
Angel	£1,650	£3,750
Half Angel	£4,500	—
Silver		
Shilling	£160	£565
Sixpence	£175	£600
Groat	£70	£260
Half Groat	£275	£700
Penny	£50	£165

Shilling

ELIZABETH I
(1558–1603)

As might be expected with a long reign there are a number of significant changes in the coinage which include several new denominations—so many in silver that every value from the shilling downwards was marked and dated to distinguish them. Early on we have old base Edward VI shillings countermarked to a new reduced value (not priced here). Also due to a lack of small change and the expense of making a miniscule farthing we have a new threehalfpence and threefarthings. Finally we see the beginnings of a milled (machine produced) coinage for a brief period from 1561–71.

	F	VF	EF
Gold			
Sovereign (30s)	£1,600	£3,500	—
Ryal (15s)	£3,000	£7,750	—
Angel	£300	£625	—
Half Angel	£300	£625	—
Quarter Angel	£250	£550	—
Pound (20s)	£700	£1,650	£3,200
Half Pound	£400	£900	—
Crown	£400	£825	—
Half Crown	£400	£825	—
Silver			
Crown	£500	£1,150	£3,000
Half Crown	£325	£775	—
Shilling	£60	£175	£350
Sixpence	£40	£100	£225
Groat	£30	£80	£175
Threepence	£25	£70	£150
Half Groat	£20	£45	—
Threehalfpence	£25	£75	—
Penny	£15	£50	£130
Threefarthings	£45	£125	—
Half Penny	£20	£50	£90

Shilling

Milled Sixpence

JAMES I
(1603–25)

Although the size of the gold coinage remains much the same as Elizabeth's reign, the name and weight or value of the denominations have several changes, i.e. Pound = Sovereign = Unite = Laurel. A new four shilling gold coin (thistle crown) was introduced. A number of the silver coins now have their value in Roman numerals on the coin. Relatively few angels were made from this period onwards and they are usually found pierced.

Half Groat

Shilling

	F	VF	EF
Gold			
Sovereign (20s)	£675	£1,500	—
Unite	£275	£525	£1,000
Double crown/half unite	£210	£450	£875
Crown	£140	£300	£650
Thistle Crown	£150	£325	£635
Half Crown	£130	£250	—
Rose Ryal (30s)	£875	£1,950	—
Spur Ryal (15s)	£1,700	£4,250	—
Angel (pierced)	£250	£550	—
Half Angel (Unpierced)	£1,300	£3,000	—
Laurel	£230	£450	£950
Half Laurel	£185	£385	£850
Quarter Laurel	£130	£250	£450
Silver			
Crown	£250	£585	—
Half Crown	£115	£275	—
Shilling	£45	£150	—
Sixpence	£40	£140	—
Half Groat	£15	£35	£75
Penny	£15	£30	£65
Half Penny	£15	£25	£50

CHARLES I
(1625–49)

This reign is probably the most difficult to simplify as there are so many different issues and whole books have been produced on this period alone. From the beginning of the King's reign and throughout the Civil War, a number of mints operated for varying lengths of time, producing both regular and irregular issues. The Tower mint was taken over by Parliament in 1642 but before this a small quantity of milled coinage was produced alongside the regular hammered issues. The Court then moved to Oxford from where, for the next three years, large quantities of gold and silver were struck (including rare triple unites and large silver pounds). The most prolific of the provincial mints were those situated at Aberystwyth, York, Oxford, Shrewsbury, Bristol, Exeter, Truro, Chester and Worcester as well as some smaller mints mainly situated in the West Country. Among the more interesting coins of the period are the pieces struck on unusually-shaped flans at Newark and Pontefract whilst those towns were under siege. As many of the coins struck during the Civil War were crudely struck on hastily gathered bullion and plate, they provide a fascinating area of study. The prices indicated below are the minimum for the commonest examples of each denomination irrespective of town of origin.

	F	VF	EF
Gold			
Triple Unite (£3)	£2,200	£5,250	—
Unite	£250	£475	—
Double crown/Half unite	£210	£425	—
Crown	£130	£275	—
Angel (pierced)	£350	£750	—
Silver			
Pound (20 shillings)	£1,000	£2,400	—
Half Pound	£375	£825	—
Crown	£200	£425	—
Half Crown	£35	£120	—
Shilling	£30	£90	£300
Sixpence	£30	£115	£275
Groat	£35	£80	£175
Threepence	£30	£65	£150
Half Groat	£15	£35	£85
Penny	£12	£28	£75
Half Penny	£12	£25	£50

Many of the coins of Charles' reign, particularly those produced during the Civil War, are poorly struck. However, the sixpence shown above is a superb example with a good portrait.

The siege coins of Newark, Pontefract and Scarborough are keenly sought.

THE COMMONWEALTH
(1649–60)

After the execution of Charles I, Parliament changed the design of the coinage. They are simple non portrait pieces with an English legend.

	F	VF	EF
Gold			
Unite	£450	£925	£1,800
Double crown/Half unite	£375	£750	£1,500
Crown	£350	£650	£1,250
Silver			
Crown	£350	£675	£1,400
Half Crown	£125	£325	£800
Shilling	£80	£185	£450
Sixpence	£75	£175	£425
Half Groat	£25	£60	£125
Penny	£25	£50	£120
Half Penny	£25	£50	£95

Unite

CHARLES II
(1660–85)

Although milled coins had been produced for Oliver Cromwell in 1656–58, after the Restoration of the monarchy hammered coins continued to be produced until 1663, when the machinery was ready to manufacture large quantities of good milled pieces.

	F	VF	EF
Gold			
Unite	£600	£1,300	—
Double crown/Half unite	£450	£950	—
Crown	£500	£1,050	—
Silver			
Half Crown	£110	£350	—
Shilling	£80	£200	—
Sixpence	£65	£185	—
Fourpence	£20	£50	£90
Threepence	£25	£50	£90
Twopence	£12	£28	£55
Penny	£20	£50	£90

Halfcrown

THE
UNITED KINGDOM
1656–1999

including

ENGLAND
SCOTLAND
ISLE OF MAN
GUERNSEY, JERSEY, ALDERNEY

and

IRELAND

When referring to this price guide one must bear a number of important points in mind. The points listed here have been taken into consideration during the preparation of this guide and we hope that the prices given will provide a true reflection of the market at the time of going to press. Nevertheless, the publishers can accept no liability for the accuracy of the prices quoted.

1. "As struck" examples with flaws will be worth less than the indicated price.
2. Any coin in superb state will command a higher price.
3. These prices refer strictly to the British market, and do not reflect outside opinions.
4. Some prices given for coins not seen in recent years are estimates based on a knowledge of   the market.
5. In the case of coins of high rarity, prices are not generally given.
6. In the listing, "—" indicates, where applicable, one of the following:
    a. Metal or bullion value only
    b. Not usually found in this grade
    c. Not collected in this condition
7. Proof coins are listed in FDC under the UNC column.
8. All prices are quoted in £ sterling, exclusive of VAT (where applicable).

FIVE GUINEAS

	F	VF	EF

CHARLES II (1660–85)

	F	VF	EF
1668 First bust	£900	£2000	£7000
1668 — Elephant	£900	£2000	£7500
1669 —	£900	£2100	—
1669 — Elephant	£1500	—	—
*1670 —	£900	£2000	£7000
1671 —	£900	£2100	—
1672 —	£900	£2000	£7000
1673 —	£900	£2000	£7000
1674 —	£900	£2000	£7500
1675 —	£900	£2000	£7000
1675 — Elephant	£1500	—	—
1675 — Elephant & Castle		Extremely rare	
1676 —	£1000	£1100	—
1676 — Elephant & Castle	£900	£2100	—
1677 —	£900	£2100	—
1677/5 —		Extremely rare	
1677 — Elephant & Castle	£950	£2100	—
1678 —	£900	£2000	£6500
1678 — Elephant & Castle	£1100	£2300	—
1678 Second bust	£1100	£2300	—
1679 —	£900	£2000	£6500
1680 —	£900	£2000	£7000
1680 — Elephant & Castle		Extremely rare	
1681 —	£900	£2000	£6500
1681 — Elephant & Castle	£1100	£2300	—
1682 —	£900	£2000	£6500
1682 — Elephant & Castle	£900	£2000	—
1683 —	£900	£2000	£6500
1683 — Elephant & Castle	£1100	£2300	—
1684 —	£900	£1850	£6500

JAMES II (1685–88)

	F	VF	EF
1686	£900	£1850	£6000
1687	£1100	£2100	£6500
1687 Elephant & Castle	£900	£1750	£6000
1688	£1100	£2100	£6500
1688 Elephant & Castle	£1100	£2100	£6500

WILLIAM AND MARY (1688–94)

	F	VF	EF
*1691	£900	£1850	£5000
1691 Elephant & Castle	£1100	£2000	£5250
1692	£900	£1850	£5000
1692 Elephant & Castle	£1250	£2100	£5500
1693	£900	£1850	£5000
1693 Elephant & Castle	£1250	£2100	£5750
1694	£900	£1850	£5000
1694 Elephant & Castle	£1250	£2000	£5500

WILLIAM III (1694–1702)

	F	VF	EF
1699 First bust	£900	£1850	£4500
1699 — Elephant & Castle	£1000	£2000	£4500
1700 —	£900	£1850	£4500
1701 Second bust "fine work"	£1100	£2300	£5000

ANNE (1702–14)

Pre-Union with Scotland
1703 VIGO below bust ....   Extremely rare

	F	VF	EF
*1705	£1250	£2500	£6750
1706	£1250	£2250	£6250
Post-Union later shields			
1706	£1000	£1600	£5000
1709 Broader shields	£1050	£1750	£5500
1711 Broader bust	£1000	£1600	£5000
1713 —	£1050	£1750	£5500
1714 —	£1000	£1600	£5000

GEORGE I (1714–27)

	F	VF	EF
1716	£1150	£2500	£7000
1717	£1150	£2750	£7500
1720	£1150	£2500	£7000
1726	£1150	£2500	£7000

GEORGE II (1727–60)

	F	VF	EF
1729 Young head	£900	£1600	£4200
1729 — E.I.C. below head	£900	£1600	£4200
1731 —	£950	£1650	£4600
1735 —	£950	£1650	£4600
1738 —	£900	£1600	£4400
1741 —	£850	£1600	£4200
1746 Old head, LIMA	£1000	£1700	£4600
1748 —	£850	£1600	£4200
1753 —	£850	£1600	£4200

GEORGE III (1760–1820)

	F	VF	EF
1770 Patterns	—	—	£35000
1773	—	—	£35000
1777	—	—	£35000

The Great Fire of London, 1666.

TWO GUINEAS

	F	VF	EF

CHARLES II (1660–85)

	F	VF	EF
1664 First bust	£425	£1350	—
*1664 — Elephant	£375	£900	£4500
1665 —		Extremely rare	
1669 —		Extremely rare	
1671 —	£500	£1600	—
1675 Second bust	£425	£1450	—
1676 —	£400	£1200	—
1676 — Elephant & Castle	£400	£1200	—
1677 —	£400	£1050	£4500
1677 — Elephant & Castle		Extremely rare	
1678 —	£400	£1050	—
1678 — Elephant		Extremely rare	
1678 — Elephant & Castle	£425	£1250	—
1679 —	£400	£1250	—
1680 —	£500	£1700	—
1681 —	£400	£1200	£4000
1682 — Elephant & Castle	£425	£1250	—
1683 —	£400	£1300	£4000
1683 — Elephant & Castle	£750	—	—
1684 —	£425	£1300	—
1684 — Elephant & Castle	£550	£1600	—

JAMES II (1685–88)

	F	VF	EF
1687	£475	£1100	£4000
*1688/7	£515	£1350	£4500

WILLIAM AND MARY (1688–94)

	F	VF	EF
1691 Elephant & Castle		Extremely rare	
1693	£450	£1150	£3500
1693 Elephant & Castle	£500	£1250	£3850
1694	£450	£1150	£3500
1694 Elephant & Castle	£500	£1375	£3850

WILLIAM III (1694–1702)

	F	VF	EF
1701 "fine work"	£550	£1750	£4500

ANNE (1702–14)

	F	VF	EF
1709	£425	£1000	£3500
1711	£425	£1000	£3000
1713	£425	£1000	£3500
1714	£425	£1100	£3750

GEORGE I (1714–27)

	F	VF	EF
1717	£425	£1150	£4000
1720	£475	£1250	£4500
*1726	£425	£1150	£4000

	F	VF	EF

GEORGE II (1727–60)

	F	VF	EF
1734 Young head	£750	£2000	—
1735 —	£350	£750	£2500
*1738 —	£275	£600	£1600
1739 —	£275	£700	£1750
1739 Intermediate head	£275	£600	£1500
1740 —	£275	£650	£1800
1748 Old head	£325	£750	£2100
1753 —	£475	£1350	—

GEORGE III (1760–1820)

	F	VF	EF
1768 Patterns only	—	—	£12000
1773 Patterns only	—	—	£12000
1777 Patterns only	—	—	£12000

GUINEAS

CHARLES II (1660–85)

	F	VF	EF
1663 First bust	£550	£1600	—
1663 — Elephant below	£550	£1600	—
1664 Second bust	£400	£1200	—
1664 — Elephant		Extremely rare	
1664 Third bust	£275	£800	£3250
1664 — Elephant	£310	£950	£3950
1665 —	£275	£725	£3250
1665 — Elephant	£325	£1000	£4000
1666 —	£275	£825	£3250
1667 —	£275	£825	£3250
1668 —	£275	£800	£3250
1668 — Elephant		Extremely rare	
1669 —	£350	£1100	—
*1670 —	£275	£750	£3250
1671 —	£275	£750	£3250
1672 —	£350	£1100	—
1672 Fourth bust	£225	£650	£3000
1673 Third bust	£400	£1400	—
1673 Fourth bust	£275	£700	£3000
1674 —	£275	£1100	—
1674 — Elephant & Castle	£2500	—	—
1675 —	£275	£750	£3250
*1675 — Elephant & Castle	£350	£1250	—
1676 —	£225	£650	£2750
1676 — Elephant & Castle	£325	£1000	£3000
1677 —	£200	£650	£2750
1677 — Elephant		Extremely rare	
1677 — Elephant & Castle	£325	£1000	£3250
1678 —	£180	£600	£2750
1678 — Elephant	£2500	—	—
1678 — Elephant & Castle	£425	£1300	—
1679 —	£200	£550	£2750

	F	VF	EF
1679 — Elephant & Castle	£350	£1250	—
1680 —	£200	£625	£2750
1680 — Elephant & Castle	£500	£1300	—
1681 —	£275	£750	£3000
1681 — Elephant & Castle	£325	£1150	—
1682 —	£275	£750	£3000
1682 — Elephant & Castle	£325	£1150	£2750
1683 —	£225	£625	£2750
1683 — Elephant & Castle	£500	£1350	£3250
1684 —	£275	£750	£3300
1684 — Elephant & Castle	£325	£850	£3250

JAMES II (1685–1688)

	F	VF	EF
1685 First bust	£225	£525	£2500
*1685 — Elephant & Castle	£270	£625	£2750
1686 —	£275	£600	£3000
1686 — Elephant & Castle		Extremely rare	
1686 Second bust	£225	£575	£2500
1686 — Elephant & Castle	£325	£825	£3000
1687 —	£225	£575	£2500
1687 —Elephant & Castle	£275	£600	£2500
*1688 —	£225	£575	£2500
1688 — Elephant & Castle	£275	£600	£2500

WILLIAM AND MARY (1688–94)

	F	VF	EF
1689	£230	£600	£2500
1689 Elephant & Castle	£260	£600	£2500
1690	£300	£650	£2500
1690 Elephant & Castle	£470	£875	£3250
1691	£325	£700	£2750
1691 Elephant & Castle	£340	£725	£2750
1692	£375	£700	£2750
1692 Elephant	£475	£1050	£3500
1692 Elephant & Castle	£375	£800	£2750
1693	£325	£700	£2750
1693 Elephant		Extremely rare	
1693 Elephant & Castle		Extremely rare	
1694	£275	£625	£2500
1694 Elephant & Castle	£375	£800	£2750

WILLIAM III (1694–1702)

	F	VF	EF
1695 First bust	£185	£460	£2000
1695 — Elephant & Castle	£350	£650	£2500
1696 —	£200	£450	£2000
1696 — Elephant & Castle		Extremely rare	
1697 —	£200	£460	£2000
1697 Second bust	£200	£460	£2000
1697 — Elephant & Castle	£650	£1500	—
1698 —	£200	£460	£2000
1698 — Elephant & Castle	£350	£650	£2500
1699 —	£300	£600	£2250
1699 — Elephant & Castle		Extremely rare	
1700 —	£200	£460	£2000
1700 — Elephant & Castle	£650	£1500	—
1701 —	£210	£460	£2000
1701 — Elephant & Castle		Extremely rare	
1701 Third bust "fine work"	£425	£1000	£2500

	F	VF	EF

ANNE (1702–1714)

	F	VF	EF
1702 (Pre-Union) First bust	£275	£750	£2750
1703 — VIGO below	£4000	£8000	—
1705 —	£275	£750	£2750
1706 —	£275	£750	£2750
1707 —	£275	£750	£2750
1707 — (Post-Union)	£185	£500	£2000
1707 — Elephant & Castle	£850	£1500	—
1707 Second bust	£650	—	—
1708 First bust		Extremely rare	
1708 Second bust	£175	£425	£1650
1708 — Elephant & Castle	£700	£1250	£3250
1709 —	£185	£425	£1750
1709 — Elephant & Castle	£700	£1250	£3250
1710 Third bust	£160	£350	£1600
1711 —	£160	£350	£1600
1712 —	£160	£350	£1600
*1713 —	£160	£350	£1500
1714 —	£160	£350	£1500

GEORGE I (1714–27)

	F	VF	EF
1714 First bust (Prince Elector)	£600	£1000	£3000
1715 Second bust	£185	£350	£1650
1715 Third bust	£185	£350	£1650
1716 —	£185	£350	£1650
1716 Fourth bust	£185	£350	£1650
1717 —	£185	£350	£1650
1718 —		Extremely rare	
1719 —	£185	£350	£1650
1720 —	£185	£350	£1650
1721 —	£185	£350	£1650
1721 — Elephant & Castle		Extremely rare	
1722 —	£185	£350	£1650
1722 — Elephant & Castle		Extremely rare	
1723 —	£185	£350	£1850
1723 Fifth bust	£185	£350	£1850
1724 —	£185	£350	£1850
1725 —	£185	£350	£1850
1726 —	£185	£350	£1650
1726 — Elephant & Castle	£600	£1500	—
1727 —	£270	£500	£2000

GEORGE II (1727–60)

	F	VF	EF
1727 First young head, early large shield	£500	£900	£2500
1727 — Larger lettering, early small shield	£350	£700	£2000
1728 — —	£350	£550	£2000
1729 — 2nd Young Head E.I.C. below	£320	£625	£2250
1730 —	£200	£450	£2000
1731 —	£190	£375	£2000
1731 — E.I.C below	£300	£450	£2500
1732 —	£190	£375	£2000
1732 — E.I.C	£250	£450	£2250
1732 — Larger lettering obverse	£225	£600	£1600
1732 — E.I.C	£300	£900	£2500
1733 — —	£190	£350	£1750
1734 — —	£190	£350	£1750
1735 — —	£190	£350	£1750
1736 ——	£190	£350	£1750
1737 — —	£190	£350	£1750

	F	VF	EF
1738 — —	£190	£350	£1500
1739 Intermediate head	£190	£380	£1500
1739 — E.I.C	£200	£450	£2250
1740 —	£190	£340	£1500
1741/39 —		Extremely rare	
1743 —		Extremely rare	
1745 — (GEORGIUS) Larger lettering obv.	£220	£400	£2000
1745 — LIMA	£400	£1250	£3250
1746 — (GEORGIVS) Larger lettering obv.	£190	£340	£1500
1747 Old head, large lettering	£190	£340	£1250
1748 —	£190	£340	£1250
1749 —	£190	£340	£1250
1750 —	£190	£340	£1250
1751 — small lettering	£190	£340	£1250
1753 —	£190	£340	£1250
1755 —	£190	£340	£1250
1756 —	£190	£340	£1250
1758 —	£190	£340	£1250
1759 —	£190	£340	£1250
1760 —	£190	£340	£1250

GEORGE III (1760–1820)

	F	VF	EF
1761 First head	£350	£850	£2400
1763 Second head	£300	£750	£2000
1764 —	£200	£500	£1500
1765 Third head	£160	£365	£875
1766 —	£130	£300	£750
1767 —	£175	£400	£900
1768 —	£130	£300	£750
1769 —	£130	£300	£750
1770 —	£175	£400	£900
*1771 —	£130	£300	£750
1772 —	£130	£300	£750
1773 —	£130	£250	£650
1774 Fourth head	£90	£160	£400
1775 —	£90	£160	£400
1776 —	£90	£160	£400
1777 —	£90	£160	£400
1778 —	£90	£180	£500
1779 —	£100	£180	£450
1781 —	£100	£170	£400
1782 —	£100	£170	£400
1783 —	£100	£170	£400
1784 —	£100	£170	£400
1785 —	£95	£160	£400
1786 —	£95	£160	£400
1787 Fifth head "Spade" rev	£80	£125	£200
1788 —	£85	£125	£250
1789 —	£85	£125	£250
1790 —	£85	£125	£250
1791 —	£85	£125	£250
1792 —	£85	£125	£250
1793 —	£85	£125	£250
1794 —	£85	£125	£250
1795 —	£100	£175	£350
1796 —	£120	£200	£500
1797 —	£90	£135	£275
*1798 —	£80	£120	£230
1799 —	£95	£180	£400
*1813 Sixth head, "Military" rev	£160	£425	£875

(*Beware of Counterfiets)

HALF GUINEAS

	F	VF	EF

CHARLES II (1660–85)

	F	VF	EF
1669 First bust	£250	£500	£2500
*1670 —	£170	£450	£2000
1671 —	£350	£900	—
1672 —	£350	£900	—
1672 Second bust	£170	£450	£2000
1673 —	£400	£1100	—
1674 —	£400	£1100	—
1675 —		Extremely rare	
1676 —	£175	£470	—
1676 — Elephant & Castle		Extremely rare	
1677 —	£190	£450	£1750
1677 — Elephant & Castle	£400	£1100	—
1678 —	£190	£500	£2000
1678 — Elephant & Castle	£350	£900	—
1679 —	£175	£420	£1750
1680 —	£400	£1100	—
1680 — Elephant & Castle		Extremely rare	
1681 —	£400	£1100	—
1682 —	£250	£575	£2000
1682 — Elephant & Castle	£450	£1350	—
1683 — —		Extremely rare	
1684 —	£175	£350	£1750
1684 — Elephant & Castle	£350	£700	£2750

JAMES II (1685–88)

	F	VF	EF
1686	£240	£500	£2500
1686 Elephant & Castle	£450	£1250	£4000
1687	£325	£600	£2750
1688	£250	£550	£2500

WILLIAM AND MARY (1688–94)

	F	VF	EF
1689 First busts	£300	£600	£2000
1690 Second busts	£350	£625	£2000
1691 —	£400	£750	£2000
1691 — Elephant & Castle	£300	£600	£2000
1692 —	£325	£620	£2250
*1692 — Elephant		Extremely rare	
1692 — Elephant & Castle	£300	£600	£2000
1693 —		Extremely rare	
1694 —	£250	£550	£1850

WILLIAM III (1694–1702)

	F	VF	EF
1695	£125	£350	£1600
1695 Elephant & Castle	£400	£800	£2250
1696 —	£220	£525	£2000
1697 Larger Harp rev.	£250	£600	£2000
1698	£125	£400	£1500
1698 Elephant & Castle	£350	£700	£2250
*1699		Extremely rare	
1700	£125	£425	£1850
1701	£125	£425	£1850

	F	VF	EF

ANNE (1702–14)

	F	VF	EF
1702 (Pre-Union)	£250	£600	£2500
1703 VIGO below bust	£2000	£4000	—
1705	£250	£600	£2500
1707 (Post-Union)	£140	£325	£1250
1708	£160	£350	£1500
1709	£140	£325	£1250
1710	£140	£270	£1100
*1711	£140	£270	£1200
1712	£130	£300	£1250
1713	£130	£275	£1100
1714	£130	£275	£1100

GEORGE I (1714–27)

	F	VF	EF
1715 First bust	£135	£280	£1100
*1718 —	£135	£270	£1000
1719 —	£135	£270	£1000
1720 —	£250	£600	—
1721 —		Extremely rare	
1721 — Elephant & Castle		Extremely rare	
1722 —	£130	£300	£1350
1723 —		Extremely rare	
1724 —	£250	£500	£1850
1725 Second bust	£135	£275	£1000
1726 —	£135	£275	£1000
1727 —	£160	£350	£1000

GEORGE II (1727–60)

	F	VF	EF
1728 Young head	£175	£375	£1500
1729 —	£175	£375	£1500
1729 — E.I.C.	£250	£600	—
1730 —		Extremely rare	
1730 — E.I.C.	£325	£850	—
1731 —	£200	£425	£1750
1731 — E.I.C.		Extremely rare	
1732 —	£160	£375	£1500
1732 — E.I.C.		Extremely rare	
1733 —		Extremely rare	
1734 —	£160	£350	£1500
1735 —		Extremely rare	
1736 —	£160	£350	£1500
*1737 —		Extremely rare	
1738 —	£140	£325	£1500
1739 —	£140	£325	£1500
1739 — E.I.C.		Extremely rare	
1740 Intermediate head	£175	£400	£1500
1743 —		Extremely rare	
1745 —	£175	£370	£1500
1745 — LIMA	£600	£1500	—
1746 —	£140	£320	£1250
1747 Old head	£250	£500	£1250
1748 —	£140	£320	£850
1749 —		Extremely rare	
*1750 —	£150	£350	£1000
1751 —	£150	£350	£900
1752 —	£150	£350	£900
1753 —	£140	£270	£750
1755 —	£130	£270	£650

	F	VF	EF
1756 —	£130	£250	£650
1758 —	£130	£250	£650
1759 —	£110	£200	£600
1760 —	£110	£200	£600

GEORGE III (1760–1820)

	F	VF	EF
1762 First head	£200	£400	£1100
1763 —	£275	£550	£1500
1764 Second head	£150	£275	£500
1765 —	£225	£450	£1250
1766 —	£175	£300	£750
1768 —	£175	£300	£750
*1769 —	£150	£275	£600
1772 —		Extremely rare	
1773 —	£175	£300	£750
1774 —	£250	£500	£1500
1774 Third head		Extremely rare	
1775 —	£250	£500	£1500
1775 Fourth head	£75	£135	£300
1776 —	£75	£135	£300
1777 —	£75	£135	£300
1778 —	£90	£150	£350
1779 —	£100	£180	£400
1781 —	£90	£150	£350
1783 —	£300	£750	—
1784 —	£75	£135	£300
1785 —	£70	£155	£300
1786 —	£70	£155	£300
1787 Fifth head, "Spade" rev.	£55	£100	£220
1788 —	£55	£100	£220
1789 —	£55	£100	£220
1790 —	£55	£100	£220
1791 —	£55	£100	£220
1792 —		Extremely Rare	
1793 —	£55	£100	£220
1794 —	£55	£100	£220
1795 —	£75	£125	£300
1796 —	£55	£100	£220
1797 —	£55	£100	£220
1798 —	£55	£100	£220
1800 —	£125	£275	£750
1801 Sixth head, Shield in Garter rev.	£55	£90	£180
1802 —	£55	£90	£180
1803 —	£55	£90	£180
1804 Seventh head	£55	£90	£180
1805		Extremely Rare	
1806 —	£55	£90	£180
1808 —	£55	£90	£180
1899 —	£55	£90	£180
1810 —	£55	£90	£180
1811 —	£75	£130	£275
1813 —	£60	£115	£260

THIRD GUINEAS

DATE	F	VF	EF

GEORGE III (1760–1820)

	F	VF	EF
*1797 First head, date in legend	£35	£65	£140
1798 — —	£35	£65	£140
1799 — —	£50	£90	£210
1800 — —	£35	£65	£140
1801 Date under crown	£35	£65	£140
1802 —	£35	£65	£140
1803 —	£35	£65	£140
1804 Second head	£35	£65	£150
1806 —	£35	£65	£150
1808 —	£35	£65	£150
1809 —	£35	£65	£150
*1810 —	£35	£65	£150
1811 —	£100	£300	£700
1813 —	£45	£90	£180

QUARTER GUINEAS

GEORGE I (1714–27)

	F	VF	EF
1718	£55	£110	£230

GEORGE III (1760–1820)

	F	VF	EF
*1762	£45	£100	£230

FIVE POUNDS

DATE	Mintage	F	VF	EF	UNC

GEORGE III (1760–1820)

	Mintage	F	VF	EF	UNC
1820 (pattern only)	—		Extremely rare		

GEORGE IV (1820–30)

	Mintage	F	VF	EF	UNC
*1826 proof only	—	—	—	£6,000	£10,000

VICTORIA (1837–1901)

	Mintage	F	VF	EF	UNC
1839 Proof Only	—	—	—	£16,000	£20,000
1887	53,844	£325	£450	£625	£825
1887 Proof	797	—	—	—	£2,000
1887 S on ground on rev. (Sydney Mint)			Excessively rare		
1893	20,405	£400	£575	£800	£1,200
1893 Proof	773	—	—	—	£2,500

EDWARD VII (1902–10)

	Mintage	F	VF	EF	UNC
1902	34,910	—	£375	£500	£700
1902 Matt proof	8,066	—	—	—	£700

DATE	MINTAGE	F	VF	EF	UNC

GEORGE V (1911–36)
1911 Proof only 2,812   —   —   —   £1,400

GEORGE VI (1937–52)
*1937 Proof only 5,501   —   —   —   £700

Later issues are listed in the Decimal section.

TWO POUNDS

GEORGE III (1760–1820)
1820 (pattern only) ....   —   —   —   Extremely rare

GEORGE IV (1820–30)
1823 St George reverse ....   —   £200   £375   £700   £1500
1826 Proof only, shield reverse   —   —   —   £2750   £4000

WILLIAM IV (1830–37)
1831 Proof only 225   —   —   £2800   £5000

VICTORIA (1837–1901)
1887 91,345   £160   £225   £325   £450
1887 Proof 797   —   —   —   £850
1887 S on ground of rev. (Sydney Mint)   Excessively rare
1893 52,212   £220   £320   £480   £650
1893 Proof 773   —   —   —   £1000

EDWARD VII (1902–10)
1902 45,807   £140   £175   £260   £325
1902 Matt proof 8,066   —   —   —   £350

GEORGE V (1911–36)
1911 Proof only 2,812   —   —   —   £650

GEORGE VI (1937–52)
*1937 Proof only 5,501   —   —   —   £360

Later issues are listed in the Decimal section.

SOVEREIGNS

DATE	MINTAGE	F	VF	EF	UNC

GEORGE III (1760–1820)

DATE	MINTAGE	F	VF	EF	UNC
1817	3,235,239	£80	£165	£425	£650
1818	2,347,230	£80	£165	£425	£650
1819	3,574		Exceedingly rare		
1820	931,994	£80	£165	£450	£700

GEORGE IV (1820–30)

DATE	MINTAGE	F	VF	EF	UNC
1821 First bust, St George reverse	9,405,114	£80	£160	£450	£850
1821 — Proof	incl. above	—	—	£1500	£2500
1822 —	5,356,787	£85	£160	£450	£850
1823 —	616,770	£125	£325	£1200	—
1824 —	3,767,904	£85	£160	£450	£850
1825 —	4,200,343	£150	£400	£1200	—
1825 Second bust, shield reverse	incl. above	£85	£140	£400	£750
1826 —	5,724,046	£85	£140	£400	£750
*1826 — Proof	—	—	—	£1500	£2500
1827 —	2,266,629	£85	£140	£400	£750
1828 —	386,182	£500	£1250	£2500	—
1829 —	2,444,652	£85	£140	£400	£750
1830 —	2,387,881	£85	£140	£400	£750

WILLIAM IV (1830–37)

DATE	MINTAGE	F	VF	EF	UNC
1831	598,547	£85	£160	£450	£900
*1831 Proof	—	—	—	£1750	£2750
1832	3,737,065	£85	£145	£450	£850
1833	1,225,269	£85	£155	£450	£800
1835	723,441	£90	£160	£450	£850
1836	1,714,349	£85	£160	£450	£850
1837	1,172,984	£85	£145	£450	£800

VICTORIA (1837–1901)

Many of the gold coins struck at the colonial mints found their way into circulation in Britain, for the sake of completeness these coins are listed here. These can easily be identified by a tiny initial letter for the appropriate mint which can be found below the base of the reverse shield or, in the case of the St George reverse, below the bust on the obverse of the Young Head issues, or on the "ground" below the horse's hoof on the later issues.

YOUNG HEAD ISSUES

Shield reverse
(Note—Shield back sovereigns in Fine/VF condition, common dates, are normally traded as bullion + a percentage)

DATE	MINTAGE	F	VF	EF	UNC
1838	2,718,694	—	£85	£200	£500
1839	503,695	—	£350	£850	£2000
*1839 Proof	—	—	—	—	£2000
1841	124,054	£500	£1100	£2000	—
1842	4,865,375	—	£65	£140	£240
1843	5,981,968	—	£65	£140	£240
1843 "Narrow shield" variety	incl. above	£275	£600	£1500	—
1844	3,000,445	—	£65	£125	£240
1845	3,800,845	—	£65	£140	£240
1846	3,802,947	—	£65	£140	£270

DATE	MINTAGE	F	VF	EF	UNC
1847	4,667,126	—	£65	£140	£240
1848	2,246,701	—	£65	£150	£325
1849	1,755,399	—	£65	£150	£325
1850	1,402,039	—	£65	£140	£275
1851	4,013,624	—	£65	£140	£240
1852	8,053,435	—	£65	£140	£240
1853	10,597,993	—	£65	£140	£240
1853 Proof	—	—	—	—	£3500
1854	3,589,611	—	£65	£140	£240
1855	8,448,482	—	£65	£140	£240
1856	4,806,160	—	£65	£140	£240
1857	4,495,748	—	£65	£140	£240
1858	803,234	—	£75	£175	£450
1859	1,547,603	—	£65	£140	£300
1859 "Ansell" (additional line on lower part of hair ribbon)	—	£160	£320	£1200	—
1860	2,555,958	—	£65	£200	£500
1861	7,624,736	—	£65	£140	£240
1862	7,836,413	—	£65	£140	£240
1863	5,921,669	—	£65	£140	£240
1863 with Die number	incl. above	—	£65	£110	£220
1864 —	8,656,352	—	£65	£110	£220
1865 —	1,450,238	—	£65	£110	£220
1866 —	4,047,288	—	£65	£110	£220
1868 —	1,653,384	—	£65	£110	£220
1869 —	6,441,322	—	£65	£110	£220
1870 —	2,189,960	—	£65	£110	£220
1871 —	8,767,250	—	£65	£110	£220
1872 —	8,767,250	—	£65	£110	£220
1872 no Die number	incl. above	—	£65	£140	£240
1873 with Die number	2,368,215	—	£65	£130	£240
1874 —	520,713	£800	—	—	—

M below (Melbourne Mint)

DATE	MINTAGE	F	VF	EF	UNC
1872	748,180	—	£75	£175	£325
1873	—	Extremely rare			
1874	1,373,298	—	£75	£150	£300
1879		Extremely rare			
1880	3,053,454	£300	£800	£3000	—
1881	2,325,303	£75	£125	£375	£850
1882	2,465,781	—	£75	£175	£325
1883	2,050,450	£100	£200	£600	—
1884	2,942,630	—	£75	£150	£300
1885	2,967,143	—	£75	£150	£300
1886	2,902,131	£500	£1300	£3000	—
1887	1,916,424	£300	£700	£1800	£3000

S below (Sydney Mint)

DATE	MINTAGE	F	VF	EF	UNC
1871	2,814,000	—	£65	£130	—
1872	1,815,000	—	£65	£130	—
1873	1,478,000	—	£65	£130	—
1875	2,122,000	—	£65	£130	—
1877	1,590,000	—	£65	£130	—
1878	1,259,000	—	£75	£140	—
1879	1,366,000	—	£65	£130	—
1880	1,459,000	—	£65	£130	—
1881	1,360,000	—	£75	£160	—
1882	1,298,000	—	£65	£130	—
1883	1,108,000	—	£75	£170	—
1884	1,595,000	—	£65	£130	—
1885	1,486,000	—	£65	£130	—
1886	1,667,000	—	£65	£130	—
1887	1,000,000	—	£75	£170	£325

DATE	MINTAGE	F	VF	EF	UNC
St George & Dragon reverse					
1871	incl. above	—	£60	£85	£160
1872	incl. above	—	£60	£85	£160
1873	incl. above	—	£60	£85	£160
1874	incl. above	—	£60	£80	£160
1876	3,318,866	—	£60	£80	£160
1878	1,091,275	—	£60	£85	£200
1879	20,013	£100	£300	£750	—
1880	3,650,080	—	£60	£80	£160
1884	2,942,630	—	£60	£80	£160
1885	2,967,143	—	£60	£80	£160
M below (Melbourne Mint)					
1872	incl. above	—	£60	£100	£160
1873	752,199	—	£60	£100	£150
1874	incl. above	—	£60	£100	£150
1875	incl. above	—	£60	£100	£150
1876	2,124,445	—	£60	£100	£160
1877	1,487,316	—	£60	£100	£150
1878	2,171,457	—	£60	£100	£150
1879	2,740,594	—	£60	£100	£150
1880	incl. above	—	£60	£100	£150
1881	incl. above	—	£60	£100	£150
1882	incl. above	—	£60	£100	£150
1883	incl. above	—	£60	£100	£150
1884	incl. above	—	£60	£100	£150
1885	incl. above	—	£60	£100	£150
1886	incl. above	—	£60	£100	£150
1887	incl. above	—	£60	£100	£150
S below (Sydney Mint)					
1871	incl. above	—	£60	£110	£175
1872	incl. above	—	£60	£110	£175
1873	incl. above	—	£60	£110	£175
1874	1,899,000	—	£60	£100	£150
1875	inc above	—	£60	£100	£150
1876	1,613,000	—	£60	£100	£150
1877	—		Extremely rare		
1879	incl. above	—	£60	£100	£150
1880	incl. above	—	£60	£100	£150
1881	incl. above	—	£60	£100	£150
1882	incl. above	—	£60	£100	£150
1883	incl. above	—	£60	£100	£150
1884	incl. above	—	£60	£100	£150
1885	incl. above	—	£60	£100	£150
1886	incl. above	—	£60	£100	£150
1887	incl. above	—	£60	£100	£150
JUBILEE HEAD ISSUES					
*1887	1,111,280	—	—	£70	£90
1887 Proof	797	—	—	—	£700
1888	2,717,424	—	—	£60	£90
1889	7,257,455	—	—	£60	£90
1890	6,529.887	—	—	£60	£90
1891	6,329,476	—	—	£60	£90
1892	7,104,720	—	—	£60	£90
M below (Melbourne Mint)					
1887	940,000	£70	£100	£200	—
1888	2,830,612	£55	£70	£110	—
1889	2,732,590	£55	£70	£110	—
1890	2,473,537	£55	£70	£110	—
1891	2,749,592	£55	£70	£110	—
1892	3,488,750	£55	£70	£110	—
1893	1,649,352	£55	£70	£110	—

DATE	MINTAGE	F	VF	EF	UNC
S below (Sydney Mint)					
1887	1,002,000	£55	£100	£110	£150
1888	2,187,000	—	£75	£100	—
1889	3,262,000	—	£75	£100	—
1890	2,808,000	—	£75	£100	
1891	2,596,000	—	£75	£100	—
1892	2,837,000	—	£75	£100	—
1893	1,498,000	—	£75	£100	—

OLD HEAD ISSUES

*1893	6,898,260	—	—	£65	£85
1893 Proof	773	—	—	—	£650
1894	3,782,611	—	—	£65	£85
1895	2,285,317	—	—	£65	£85
1896	3,334,065	—	—	£65	£85
1898	4,361,347	—	—	£65	£85
1899	7,515,978	—	—	£65	£85
1900	10,846,741	—	—	£65	£85
1901	1,578,948	—	—	£65	£85
M below (Melbourne Mint)					
1893	1,914,000	—	—	£90	£100
1894	4,166,874	—	—	£90	£100
1895	4,165,869	—	—	£90	£100
1896	4,456,932	—	—	£90	£100
1897	5,130,565	—	—	£90	£100
1898	5,509,138	—	—	£90	£100
1899	5,579,157	—	—	£90	£100
1900	4,305,904	—	—	£90	£100
1901	3,987,701	—	—	£90	£100
P below (Perth Mint)					
1899	690,992	—	£65	£110	£150
1900	1,886,089	—	—	£90	£130
1901	2,889,333	—	—	£90	£130
S below (Sydney Mint)					
1893	1,346,000	—	—	£75	£100
1894	3,067,000	—	—	£75	£100
1895	2,758,000	—	—	£75	£100
1896	2,544,000	—	—	£100	£140
1897	2,532,000	—	—	£75	£100
1898	2,548,000	—	—	£75	£100
1899	3,259,000	—	—	£75	£100
1900	3,586,000	—	—	£75	£100
1901	3,012,000	—	—	£75	£100

EDWARD VII (1902–10)

*1902	4,737,796	—	—	£60	£75
1902 Matt proof	15,123	—	—	—	£150
1903	8,888,627	—	—	£60	£75
1904	10,041,369	—	—	£60	£75
1905	5,910,403	—	—	£60	£75
1906	10,466,981	—	—	£60	£75
1907	18,458,663	—	—	£60	£75
1908	11,729,006	—	—	£60	£75
1909	12,157,099	—	—	£60	£75
1910	22,379,624	—	—	£60	£75
C below (Ottawa Mint)					
1908 Satin finish Proof only	636		Extremely rare		
1909	16,273	—	£80	£220	—
1910	28,012	—	£80	£220	—

DATE	MINTAGE	F	VF	EF	UNC
M below (Melbourne Mint)					
1902	4,267,157	—	—	£80	£120
1903	3,521,780	—	—	£80	£120
1904	3,743,897	—	—	£80	£120
1905	3,633,838	—	—	£80	£120
1906	3,657,853	—	—	£80	£120
1907	3,332,691	—	—	£80	£120
1908	3,080,148	—	—	£80	£120
1909	3,029,538	—	—	£80	£120
1910	3,054,547	—	—	£80	£120
P below (Perth Mint)					
1902	3,289,122	—	—	£80	£120
1903	4,674,783	—	—	£80	£120
1904	4,506,756	—	—	£80	£120
1905	4,876,193	—	—	£80	£120
1906	4,829,817	—	—	£80	£120
1907	4,972,289	—	—	£80	£120
1908	4,875,617	—	—	£80	£120
1909	4,524,241	—	—	£80	£120
1910	4,690,625	—	—	£80	£120
S below (Sydney Mint)					
1902	2,813,000	—	—	£80	£120
1902 Proof	*incl. above*		Extremely rare		
1903	2,806,000	—	—	£80	£120
1904	2,986,000	—	—	£80	£120
1905	2,778,000	—	—	£80	£120
1906	2,792,000	—	—	£80	£120
1907	2,539,000	—	—	£80	£120
1908	2,017,000	—	—	£80	£120
1909	2,057,000	—	—	£80	£120
1910	2,135,000	—	—	£80	£120

GEORGE V (1911–36)

(Extra care should be exercised when purchasing as good quality forgeries exist of virtually all dates and mintmarks)

	MINTAGE	F	VF	EF	UNC
1911	30,044,105	—	—	£60	£70
1911 Proof	3,764	—	—	—	£250
1912	30,317,921	—	—	£60	£70
1913	24,539,672	—	—	£60	£70
1914	11,501,117	—	—	£60	£70
1915	20,295,280	—	—	£60	£70
1916	1,554,120	—	—	£60	£75
1917	1,014,714	£2500	£3250	£4000	—
1925	4,406,431	—	—	—	£70
C below (Ottawa Mint)					
1911	256,946	—	£70	£100	£150
1913	3,715	£100	£120	£500	—
1914	14,891	£100	£180	£300	—
1916	6,111		Extremely rare		
1917	58,845	—	£70	£110	—
1918	106,516	—	£70	£110	—
1919	135,889	—	£70	£110	—
I below (Bombay Mint)					
1918	1,295,372	—	—	£75	—
M below (Melbourne Mint)					
1911	2,851,451	—	—	£75	£100
1912	2,469,257	—	—	£75	£100
1913	2,323,180	—	—	£75	£100
1914	2,012,029	—	—	£75	£100
1915	1,637,839	—	—	£75	£100

DATE	MINTAGE	F	VF	EF	UNC
1916	1,273,643	—	—	£75	£100
1917	934,469	—	—	£75	£100
1918	4,969,493	—	—	£75	£100
1919	514,257	—	—	£85	£125
1920	530,266	£200	£600	£1000	—
1921	240,121	—	—	£4000	—
1922	608,306	£300	£800	£3000	—
1923	510,870	—	—	£100	£140
1924	278,140	—	—	£100	£140
1925	3,311,622	—	—	£75	£100
1926	211,107	—	—	£75	£100
1928	413,208	£200	£500	£600	—
1929	436,719	£100	£275	£800	—
1930	77,547	—	£75	£125	—
1931	57,779	£70	£110	£250	—

P below (Perth Mint)

DATE	MINTAGE	F	VF	EF	UNC
1911	4,373,165	—	—	£75	£100
1912	4,278,144	—	—	£75	£100
1913	4,635,287	—	—	£75	£100
1914	4,815,996	—	—	£75	£100
1915	4,373,596	—	—	£75	£100
1916	4,096,771	—	—	£75	£100
1917	4,110,286	—	—	£75	£100
1918	3,812,884	—	—	£75	£100
1919	2,995,216	—	—	£75	£100
1920	2,421,196	—	—	£75	£100
1921	2,134,360	—	—	£75	£100
1922	2,298,884	—	—	£75	£100
1923	2,124,154	—	—	£75	£100
1924	1,464,416	—	—	£75	£100
1925	1,837,901	—	—	£75	£110
1926	1,313,578	—	—	£75	£120
1927	1,383,544	—	—	£75	£120
1928	1,333,417	—	—	£100	£140
1929	1,606,625	—	—	£75	£100
1930	1,915,352	—	—	£75	£100
1931	1,173,568	—	—	£75	£100

S below (Sydney Mint)

DATE	MINTAGE	F	VF	EF	UNC
1911	2,519,000	—	—	£70	£90
1912	2,227,000	—	—	£70	£90
1913	2,249,000	—	—	£70	£90
1914	1,774,000	—	—	£70	£90
1915	1,346,000	—	—	£70	£90
1916	1,242,000	—	—	£70	£90
1917	1,666,000	—	—	£70	£90
1918	3,716,000	—	—	£70	£90
1919	1,835,000	—	—	£70	£90
1920	—		Excessively rare		
1921	839,000	—	£500	£1200	—
1922	578,000		Extremely rare		
1923	416,000		Extremely rare		
1924	394,000	—	£400	£800	—
1925	5,632,000	—	—	£75	£100
1926	1,031,050		Extremely rare		

SA below (Pretoria Mint)

DATE	MINTAGE	F	VF	EF	UNC
1923	719		Extremely rare		
1923 Proof	655		Extremely rare		
1924	3,184		Extremely rare		
1925	6,086,264	—	£60	£80	£95
1926	11,107,611	—	£60	£80	£95
1927	16,379,704	—	£60	£80	£95
1928	18,235,057	—	£60	£80	£95

157

DATE	MINTAGE	F	VF	EF	UNC
1929	12,024,107	—	—	£80	£95
1930	10,027,756	—	—	£80	£95
1931	8,511,792	—	—	£80	£95
1932	1,066,680	—	—	£90	£110

GEORGE VI (1937–52)

*1937 Proof only	5,501	—	—	£275	£325

ELIZABETH II (1952–   )

Pre Decimal Issues

1957	2,072,000	—	—	—	£65
1958	8,700,140	—	—	—	£60
1959	1,358,228	—	—	—	£65
1962	3,000,000	—	—	—	£60
1963	7,400,000	—	—	—	£60
1964	3,000,000	—	—	—	£60
1965	3,800,000	—	—	—	£60
1966	7,050,000	—	—	—	£60
1967	5,000,000	—	—	—	£60
1968	4,203,000	—	—	—	£60

Later issues are included in the Decimal section.

HALF SOVEREIGNS

GEORGE III (1760–1820)

1817	2,080,197	£50	£80	£160	£325
1818	1,030,286	£50	£80	£160	£325
1820	35,043	£50	£80	£160	£325

GEORGE IV (1820–30)

1821 First bust, ornate shield reverse	231,288	£150	£400	£1500	£2250
1821 — Proof	unrecorded	—	—	£2000	£3000
1823 First bust, Plain shield rev.	224,280	£70	£150	£400	£675
1824 —	591,538	£70	£150	£425	£675
1825 —	761,150	£70	£150	£425	£675
1826 bare head, shield with full legend reverse	344,830	£65	£130	£400	£600
1826 — Proof	unrecorded	—	—	£750	£1000
1827 —	492,014	£70	£150	£400	£650
1828 —	1,224,754	£65	£130	£400	£675

WILLIAM IV (1830–37)

1831 Proof only	uncrecorded	—	—	£750	£1250
1834	133,899	£75	£150	£450	£800
1835	772,554	£65	£125	£400	£775
1836	146,865	£75	£150	£450	£850
1836 obverse from 6d die	incl. above	£450	£1000	£2500	—
1837	160,207	£65	£130	£400	£750

DATE	MINTAGE	F	VF	EF	UNC

VICTORIA (1837–1901)

YOUNG HEAD ISSUES
Shield reverse

DATE	MINTAGE	F	VF	EF	UNC
1838	273,341	—	£60	£225	£450
1839 Proof only	1,230	—	—	—	£900
1841	508,835	—	£65	£250	£500
1842	2,223,352	—	£60	£180	£320
1843	1,251,762	—	£65	£250	£500
1844	1,127,007	—	£60	£180	£320
1845	887,526	£50	£150	£350	£525
1846	1,063,928	—	£60	£180	£325
1847	982,636	—	£60	£180	£325
1848	410,595	—	£60	£180	£325
1849	845,112	—	£60	£180	£325
1850	179,595	£50	£150	£375	£600
1851	773,573	—	£60	£180	£325
1852	1,377,671	—	£60	£180	£325
1853	2,708,796	—	£60	£180	£300
1853 Proof	unrecorded	—	—	—	£2750
1854	1,125,144		Extremely rare		
1855	1,120,362	—	£60	£180	£325
1856	2,391,909	—	£60	£180	£325
1857	728,223	—	£60	£180	£325
1858	855,578	—	£60	£180	£325
1859	2,203,813	—	£60	£180	£325
1860	1,131,500	—	£60	£180	£325
1861	1,130,867	—	£60	£180	£325
1862	unrecorded		Extremely rare		
1863	1,571,574	—	£60	£180	£325
1863 with Die number	incl. above	—	£60	£180	£325
1864 —	1,758,490	—	£60	£180	£325
1865 —	1,834,750	—	£60	£180	£325
1866 —	2,058,776	—	£60	£180	£325
1867 —	992,795	—	£60	£180	£325
1869 —	1,861,764	—	£60	£180	£325
1870 —	1,159,544	—	£60	£150	£225
1871 —	2,062,970	—	£55	£125	£225
1872 —	3,248,627	—	£55	£130	£240
1873 —	1,927,050	—	£55	£125	£225
1874 —	1,884,432	—	£55	£130	£240
1875 —	516,240	—	£55	£125	£225
1876 —	2,785,187	—	£55	£125	£225
1877 —	2,197,482	—	£55	£120	£220
1878 —	2,081,941	—	£55	£120	£220
1879 —	35,201	—	£55	£120	£220
1880 —	1,009,049	—	£55	£120	£220
1880 no Die number	incl. above	—	£55	£130	£230
1883 —	2,870,457	—	£55	£120	£220
1884 —	1,113,756	—	£55	£120	£220
1885 —	4,468,871	—	£55	£120	£220

M below (Melbourne Mint)

DATE	MINTAGE	F	VF	EF	UNC
1873	165,034	£75	£140	£440	—
1877	80,016	£60	£110	£430	—
1881	42,009	£100	£200	£600	—
1882	107,522	£75	£140	£500	—
1884	48,009	£100	£200	£600	—
1885	11,003	£150	£350	£1500	—
1886	38,008	£85	£150	£650	—
1887	64,013	£140	£300	£1000	—

S below (Sydney Mint)

DATE	MINTAGE	F	VF	EF	UNC
1871	unrecorded	£60	£95	£400	—
1872	356,000	£65	£110	£400	—

Date	Mintage	F	VF	EF	UNC
1875	*unrecorded*	£70	£120	£400	—
1879	94,000	£70	£120	£400	—
1880	80,000	£70	£120	£400	—
1881	62,000	£100	£175	£700	—
1882	52,000	£150	£250	£1000	—
1883	220,000	£65	£100	£400	—
1886	82,000	£65	£100	£350	—
1887	134,000	£65	£100	£350	—

JUBILEE HEAD ISSUES

1887	871,770	—	—	£60	£80
1887 Proof	797	—	—	—	£400
1890	2.266,023	—	—	£60	£95
1891	1,079,286	—	—	£60	£95
1892	13,680,486	—	—	£60	£90
1893	4,426,625	—	—	£65	£120

M below (Melbourne Mint)

1887	*incl. above*	£50	£90	£250	£450
1893	110,024	£60	£100	£325	—

S below (Sydney Mint)

1887	*incl. above*	£50	£80	£200	£375
1889	64,000	£60	£100	£300	—
1891	154,000	£60	£100	£325	—

OLD HEAD ISSUES

1893	*incl. above*	—	£42	£55	£80
1893 Proof	773	—	—	—	£500
1894	3,794,591	—	£42	£60	£85
1895	2,869,183	—	£42	£60	£85
1896	2,946,605	—	£42	£60	£85
1897	3,568,156	—	£42	£60	£85
1898	2,868,527	—	£42	£60	£85
1899	3,361,881	—	£42	£60	£85
1900	4,307,372	—	£42	£60	£85
1901	2,037,664	—	£42	£60	£85

M below (Melbourne Mint)

1893	*unrecorded*		Extremely rare		
1896	218,946	£50	£90	£300	—
1899	97,221	£50	£90	£300	—
1900	112,920	£50	£90	£300	—

P below (Perth Mint)

1899			Extremely rare		
1900	119,376	£60	£100	£450	—

S below (Sydney Mint)

1893	250,000	£50	£90	£300	—
1897	*unrecorded*	£50	£90	£300	—
1900	260,00	£50	£90	£300	—

EDWARD VII (1902–10)

1902	4,244,457	—	—	£45	£55
1902 Matt proof	15,123	—	—	—	£100
1903	2,522,057	—	—	£45	£55
1904	1,717,440	—	—	£45	£55
1905	3,023,993	—	—	£45	£55
1906	4,245,437	—	—	£45	£55
1907	4,233,421	—	—	£45	£55
1908	3,996,992	—	—	£45	£55
1909	4,010,715	—	—	£45	£55
1910	5,023,881	—	—	£45	£55

DATE	F	VF	EF	UNC
M below (Melbourne Mint)				
1906	82,042	—	£40	£80	£165
1907	405,034	—	£40	£80	£165
1908	incl. above	—	£40	£80	£165
1909	186,094	—	£40	£80	£165
P below (Perth Mint)				
1904	60,030	£80	£150	£550	—
1908	24,668	£80	£150	£550	—
1909	44,022	£70	£130	£350	—
S below (Sydney Mint)				
1902	84,000	—	£45	£90	£160
1903	231,000	—	£45	£90	£160
1906	308,00	—	£45	£90	£160
1908	538,000	—	£45	£90	£160
1910	474,000	—	£45	£90	£160

GEORGE V (1911–36)

DATE		F	VF	EF	UNC
1911	6,104,106	—	£40	£60	£80
1911 Proof	3,764	—	—	—	£175
1912	6,224,316	—	£40	£60	£80
1913	6,094,290	—	£40	£60	£80
1914	7,251,124	—	£40	£60	£80
1915	2,042,747	—	£40	£60	£80
M below (Melbourne Mint)				
1915	125,664	—	—	£70	£110
P below (Perth Mint)				
1911	130,373	—	—	£70	£100
1915	136,219	—	—	£70	£100
1918	unrecorded	£175	£375	£700	—
S below (Sydney Mint)				
1911	252,000	—	—	£70	£110
1912	278,000	—	—	£70	£110
1914	322,000	—	—	£70	£110
1915	892,000	—	—	£70	£110
1916	448,000	—	—	£70	£110
SA below (Pretoria Mint)				
1923 Proof only	655	—	—	—	£450
1925	946,615	—	—	£65	£100
1926	806,540	—	—	£65	£100

GEORGE VI (1937–52)

DATE		F	VF	EF	UNC
1937 Proof only	5,501	—	—	—	£165

Later issues are included in the Decimal section.

CROWNS

DATE	F	VF	EF	UNC

OLIVER CROMWELL

	F	VF	EF	UNC
1658 8 over 7 (always)	£550	£925	£1800	—
1658 Dutch Copy		Extremely rare		
1658 Patterns. In Various Metals		Extremely rare		

CHARLES II (1660–85)

	F	VF	EF	UNC
1662 First bust, rose (2 varieties)	£60	£230	£2000	—
1662 — no rose (2 varieties)	£60	£230	£2000	—
1663 —	£60	£230	£2000	—
1664 Second bust	£60	£300	£2500	—
1665 —	£150	£450	—	—
*1666 —	£70	£300	£2500	—
1666 — Elephant below bust	£175	£500	£3500	—
1667 —	£60	£230	£2000	—
1668 —	£60	£230	£2000	—
1669 —	£125	£300	£2250	—
1670 —	£60	£230	£1850	—
1671	£60	£230	£1850	—
1671 Third Bust	£60	£230	£1700	—
1672 —	£60	£230	£1700	—
1673 —	£60	£230	£1700	—
1674 —		Extremely rare		
1675 —	£175	—	—	—
1675/3 —	£160	£600	—	—
1676 —	£60	£230	£1650	—
1677 —	£60	£220	£1650	—
1678/7 —	£75	£300		—
1679 —	£60	£230	£1650	—
1679 Fourth bust	£60	£230	£1800	—
1680 Third bust	£60	£230	£1850	—
1680 Fourth bust	£60	£230	£1850	—
1681 —	£60	£230	£1850	—
1681 — Elephant & Castle below bust	£500	£1000		—
1682/1 —	£60	£275	£1850	—
1683 —	£75	£350	£2000	—
1684 —	£110	£500	—	—

JAMES II (1685–88)

	F	VF	EF	UNC
1686 First bust	£85	£325	£1300	—
1686 — No stops on obv	£100	£325	—	—
1687 Second bust	£75	£285	£850	—
*1688 —	£75	£285	£850	—

WILLIAM AND MARY (1688–94)

	F	VF	EF	UNC
1691	£160	£450	£1850	—
1692	£160	£425	£1800	—
1692 2 over upside down 2	£160	£425	£1800	—

WILLIAM III (1694–1702)

	F	VF	EF	UNC
1695 First bust	£45	£150	£475	—
1696 — GEI for DEI	£75	£220	—	—
1696 —	£45	£150	£475	—
1696 Second bust		Only one known		
1696 Third bust	£45	£150	£550	—
1697 —	£150	£650	£800	—
1700 Third bust variety edge year Duodecimo	£70	£175	£600	—
1700 — edge year Duodecimo Tertio	£70	£175	£600	—

DATE	F	VF	EF	UNC

ANNE (1702–14)

	F	VF	EF	UNC
1703 First bust, VIGO	£130	£375	£1200	—
1705 — Plumes in angles on rev.	£250	£600	£2000	—
1706 — Roses & Plumes in angles on rev	£140	£350	£950	—
1707 — Roses & Plumes in angles on rev	£140	£350	£950	—
1707 Second bust, E below	£75	£225	£700	—
1707 — Plain	£80	£250	£750	—
1708 — E below	£80	£250	£700	—
1708 — Plain	£75	£225	£750	—
1708 — Plumes in angles on rev.	£125	£350	£1100	—
*1713 Third bust, Roses & Plumes rev	£150	£400	£1100	—

GEORGE I (1714–27)

	F	VF	EF	UNC
1716	£200	£425	£1400	—
1718	£200	£425	£1550	—
1720	£200	£425	£1550	—
1723 SSC in angles on rev(South Sea Co.)	£200	£425	£1150	—
1726	£220	£500	£1800	—

GEORGE II (1727–60)

	F	VF	EF	UNC
1732 Young head, Plain Proof	—	—	£3000	
1732 — Roses & Plumes in angles on rev	£150	£325	£800	—
1734 —	£150	£325	£800	—
1735 —	£150	£325	£800	—
1736 —	£165	£350	£900	—
1739 — Roses in angles on rev	£140	£300	£650	—
1741 —	£140	£300	£650	—
1743 Old head, Roses in angles on rev	£125	£300	£700	—
*1746 — LIMA below bust	£125	£300	£700	—
1746 — Plain Proof	—	—	£1750	
1750 — Plain	£180	£360	£900	—
1751 —	£210	£425	£1000	—

GEORGE III (1760–1820)

	F	VF	EF	UNC
Dollar with oval counterstamp	£75	£170	£400	—
Dollar with octagonal counterstamp	£90	£180	£425	—
1804 Bank of England Dollar, Britannia rev.	£60	£110	£275	—
1818 LVIII	£18	£60	£210	£450
1818 LIX	£18	£60	£210	£450
1819 LIX	£18	£60	£210	£450
1819 LX	£18	£60	£210	£450
1820 LX	£18	£60	£210	£450
1820 LX 20 over 19	£20	£75	£250	—

GEORGE IV (1820–30)

	F	VF	EF	UNC
1821 First bust, St George rev. SECUNDO on edge	£18	£70	£250	£650
1821 — — Proof	—	—	—	£2000
1821 — — Proof TERTIO (error edge)	—	—	—	£3000
1822 — — SECUNDO	£18	£80	£350	£900
1822 — — TERTIO	£18	£70	£300	£750
1823 — — Proof only			Extremely rare	
1826 Second bust, shield rev, SEPTIMO Proof only	—	—	£1750	£2250

WILLIAM IV (1830–37)

	F	VF	EF	UNC
1831 Proof only W.W. on truncation	—	—	£2500	£4500
1831 Proof only W. WYON on truncation	—	—	£3000	£5250
1834 Proof only	—	—	—	—

DATE	MINTAGE	F	VF	EF	UNC

VICTORIA (1837–1901)

YOUNG HEAD ISSUES

1839 Proof Only	—	—	—	—	£2500
1844 (two edge varieties)	94,248	£28	£130	£550	£1800
1845	159,192	£28	£130	£550	£1800
1847	140,976	£32	£140	£575	£2000
1847 "Gothic" Proof only UNDECIMO edge	8,000	£225	£400	£650	£1100
1847 Plain edge, Proof only	—	—	—	£800	£1400
1853 D. SEPTIMO edge, Proof only	460	—	—	—	£5000
1853 Plain edge, Proof only	—	—	£2200	—	£5000

JUBILEE HEAD ISSUES

*1887	173,581	£10	£20	£40	£70
1887 Proof	1,084	—	—	—	£300
1888	131,899	£12	£25	£60	£110
1889	1,807,224	£10	£18	£32	£65
1890	997,862	£10	£22	£55	£90
1891	556,394	£10	£22	£55	£90
1892	451,334	£10	£22	£60	£110

OLD HEAD ISSUES (Regnal date on edge in Roman numerals)

1893 LVI	497,845	£12	£20	£65	£135
1893 LVII	*incl. above*	£14	£35	£150	£350
1893 Proof	1,312	—	—	—	£350
1894 LVII	144,906	£14	£35	£75	£145
1894 LVIII	*incl. above*	£14	£35	£75	£140
1895 LVIII	252,862	£12	£30	£75	£140
1895 LIX	*incl. above*	£12	£30	£75	£140
1896 LIX	317,599	£14	£30	£125	£300
1896 LX	*incl. above*	£12	£30	£75	£140
1897 LX	262,118	£12	£30	£75	£140
1897 LXI	*incl. above*	£12	£30	£75	£140
1898 LXI	166,150	£14	£35	£90	£200
1898 LXII	*incl. above*	£12	£30	£75	£150
1899 LXII	166,300	£12	£30	£75	£150
1899 LXIII	*incl. above*	£12	£30	£75	£150
1900 LXIII	353,356	£12	£30	£65	£140
1900 LXIV	*incl. above*	£12	£30	£65	£130

EDWARD VII (1901–10)

1902	256,020	£20	£40	£80	£120
1902 "Matt Proof"	15,123	—	—	—	£110

GEORGE V (1910–36)

1927 Proof only	15,030	—	£50	£80	£125
1928	9,034	£40	£60	£100	£150
1929	4,994	£40	£60	£105	£155
1930	4,847	£40	£60	£110	£170
1931	4,056	£40	£60	£100	£150
1932	2,395	£70	£125	£200	£325
1933	7,132	£40	£60	£100	£140
*1934	932	£325	£525	£1000	£1500
1935 Jubilee issue	714,769	£7	£10	£15	£22
1935 Specimen	—	—	—	—	£30
1935 Proof Raised Edge inscription	2,500	—	—	£150	£200
1936	2,473	£65	£125	£210	£320

GEORGE VI (1936–52)

1937 Coronation	418,699	£9	£14	£18	£30
1937 Proof	26,402	—	—	—	£30
1951 Festival of Britain, Proof-like	1,983,540	—	—	£2.50	£5

DATE	MINTAGE	F	VF	EF	UNC

ELIZABETH II (1952–   )

Pre-Decimal issues (Five Shillings)

DATE	MINTAGE	F	VF	EF	UNC
1953	5,962,621	—	—	£3	£6
1953 Proof	40,000	—	—	—	£15
1960	1,024,038	—	—	£3	£6
1960 Polished dies	70,000	—	—	—	£8
1965	19,640,000	—	—	—	£1

Later issues are listed in the Decimal section.

DOUBLE FLORINS

VICTORIA (1837–1901)

	MINTAGE	F	VF	EF	UNC
1887 Roman I	483,347	£9	£16	£35	£55
1887 Roman I Proof	incl. above	—	—	—	£200
1887 Arabic 1	incl. above	£9	£16	£35	£55
1887 Arabic 1 Proof	incl. above	—	—	—	£175
1888	243,340	£11	£22	£50	£75
1888 Second I in VICTORIA an inverted 1	incl. above	£15	£30	£60	£140
1889	1,185,111	£10	£18	£32	£60
1889 inverted 1	incl. above	£15	£28	£60	£140
1890	782,146	£11	£28	£50	£95

Patterns were also produced in 1911, 1914 and 1950 and are all extremely rare.

HALFCROWNS

OLIVER CROMWELL

1656			Extremely rare	
1658	£280	£500	£900	—
1658 Proof in Gold			Extremely rare	

CHARLES II (1660–1685)

	F	VF	EF	UNC
1663 First bust	£55	£300	£1250	—
1664 Second bust	£60	£350	£1750	—
1666 Third bust	£300	—	—	—
1666 — Elephant	£150	£450	£2500	—
1667/4 —			Extremely rare	
1668/4 —	£70	—	—	—
1669 —	£110	£400	—	—
1670 —	£40	£130	£850	—
1671 —	£40	£130	£850	—
1672 —	£40	£140	£850	—
1672 Fourth bust	£50	£175	£1000	—
1673 —	£40	£130	£850	—
1673 — Plumes both sides			Extremely rare	
1673 — Plume below bust	£800	—	—	—
1674 —	£60	£180	—	—
1675 —	£40	£140	£850	—
1676 —	£40	£130	£750	—
1677 —	£40	£130	£750	—
1678 —	£100	£300	—	—
1679 —	£45	£140	£750	—
1680 —	£100	£250	—	—
1681 —	£60	£149	£850	—
1681 — Elephant & Castle	£600	—	—	—
1682 —	£70	£180	£1350	—

DATE	MINTAGE	F	VF	EF	UNC
1683 —		£70	£160	£850	—
1683 — Plume below bust			Extremely rare		
1684/3 —		£100	£300	£1500	—

JAMES II (1685–1688)

1685 First bust	£65	£175	£600	—
1686 —	£65	£175	£600	—
1687 —	£70	£175	£650	—
1687 Second bust	£65	£175	£700	—
1688 —	£65	£175	£700	—

WILLIAM AND MARY (1688–1694)

1689 First busts; first shield	£50	£110	£400	—
1689 — second shield	£50	£110	£400	—
1690 — —	£50	£160	£550	—
1690 — — variety GRETIA for GRATIA	£110	£300	—	—
1691 Second busts	£65	£150	£450	—
1692 —	£65	£150	£450	—
1693 —	£65	£150	£400	—

WILLIAM III (1694–1702)

1696 First bust, large shields, early harp	£25	£70	£230	—
1696 — — — B (Bristol) below bust	£30	£100	£325	—
1696 — — — C (Chester)	£32	£100	£400	—
1696 — — — E (Exeter)	£32	£100	£450	—
1696 — — — N (Norwich)	£50	£160	—	—
1696 — — — y (York)	£32	£110	£325	—
1696 — — ordinary harp	£65	£180	—	—
1696 — — — C	£65	£180	—	—
1696 — — — E	£65	£180	—	—
1696 — — — N	£75	£275	—	—
1696 — Small shields, ordinary harp	£28	£100	£260	—
1696 — — — B	£32	£120	£450	—
1696 — — — C	£35	£150	£500	—
1696 — — — E	£50	£150	—	—
1696 — — — N	£32	£120	£450	—
1696 — — — y	£32	£120	£450	—
1696 Second bust			Only one known	
1697 First bust, large shields, ordinary harp	£28	£90	£225	—
1697 — — — B	£32	£100	£325	—
1697 — — — C	£32	£110	£350	—
1697 — — — E	£32	£120	£325	—
1697 — — — N	£32	£120	£350	—
1697 — — — y	£32	£120	£325	—
1698 —	£32	£100	£240	—
1699 —	£55	£150	£450	—
1700 —	£45	£120	£320	—
1701 —	£50	£130	£370	—
1701 — Elephant & Castle			Extremely Rare	
1701 — Plumes in angles on rev.	£65	£220	£575	—

ANNE (1702–1714)

1703 Plain (pre-Union)	£110	£375	—	—
1703 VIGO below bust	£55	£120	£400	—
1704 Plumes in angles on rev.	£70	£140	£500	—
1705 —	£40	£140	£500	—
1706 Roses & Plumes in angles on rev.	£40	£110	£370	—
*1707 —	£35	£100	£350	—
1707 Plain (post-Union)	£32	£80	£250	—
1707 E below bust	£32	£80	£350	—
1708 Plain	£30	£75	£250	—
1708 E below bust	£30	£80	£350	—

DATE	MINTAGE	F	VF	EF	UNC
1708 Plumes in angles on rev.		£32	£90	£400	—
1709 Plain		£32	£90	£250	—
1709 E below bust		£65	£150	—	—
1710 Roses & Plumes in angles on rev.		£38	£100	£350	—
1712 —		£38	£100	£350	—
1713 Plain		£35	£100	£400	—
1713 Roses & Plumes in angles on rev.		£35	£100	£350	—
1714 —		£35	£100	£350	—

GEORGE I (1714–1727)

	MINTAGE	F	VF	EF	UNC
1715 Roses & Plumes in angles on rev.		£100	£300	£750	—
1717 —		£100	£300	£750	—
*1720 —		£100	£300	£750	—
1723 SSC in angles on rev.		£100	£300	£700	—
1726 Small Roses & Plumes in angles on rev..		£800	£1750	—	—

GEORGE II (1727–1760)

	MINTAGE	F	VF	EF	UNC
1731 Young head, Plain, proof only		—	—	£1850	—
1731 — Roses & Plumes in angles on rev.		£55	£125	£400	—
1732 — —		£55	£125	£400	—
1734 — —		£55	£125	£400	—
1735 — —		£55	£135	£400	—
1736 — —		£55	£135	£400	—
1739 — Roses in angles on rev.		£45	£115	£325	—
1741 —		£45	£115	£325	—
1743 Old head, Roses in angles on rev.		£35	£70	£200	—
1745 — —		£35	£70	£200	—
1745 — LIMA below bust		£28	£55	£175	—
1746 — —		£28	£55	£175	—
1746 — Plain, Proof		—	—	—	£750
1750 — —		£50	£175	£500	—
1751 — —		£60	£200	£600	—

GEORGE III (1760–1820)

	MINTAGE	F	VF	EF	UNC
1816 "Bull head"	—	£8	£35	£90	£165
1817 —	8,092,656	£8	£35	£90	£170
1817 "Small head"	incl. above	£8	£35	£95	£185
1818 —	2,905,056	£8	£35	£95	£185
1819 —	4,790,016	£8	£35	£95	£185
1820 —	2,396,592	£14	£45	£130	£260

GEORGE IV (1820–30)

	MINTAGE	F	VF	EF	UNC
1820 First bust, first reverse	incl. above	£10	£35	£120	£240
1821 — —	1,435,104	£10	£35	£120	£240
1821 — — Proof	incl. above	—	—	—	£650
1823 —	2,003,760	£250	£500	£1750	—
1823 — Second reverse	incl. above	£12	£40	£110	£240
1824 — —	465,696	£15	£45	£140	£260
1824 Second bust, third reverse .	incl. above		Extremely rare		
*1825 — —	2,258,784	£12	£32	£100	£220
1826 — —	2,189,088	£12	£32	£100	£220
1826 — — Proof	incl. above	—	—	£325	£450
1828 — —	49,890	£35	£70	£175	£350
1829 —	508,464	£30	£60	£150	£300

WILLIAM IV (1830–37)

	MINTAGE	F	VF	EF	UNC
1831	—		Extremely rare		
1831 Proof (W.W. in script & block)	—	—	—	£350	£600
1834 W.W. in block	993,168	£10	£45	£150	£275
1834 W.W. in script	incl. above	£10	£40	£120	£240
1835	281,952	£10	£45	£150	£260
*1836	1,588,752	£10	£35	£120	£240
1837	150,526	£10	£45	£160	£275

DATE	MINTAGE	F	VF	EF	UNC

VICTORIA (1837–1901)

YOUNG HEAD ISSUES

DATE	MINTAGE	F	VF	EF	UNC
1839 (two varieties)	—	£400	£800	£2000	—
1839 Proof	—	—	—	—	£1000
1840	386,496	£25	£90	£175	£300
1841	42,768	£250	£500	£1500	£2200
1842	486,288	£20	£50	£160	£275
1843	454,608	£50	£130	£550	£850
*1844	1,999,008	£15	£35	£130	£240
1845	2,231,856	£15	£35	£130	£250
1846	1,539,668	£15	£40	£140	£275
1848 Plain 8	367,488	£35	£100	£400	£700
1848/6	incl. above	£30	£80	£300	£600
1849	261,360	£30	£65	£250	£450
1850	484,613	£25	£60	£250	£350
1853 Proof only	—	—	—	—	£1800
1874	2,188,599	£12	£30	£80	£150
1875	1,113,483	£12	£30	£80	£150
1876	633,221	£12	£30	£80	£150
1877	447,059	£12	£30	£80	£150
1878	1,466,323	£12	£30	£80	£150
1879	901,356	£16	£32	£110	£200
1880	1,346,350	£12	£30	£80	£130
1881	2,301,495	£12	£30	£80	£130
1882	808,227	£12	£30	£80	£130
1883	2,982,779	£12	£30	£80	£130
1884	1,569,175	£12	£30	£80	£130
1885	1,628,438	£12	£30	£80	£130
1886	891,767	£12	£30	£80	£130
1887	1,438,046	£12	£30	£80	£140

JUBILEE HEAD ISSUES

DATE	MINTAGE	F	VF	EF	UNC
1887	incl. above	£5	£8	£15	£35
1887 Proof	1,084	—	—	—	£125
1888	1,428,787	£8	£12	£30	£50
1889	4,811,954	£8	£12	£30	£50
1890	3,228,111	£8	£12	£35	£55
1891	2,284,632	£8	£15	£45	£75
1892	1,710,946	£8	£12	£35	£55

OLD HEAD ISSUES

DATE	MINTAGE	F	VF	EF	UNC
1893	1,792,600	£5	£12	£30	£55
1893 Proof	1,312	—	—	—	135
1894	1,524,960	£10	£20	£50	£80
1895	1,772,662	£8	£16	£40	£70
1896	2,148,505	£6	£14	£38	£65
1897	1,678,643	£6	£14	£38	£60
1898	1,870,055	£6	£14	£38	£60
1899	2,865,872	£6	£14	£38	£55
1900	4,479,128	£6	£14	£38	£55
1901	1,516,570	£6	£14	£38	£55

EDWARD VII (1901–10)

DATE	MINTAGE	F	VF	EF	UNC
1902	1,316,008	£5	£15	£45	£60
1902 "Matt Proof"	15,123	—	—	—	£60
*1903	274,840	£45	£120	£380	£800
1904	709,652	£40	£110	£350	£575
1905	166,008	£125	£325	£750	£1200
1906	2,886,206	£8	£25	£75	£130
1907	3,693,930	£8	£25	£80	£150
1908	1,758,889	£12	£35	£130	£240
1909	3,051,592	£8	£25	£80	£160
1910	2,557,685	£8	£25	£65	£125

GEORGE V (1910–36)

First issue

DATE	MINTAGE	F	VF	EF	UNC
1911	2,914,573	£5	£10	£30	£55
1911 Proof	6,007	—	—	—	£75
1912	4,700,789	£4	£10	£30	£60
1913	4,090,169	£4	£11	£40	£75
1914	18,333,003	£3	£8	£20	£32

George V first type reverse

DATE	MINTAGE	F	VF	EF	UNC
1915	32,433,066	£3	£8	£16	£30
1916	29,530,020	£3	£8	£16	£30
1917	11,172,052	£3	£8	£18	£30
1918	29,079,592	£3	£8	£16	£30
1919	10,266,737	£3	£10	£20	£40

Second issue—debased silver

1920	17,982,077	£2	£7	£15	£35
1921	23,677,889	£2	£7	£16	£35
1922	16,396,724	£2	£7	£16	£35
1923	26,308,526	£6	£7	£15	£25
1924	5,866,294	£6	£12	£35	£65
1925	1,413,461	£8	£25	£100	£195
1926	4,473,516	£4	£12	£30	£65

Third issue —Modified effigy

1926	incl. above	£4	£10	£25	£60
1927	6,837,872	£3	£8	£20	£40

Fourth issue—New shield reverse

1927 Proof	15,000	—	—	—	£35
1928	18,762,727	£2	£5	£12	£22
1929	17,632,636	£2	£5	£12	£22
1930	809,051	£5	£35	£85	£180
1931	11,264,468	£2	£5	£12	£22
1932	4,793,643	£2	£5	£16	£50
1933	10,311,494	£2	£5	£12	£28
1934	2,422,399	£3	£8	£35	£65
1935	7,022,216	£2	£5	£12	£16
1936	7,039,423	£2	£5	£10	£15

GEORGE VI (1936–52)

1937	9,106,440	—	£2	£4	£10
1937 Proof	26,402	—	—	—	£12
1938	6,426,478	£1	£3	£10	£17
1939	15,478,635	—	£1	£3	£8
1940	17,948,439	—	£1	£3	£6
1941	15,773,984	—	£1	£3	£6
1942	31,220,090	—	£1	£3	£6
1943	15,462,875	—	£1	£3	£6
1944	15,255,165	—	£1	£3	£6
1945	19,849,242	—	£1	£3	£6
1946	22,724,873	—	£1	£3	£6

Cupro-nickel

1947	21,911,484	—	£1	£2	£4
1948	71,164,703	—	£1	£2	£4
1949	28,272,512	—	£1	£2	£6
1950	28,335,500	—	£1	£2	£6
1950 Proof	17,513	—	£1	£2	£9
1951	9,003,520	—	£1	£2	£6
1951 Proof	20,000	—	—	—	£9
1952			Only one known		

ELIZABETH II (1952–)

1953	4,333,214	—	—	£1	£3
1953 Proof	40,000	—	—	—	£5
1954	11,614,953	—	£1	£3	£15
1955	23,628,726	—	—	£1	£4
1956	33,934,909	—	—	£1	£4
1957	34,200,563	—	—	£1	£4
1958	15,745,668	—	£1	£3	£15
1959	9,028,844	—	£1	£5	£18
1960	19,929,191	—	—	£1	£2
1961	25,887,897	—	—	—	£1
1962	24,013,312	—	—	—	£1
1963	17,625,200	—	—	—	£1
1964	5,973,600	—	—	—	£1
1965	9,778,440	—	—	—	£1
1966	13,375,200	—	—	—	£1
1967	33,058,400	—	—	—	—

FLORINS

DATE	MINTAGE	F	VF	EF	UNC

VICTORIA (1837–1901)

YOUNG (CROWNED) HEAD ISSUES

"Godless" type (without D.G.—"Dei Gratia")

*1849	413,820	£10	£26	£75	£140

"Gothic" type i.e. date in roman numerals in obverse legend

"brit." in legend. No die no.

1851 mdcccli Proof	1,540	Extremely rare			
1852 mdccclii	1,014,552	£12	£38	£90	£160
1853 mdcccliii	3,919,950	£12	£38	£90	£160
1853 — Proof	*incl. above*	—	—	—	£1200
1854 mdcccliv	550,413	£500	—	—	—
1855 mdccclv	831,017	£12	£38	£90	£160
1856 mdccclvi	2,201,760	£12	£38	£90	£160
1857 mdccclvii	1,671,120	£12	£38	£90	£160
1858 mdccclviii	2,239,380	£12	£38	£90	£160
1859 mdccclix	2,568,060	£12	£38	£90	£160
1860 mdccclx	1,475,100	£15	£45	£135	£250
1862 mdccclxii	594,000	£60	£170	£500	£900
1863 mdccclxiii	938,520	£150	£325	£1000	£1400

"brit" in legend. Die no. below bust

1864 mdccclxiv	1,861,200	£12	£38	£90	£160
1865 mdccclxv	1,580,044	£12	£38	£95	£160
1866 mdccclxvi	914,760	£12	£38	£95	£165
*1867 mdccclxvii	423,720	£20	£55	£220	£375
1867—only 42 arcs in border	*incl. above*	Extremely rare			

"britt" in legend. Die no. below bust

1868 mdccclxviii	896,940	£12	£38	£100	£160
1869 mdccclxix	297,000	£16	£40	£125	£250
1870 mdccclxx	1,080,648	£12	£35	£90	£160
1871 mdccclxxi	3,425,605	£12	£35	£90	£150
1872 mdccclxxii	7,199,690	£12	£35	£90	£150
1873 mdccclxxiii	5,921,839	£12	£35	£90	£150
1874 mdccclxxiv	1,642,630	£12	£35	£90	£150
1875 mdccclxxv	1,117,030	£12	£35	£90	£150
1876 mdccclxxvi	580,034	£12	£35	£90	£160
1877 mdccclxxvii	682,292	£12	£35	£90	£150
1877 — 48 arcs in border no W.W.	*incl. above*	£15	£45	£120	£240
1877 — 42 arcs	*incl. above*	£15	£45	£120	£240
1877 — — no die number	*incl. above*	Extremely rare			
1878 mdccclxxviii with die number	1,786,680	£14	£40	£120	£185
1879 mdccclxxix no die no	1,512,247	Extremely rare			
1879 — 48 arcs in border	*incl. above*	£12	£35	£120	£185
1879 — no die number	*incl. above*	Extremely rare			
1879 — 38 arcs, no W.W.	*incl. above*	£12	£45	£125	£200
1880 mdccclxxx Younger portrait	—	Extremely rare			
1880 — 34 arcs, Older portrait	2,167,170	£12	£40	£90	£160
1881 mdccclxxxi — —	2,570,337	£12	£40	£90	£150
1883 mdccclxxxiii — —	3,555,667	£12	£40	£90	£150
1884 mdccclxxxiv — —	1,447,379	£12	£40	£90	£150
1885 mdccclxxxv — —	1,758,210	£12	£40	£90	£150
1886 mdccclxxxvi — —	591,773	£12	£40	£90	£150
1887 mdccclxxxvii — —	1,776,903	£15	£55	£165	£300
1887 — 46 Arcs	*incl. above*	£20	£65	£200	£350

JUBILEE HEAD ISSUES

1887	*incl. above*	£3	£6	£15	£28
1887 Proof	1,084	—	—	—	£90
1888	1,547,540	£4	£8	£28	£45

"Godless" florin

"Gothic" florin

DATE	MINTAGE	F	VF	EF	UNC
1889	2,973,561	£4	£10	£28	£45
1890	1,684,737	£7	£20	£60	£110
1891	836,438	£12	£40	£100	£175
1892	283,401	£20	£55	£140	£300

VICTORIA—OLD HEAD ISSUES

1893	1,666,103	£3	£11	£25	£45
1893 Proof	1,312	—	—	—	£100
1894	1,952,842	£6	£20	£45	£80
1895	2,182,968	£5	£18	£45	£75
1896	2,944,416	£5	£15	£35	£55
1897	1,699,921	£5	£15	£35	£55
1898	3,061,343	£5	£15	£35	£55
1899	3,966,953	£5	£15	£35	£55
*1900	5,528,630	£5	£15	£35	£55
1901	2,648,870	£5	£15	£35	£55

EDWARD VII (1901–10)

*1902	2,189,575	£5	£12	£30	£55
1902 "Matt Proof"	15,123	—	—	—	£50
1903	1,995,298	£8	£28	£70	£150
1904	2,769,932	£8	£28	£70	£160
1905	1,187,596	£25	£60	£230	£500
1906	6,910,128	£8	£28	£70	£130
1907	5,947,895	£8	£28	£70	£130
1908	3,280,010	£9	£34	£110	£240
1909	3,482,829	£8	£30	£100	£175
1910	5,650,713	£6	£22	£60	£100

GEORGE V (1910–36)

First issue

1911	5,951,284	£3	£8	£20	£50
1911 Proof	6,007	—	—	—	£60
1912	8,571,731	£3	£10	£28	£60
1913	4,545,278	£4	£15	£32	£70
1914	21,252,701	£2	£12	£20	£35
1915	12,367,939	£2	£12	£20	£35
1916	21,064,337	£2	£12	£20	£35
1917	11,181,617	£2	£10	£20	£40
1918	29,211,792	£2	£12	£20	£35
1919	9,469,292	£3	£14	£28	£50

Second issue —*debased silver*

1920	15,387,833	£2	£12	£32	£55
1921	34,863,895	£2	£12	£28	£45
1922	23,861,044	£2	£12	£28	£45
1923	21,546,533	£2	£10	£20	£35
1924	4,582,372	£3	£12	£40	£70
1925	1,404,136	£8	£30	£90	£170
1926	5,125,410	£5	£15	£40	£70

Fourth issue—*new reverse*

1927 Proof only	101,497	—	—	—	£35
1928	11,087,186	£2	£4	£12	£22
1929	16,397,279	£2	£4	£12	£22
1930	5,753,568	£2	£5	£15	£35
1931	6,556,331	£2	£5	£10	£25
1932	717,041	£6	£15	£80	£150
1933	8,685,303	£1	£3	£12	£30
1935	7,540,546	£1	£2	£8	£15
*1936	9,897,448	£1	£2	£8	£14

DATE	MINTAGE	F	VF	EF	UNC

GEORGE VI (1936–52)

DATE	MINTAGE	F	VF	EF	UNC
1937	13,006,781	—	£1	£3	£6
1937 Proof	26,402	—	—	—	£8
1938	7,909,388	£1	£2	£8	£16
1939	20,850,607	£1	£2	£3	£5
1940	18,700,338	£1	£2	£3	£5
1941	24,451,079	£1	£2	£3	£5
1942	39,895,243	£1	£2	£3	£5
1943	26,711,987	£1	£2	£3	£5
*1944	27,560,005	£1	£2	£3	£5
1945	25,858,049	£1	£2	£3	£5
1946	22,300,254	£1	£2	£3	£5
1947	22,910,085	—	—	£1	£3
1948	67,553,636	—	—	£1	£3
1949	28,614,939	—	—	£1	£5
1950	24,357,490	—	—	£2	£7
1950 Proof	17,513	—	—	£1	£8
1951	27,411,747	—	—	£2	£7
1951 Proof	20,000	—	—	£1	£8

ELIZABETH II (1952–)

DATE	MINTAGE	F	VF	EF	UNC
1953	11,958,710	—	—	—	£2
1953 Proof	40,000	—	—	—	£5
1954	13,085,422	—	—	£5	£15
1955	25,887,253	—	—	£1	£3
1956	47,824,500	—	—	£1	£3
1957	33,071,282	—	—	£4	£15
1958	9,564,580	—	—	£3	£12
1959	14,080,319	—	—	£4	£15
1960	13,831,782	—	—	£1	£2
1961	37,735,315	—	—	£1	£2
1962	35,147,903	—	—	£1	£2
1963	26,471,000	—	—	£1	£2
1964	16,539,000	—	—	£1	£2
1965	48,163,000	—	—	—	£1
1966	83,999,000	—	—	—	£1
1967	39,718,000	—	—	—	£1

SHILLINGS

OLIVER CROMWELL

		F	VF	EF	UNC
1658		£275	£450	£800	—
1658 Dutch Copy			Extremely rare		

CHARLES II (1660–85)

	F	VF	EF	UNC
*1663 First bust	£45	£120	£400	—
1663 First bust variety	£45	£120	£400	—
1666 — Elephant below bust	£200	£550	£1500	—
1666 "Guinea" head, elephant	£500	£950	—	—
1666 Second bust		Extremely rare		
1669/6 First bust variety		Extremely rare		
1668 Second bust	£45	£115	£400	—
1669 —		Extremely rare		
1670 —	£65	£200	£550	—
1671 —	£75	£250	£675	—
1671 — Plume below, plume in centre rev.	£160	£325	£1050	—
1672 —	£50	£150	£475	—
1673 —	£75	£250	£675	—
1673 — Plume below, plume in centre rev.	£170	£325	£1150	—
1674 —	£75	£250	£675	—
1674 — Plume below, plume in centre rev.	£170	£360	£1050	—
1674 — Plume rev. only	£160	£350	£1000	—

DATE	F	VF	EF	UNC
1674 Third bust	£225	£575	—	—
1675 Second bust	£90	£275	—	—
1675 — Plume below, plume in centre rev.	£170	£360	£1050	—
1675 Third bust	£175	£450	—	—
1676 Second bust	£50	£150	£400	—
1676 — Plume below, plume in centre rev.	£170	£360	£1050	—
1677 —	£60	£150	£450	—
1677 — Plume below	£180	£400	£1100	—
1678 —	£65	£200	£600	—
1679 —	£55	£150	£450	—
1679 — Plume below, plume in centre rev.	£180	£375	£1050	—
1679 — Plume below	£180	£400	£1050	—
1680 —	£225	—	—	—
1680 — Plume below, plume in centre rev.	£180	£425	£1050	—
1681 —	£75	£250	£800	—
1681 — Elephant & Castle	£750	—	—	—
1682 —	£200	£600	—	—
1683 —	£600	—	—	—
1683 Fourth bust	£90	£280	£750	—
1684 —	£80	£280	£750	—

William III First bust

JAMES II (1685–88)

	F	VF	EF	UNC
1685	£70	£180	£475	—
1685 Plume rev		Extremely Rare		
1686	£70	£180	£475	—
1687	£70	£190	£475	—
1688	£75	£200	£500	—

William III Second bust

WILLIAM & MARY (1688–94)

	F	VF	EF	UNC
1692	£75	£200	£525	—
1693	£75	£200	£525	—

WILLIAM III (1694–1702)

Provincial shillings carry privy marks or initials below the bust:
B: Bristol. C: Chester. E: Exeter. N: Norwich. Y or y: York.

	F	VF	EF	UNC
1695 First bust	£25	£60	£160	—
1696 —	£20	£50	£150	—
1696 — B below bust	£24	£60	£175	—
1696 — C	£25	£70	£200	—
1696 — E	£25	£70	£220	—
1696 — N	£25	£70	£220	—
1696 — y	£25	£70	£220	—
1696 — Y	£30	£80	£250	—
1696 Second bust		Only one known		
1696 Third bust C below	£75	£175	£500	—
1696 — Y	£300	—	—	—
1697 First bust	£20	£55	£160	—
1697 — B	£25	£65	£220	—
1697 — C	£25	£65	£220	—
1697 — E	£25	£65	£220	—
1697 — N	£25	£65	£220	—
1697 — y	£25	£65	£220	—
1697 — Y	£25	£65	£230	—
1697 Third bust	£20	£50	£150	—
1697 — B	£25	£70	£225	—
1697 — C	£25	£70	£225	—
1697 — E	£25	£70	£225	—
1697 — N	£25	£70	£225	—
1697 — y	£25	£70	£225	—
1697 Third bust variety	£22	£55	£160	—
1697 — B	£25	£70	£240	—
1697 — C	£40	£150	—	—
1698 —	£40	£80	£250	—
1698 — Plumes in angles of rev.	£55	£225	£550	—

William III Third bust

William III Fourth bust

William III Fifth bust

173

DATE	F	VF	EF	UNC
1698 Fourth bust "Flaming hair"	£70	£230	£750	—
1699 —	£70	£220	£750	—
1699 Fifth bust	£60	£120	£425	—
1699 — Plumes in angles on rev.	£60	£170	£500	—
1699 — Roses in angles on rev.	£60	£180	£550	
1700 —	£35	£75	£190	
1700 — Plume below bust	£750	—	—	—
1701 —	£50	£115	£260	—
1701 — Plumes in angles on rev.	£70	£175	£450	—

ANNE (1702–14)

	F	VF	EF	UNC
1702 First bust (pre-Union with Scotland)	£30	£75	£225	—
1702 — Plumes in angles on rev.	£30	£80	£250	—
*1702 — VIGO below bust	£30	£80	£210	—
1703 Second bust, VIGO below	£30	£75	£200	—
1704 — Plain	£70	£175	—	—
1704 — Plumes in angles on rev.	£35	£110	£350	—
1705 — Plain	£35	£110	£300	—
1705 — Plumes in angles on rev.	£30	£110	£300	—
1705 — Roses & Plumes in angles on rev.	£30	£110	£300	—
1707 — —	£30	£110	£300	—
1707 Second bust (post-Union) E below bust	£25	£55	£200	—
1707 — E* below bust	£60	£140	£400	—
1707 Third bust, Plain	£25	£55	£130	—
1707 — Plumes in angles on rev.	£35	£90	£300	—
1707 — E below bust	£22	£55	£200	—
1707 "Edinburgh" bust, E* below		Extremely Rare		
1708 Second bust, E below	£25	£55	£250	—
1708 — E below bust	£30	£100	£300	—
1708 — Roses & Plumes in angles on rev.	£70	£200	£425	—
1708 Third bust, Plain	£25	£50	£145	—
1708 — Plumes in angles on rev.	£35	£90	£250	—
1708 — E below bust	£35	£110	£250	—
1708 — Roses & Plumes in angles on rev.	£30	£90	£250	—
1708 "Edinburgh" bust, E* below	£35	£100	£300	—
1709 Third bust, Plain	£22	£55	£155	—
1709 "Edinburgh" bust, E* below	£35	£100	£300	—
1709 — E no star (filled in die?)	£60	£150	£300	—
1710 Third bust, Roses & Plumes in angles	£28	£70	£225	—
1710 Fourth bust, Roses & Plumes in angles	£35	£100	£260	—
1711 Third bust, Plain	£60	£120	£325	—
1711 Fourth bust, Plain	£20	£40	£125	—
1712 —Roses & Plumes in angles on rev.	£28	£60	£180	—
1713 — —	£25	£60	£180	—
1714 — —	£25	£60	£180	—

GEORGE I (1714–27)

	F	VF	EF	UNC
*1715 First bust, Roses & Plumes in angles on rev.	£25	£75	£225	—
1716 — —	£60	£150	£400	—
1717 — —	£30	£75	£225	—
1718 — —	£30	£70	£190	—
1719 — —	£70	£150	£500	—
1720 — —	£30	£75	£190	—
1720 — Plain	£20	£65	£180	—
1721 — Roses & Plumes in angles on rev.	£40	£100	£300	—
1721 — Plain	£100	£225	£700	—
1722 — Roses & Plumes in angles on rev.	£50	£140	£450	—
1723 — —	£50	£130	£425	—
1723 — SSC in angles of rev.	£15	£35	£120	—
1723 Second bust, SSC in angles on rev.	£25	£70	£260	—
1723 First bust, SSC rev., Arms of France at date	£60	£120	£425	—
1723 Second bust, Roses & Plumes in angles .	£40	£110	£350	—
1723 — WCC (Welsh Copper Co) below bust ..	£200	£475	£1800	—
1724 — Roses & Plumes in angles on rev.	£35	£90	£250	—
1724 — WCC below bust	£220	£500	£2000	—
1725 — Roses & Plumes in angles on rev.	£35	£100	£270	—
1725 — WCC below bust	£220	£500	£2000	—
1726 — —.	£220	£500	£2000	—

DATE	MINTAGE	F	VF	EF	UNC
1726 — Roses & Plumes in angles on rev.		£200	£700	—	—
1727 — —			Extremely rare		
1727 — — no stops on obv.			Extremely rare		

GEORGE II (1727–60)

DATE	MINTAGE	F	VF	EF	UNC
1727 Young head, Plumes in angles on rev.		£30	£100	£300	—
1727 — Roses & Plumes in angles on rev.		£30	£95	£250	—
1728 — —		£30	£90	£300	—
1728 — Plain		£35	£100	£350	—
1729 — Roses & Plumes in angles on rev.		£30	£90	£250	—
1731 — —		£30	£70	£175	—
1731 — Plumes in angles on rev.		£40	£125	£375	—
1732 — Roses & Plumes in angles on rev.		£30	£70	£180	—
1734 — —		£30	£70	£180	—
1735 — —		£30	£70	£180	—
1736 — —		£30	£70	£180	—
1737 — —		£30	£70	£180	—
*1739 — Roses in angles on rev.		£25	£65	£160	—
1741 — —		£25	£65	£160	—
1743 Old head, Roses in angles on rev.		£18	£45	£140	—
1745 — —		£18	£45	£140	—
1745 — — LIMA beow bust		£15	£35	£110	—
1746 — — —		£30	£100	£350	—
1746 — Plain, Proof		—	—	£425	—
*1747 — Roses in angles on rev.		£18	£45	£145	—
1750 — Plain		£15	£45	£160	—
1751 — —		£25	£60	£175	—
1758 — —		£8	£25	£75	—

GEORGE III (1760–1820)

DATE	MINTAGE	F	VF	EF	UNC
*1763 "Northumberland" bust		£140	£290	£475	—
1787 rev. no semée of hearts in 4th shield		£6	£15	£45	—
1787 rev. with semée of hearts		£6	£14	£45	—
1798 "Dorrien Magens" bust		—	—	£3500	—

NEW COINAGE—shield in garter reverse

DATE	MINTAGE	F	VF	EF	UNC
1816	—	£5	£14	£35	£70
1817	3,031,360	£5	£14	£35	£70
1818	1,342,440	£6	£16	£55	£85
1819	7,595,280	£5	£14	£35	£70
1820	7,975,440	£5	£14	£35	£70

GEORGE IV (1820–30)

DATE	MINTAGE	F	VF	EF	UNC
1821 First bust, first reverse	2,463,120	£8	£25	£80	£140
1821 — — Proof	incl. above	—	—	—	£400
1823 — Second reverse	693,000	£20	£50	£150	£225
1824 — —	4,158,000	£8	£25	£70	£130
1825 — —	2,459,160	£15	£28	£70	£130
1825 Second bust, third reverse .	incl. above	£3	£10	£45	£95
1826 — —	6,351,840	£3	£10	£45	£95
1826 — — Proof	incl. above	—	—	—	£175
1827 — —	574,200	£20	£45	£100	£180
1829 — —	879,120	£15	£30	£80	£160

WILLIAM IV (1830–37)

DATE	MINTAGE	F	VF	EF	UNC
1831 Proof only	—	—	—	£140	£245
1834	3,223,440	£6	£20	£60	£130
1835	1,449,360	£6	£20	£65	£140
1836	3,567,960	£6	£20	£55	£130
1837	478,160	£7	£20	£80	£200

VICTORIA (1837–1901)

YOUNG HEAD ISSUES
First head

DATE	MINTAGE	F	VF	EF	UNC
1838 WW on truncation	1,956,240	£6	£20	£60	£120
1839 —	5,666,760	£6	£20	£60	£120

George II Young head

George II Old head

George III "Northumberland" shilling

175

DATE	MINTAGE	F	VF	EF	UNC
Second head					
1839 WW on truncation, Proof only	incl. above	—	—	—	£250
1839 no WW	incl. above	£6	£20	£65	£120
1840	1,639,440	£7	£20	£80	£180
1841	875,160	£6	£20	£80	£130
1842	2,094,840	£6	£20	£60	£120
1843	1,465,200	£6	£22	£80	£140
1844	4,466,880	£6	£20	£65	£120
1845	4,082,760	£6	£20	£65	£120
1846	4,031,280	£6	£20	£55	£110
1848 last 8 of date over 6	1,041,480	£25	£45	£135	£275
1849	845,480	£8	£30	£75	£140
1850	685,080	£160	£300	£800	£1400
1851	470,071	£25	£100	£250	£350
1852	1,306,574	£6	£20	£65	£110
1853	4,256,188	£6	£20	£65	£110
1853 Proof	incl. above	—	—	—	£400
1854	552,414	£60	£130	£270	£525
1855	1,368,400	£6	£20	£65	£110
1856	3,168,000	£6	£20	£65	£110
1857	2,562,120	£6	£20	£65	£110
1858	3,108,600	£6	£20	£65	£110
1859	4,561,920	£6	£20	£60	£100
1860	1,671,120	£6	£22	£65	£110
1861	1,382,040	£7	£25	£75	£140
1862	954,360	£40	£90	£200	£350
1863	859,320	£70	£140	£275	£500
Die no. added above date up to 1879					
1864	4,518,360	£5	£20	£50	£90
1865	5,619,240	£5	£20	£50	£90
1866	4,984,600	£5	£20	£50	£90
1867	2,166,120	£5	£20	£50	£90
Third head—with die no.					
1867	incl. above	£20	£50	£125	£200
1868	3,330,360	£5	£20	£50	£85
1869	736,560	£5	£20	£50	£85
1870	1,467,471	£5	£20	£50	£85
1871	4,910,010	£5	£16	£45	£80
1872	8,897,781	£5	£16	£45	£80
1873	6,489,598	£5	£16	£45	£80
1874	5,503,747	£5	£16	£45	£80
1875	4,353,983	£5	£16	£45	£80
1876	1,057,487	£5	£16	£45	£90
1877	2,989,703	£5	£16	£45	£80
1878	3,127,131	£5	£16	£45	£80
1879	3,611,507	£6	£30	£60	£125
Fourth head—no die no					
1879 no Die no.	incl. above	£5	£15	£50	£10
1880	4,842,786	£5	£15	£40	£70
1881	5,255,332	£5	£15	£40	£70
1882	1,611,786	£7	£22	£90	£175
1883	7,281,450	£4	£15	£40	£60
1884	3,923,993	£4	£15	£40	£60
1885	3,336,526	£4	£15	£40	£60
1886	2,086,819	£4	£15	£40	£60
1887	4,034,133	£5	£15	£50	£100
JUBILEE HEAD ISSUES					
1887	incl. above	£2	£4	£8	£18
1887 Proof	1,084	—	—	—	£60
1888	4,526,856	£2	£7	£15	£35
1889	7,039,628	£12	£40	£150	—
1889 Large bust (until 1892)	incl. above	£2	£7	£30	£55
1890	8,794,042	£2	£7	£30	£55
*1891	5,665,348	£2	£7	£30	£55
1892	4,591,622	£2	£7	£30	£55
OLD HEAD ISSUES					
1893	7,039,074	£3	£7	£17	£40
1893 Proof	1,312	—	—	—	£75
1894	5,953,152	£6	£15	£40	£75
1895	8,880,651	£5	£12	£35	£60
1896	9,264,551	£5	£11	£30	£45

Victoria Small Jubilee head

Victoria Large Jubilee head

DATE	MINTAGE	F	VF	EF	UNC
1897	6,270,364	£4	£10	£30	£45
*1898	9,768,703	£4	£10	£30	£45
1899	10,965,382	£4	£10	£30	£50
1900	10,937,590	£4	£10	£30	£40
1901	3,426,294	£4	£10	£30	£40

EDWARD VII (1901–10)

	MINTAGE	F	VF	EF	UNC
1902	7,809,481	£3	£6	£15	£35
1902 Proof matt	13,123	—	—	—	£30
1903	2,061,823	£5	£25	£65	£175
1904	2,040,161	£5	£25	£65	£175
1905	488,390	£32	£110	£375	£750
1906	10,791,025	£2	£8	£30	£45
1907	14,083,418	£3	£9	£35	£70
1908	3,806,969	£5	£18	£65	£130
1909	5,664,982	£3	£12	£50	£100
*1910	26,547,236	£2	£5	£20	£35

GEORGE V (1910–36)

First issue

	MINTAGE	F	VF	EF	UNC
1911	20,065,901	£1.50	£5	£15	£30
1911 Proof	6,007	—	—	—	£35
*1912	15,594,009	£1.50	£6	£20	£40
1913	9,011,509	£2	£7	£25	£55
1914	23,415,843	£1	£4	£15	£30
1915	39,279,024	£1	£4	£15	£30
1916	35,862,015	£1	£4	£15	£30
1917	22,202,608	£1	£4	£15	£30
1918	34,915,934	£1	£4	£15	£30
1919	10,823,824	£1	£5	£15	£35

Second issue —*debased silver*

1920	22,825,142	—	£2	£15	£30
1921	22,648,763	—	£2	£15	£30
1922	27,215,738	—	£2	£15	£30
1923	14,575,243	—	£2	£15	£25
1924	9,250,095	£2	£5	£25	£55
1925	5,418,764	£2	£5	£25	£60
1926	22,516,453	—	£4	£18	£38

George V First obverse

Third issue—*Modified bust*

1926	incl. above	—	£3	£18	£30
1927 —	9,247,344	£1	£3	£18	£30

Fourth issue —*large lion and crown on rev., date in legend*

1927	incl. above	£1	£2	£15	£30
1927 Proof	15,000	—	—	—	£25
1928	18,136,778	—	£2	£10	£25
1929	19,343,006	—	£2	£12	£25
1930	3,172,092	—	£2	£12	£35
1931	6,993,926	—	£2	£10	£25
1932	12,168,101	—	£2	£10	£25
1933	11,511,624	—	£2	£10	£25
*1934	6,138,463	—	£2	£12	£35
1935	9,183,462	—	£2	£6	£15
1936	11,910,613	—	£2	£4	£10

George V Second obverse

GEORGE VI (1936–52)

E = England rev. (lion standing on large crown). S = Scotland rev. (lion seated on small crown holding sword and mace)

	MINTAGE	F	VF	EF	UNC
1937 E	8,359,122	—	£1	£2	£5
1937 E Proof	26,402	—	—	—	£8
1937 S	6,748,875	—	£1	£2	£5
1937 S Proof	26,402	—	—	—	£8
1938 E	4,833,436	—	£1	£7	£12

DATE	MINTAGE	F	VF	EF	UNC
1938 S	4,797,852	—	£1	£7	£12
1939 E	11,052,677	—	£1	£2	£5
1939 S	10,263,892	—	£1	£2	£5
1940 E	11,099,126	—	—	£2	£5
1940 S	9,913,089	—	—	£2	£5
1941 E	11,391,883	—	—	£2	£5
1941 S	8,086,030	—	—	£2	£5
1942 E	17,453,643	—	—	£2	£4
1942 S	13,676,759	—	—	£2	£4
1943 E	11,404,213	—	—	£2	£4
1943 S	9,824,214	—	—	£2	£4
*1944 E	11,586,751	—	—	£2	£4
*1944 S	10,990,167	—	—	£2	£4
1945 E	15,143,404	—	—	£2	£5
1945 S	15,106,270	—	—	£2	£5
1946 E	16,663,797	—	—	£2	£5
1946 S	16,381,501	—	—	£2	£5
1947 E	12,120,611	—	—	—	£2
1947 S	12,283,223	—	—	—	£2
1948 E	45,576,923	—	—	—	£2
1948 S	45,351,937	—	—	—	£2
1949 E	19,328,405	—	—	—	£4
1949 S	21,243,074	—	—	—	£4
1950 E	19,243,872	—	—	—	£4
1950 E Proof	17,513	—	—	—	£8
1950 S	14,299,601	—	—	—	£4
1950 S Proof	17,513	—	—	—	£8
1951 E	9,956,930	—	—	—	£4
1951 E Proof	20,000	—	—	—	£8
1951 S	10,961,174	—	—	—	£4
1951 S Proof	20,000	—	—	—	£8

English reverse

Scottish reverse

ELIZABETH II (1952–   )

E = England rev. (shield with three lions). S = Scotland rev. (shield with one lion).

1953 E	41,942,894	—	—	—	£1
1953 E Proof	40,000	—	—	—	£3
1953 S	20,663,528	—	—	—	£1
1953 S Proof	40,000	—	—	—	£3
*1954 E	30,262,032	—	—	—	£2
*1954 S	26,771,735	—	—	—	£2
1955 E	45,259,908	—	—	—	£2
1955 S	27,950,906	—	—	—	£2
1956 E	44,907,008	—	—	—	£8
1956 S	42,853,639	—	—	—	£8
1957 E	42,774,217	—	—	—	£1
1957 S	17,959,988	—	—	—	£9
1958 E	14,392,305	—	—	—	£9
1958 S	40,822,557	—	—	—	£1
1959 E	19,442,778	—	—	—	£1
1959 S	1,012,988	£1	£2	£4	£15
1960 E	27,027,914	—	—	—	£1
1960 S	14,376,932	—	—	—	£1
1961 E	39,816,907	—	—	—	£1
1961 S	2,762,558	—	—	—	£3
1962 E	36,704,379	—	—	—	£1
1962 S	17,475,310	—	—	—	£1
1963 E	49,433,607	—	—	—	£1
1963 S	32,300,000	—	—	—	£1
1964 E	8,590,900	—	—	—	£1
1964 S	5,239,100	—	—	—	£1
1965 E	9,216,000	—	—	—	£1
1965 S	2,774,000	—	—	—	£2
1966 E	15,002,000	—	—	—	£1
1966 S	15,604,000	—	—	—	£1

English reverse

Scottish reverse

SIXPENCES

DATE	F	VF	EF	UNC

OLIVER CROMWELL

1658 Patterns by Thos. Simon & Tanner
All are very Rare 4 Varieties .... Extremely Rare

CHARLES II (1660–85)

DATE	F	VF	EF	UNC
1674	£45	£95	£250	—
1675	£45	£95	£250	—
1676	£45	£95	£250	—
*1677	£45	£95	£250	—
1678/7	£45	£95	£250	—
1679	£45	£95	£250	—
1680	£50	£110	£350	—
1681	£40	£95	£250	—
1682/1	£45	£95	£250	—
1682	£45	£95	£250	—
1683	£45	£95	£250	—
1684	£55	£110	£275	—

JAMES II (1685–88)

	F	VF	EF	UNC
1686 Early shields	£65	£150	£425	—
1687/6 —	£65	£150	£425	—
1687 Late shields	£65	£150	£400	—
1688 —	£65	£150	£425	—

WILLIAM & MARY (1688–94)

	F	VF	EF	UNC
*1693	£70	£160	£400	—
1694	£70	£165	£450	—

WILLIAM III (1694–1702)

Provincial 6d carry privy marks or initials below the bust:
B: Bristol. C: Chester. E: Exeter. N: Norwich. Y or y: York.

	F	VF	EF	UNC
1695 First bust, early harp in 4th shield on rev.	£15	£50	£140	—
1696 — —	£14	£40	£100	—
1696 — — B	£18	£50	£145	—
1696 — — C	£18	£50	£160	—
1696 — — E	£18	£50	£180	—
1696 — — N	£18	£50	£150	—
1696 — — y	£18	£50	£150	—
1696 — — Y	£24	£60	£200	—
1696 — Later harp	£30	£100	£300	—
1696 — — B	£25	£90	£260	—
1696 — — C	£40	£140	—	—
1696 — — N	£35	£125	—	—
1696 Second bust	£150	£375	—	—
1697 First bust, later harp	£18	£30	£100	—
1697 — — B	£20	£55	£160	—
1697 — — C	£20	£55	£170	—
1697 — — E	£20	£55	£160	—
1697 — — N	£20	£55	£160	—
1697 — — Y	£20	£55	£160	—
1697 Second bust	£70	£160	£600	—
1697 Third bust	£12	£35	£100	—
1697 — B	£18	£55	£170	—
1697 — C	£20	£80	£250	—
1697 — E	£25	£80	£220	—
1697 — Y	£25	£80	£225	—
1698 —	£25	£80	£200	—

DATE	MINTAGE	F	VF	EF	UNC
1698 — Plumes in angles on rev.		£30	£80	£250	—
1699 —		£40	£120	£375	—
1699 — Plumes in angles on rev.		£40	£120	£275	—
1699 — Roses in angles on rev.		£40	£120	£275	—
1700 —		£20	£55	£165	—
1700 — Plume below bust	£500	—	—	—	—
1701 —		£24	£70	£200	—

ANNE (1702–14)

	MINTAGE	F	VF	EF	UNC
1703 VIGO below bust Before Union with Scotland	£20	£50	£140	—	
1705 Plain		£35	£100	£250	—
*1705 Plumes in angles on rev.		£20	£55	£170	—
1705 Roses & Plumes in angles on rev.		£20	£55	£160	—
1707 Roses & Plumes in angles on rev.		£20	£55	£150	—
1707 (Post-Union), Plain		£18	£35	£125	—
1707 E (Edinburgh) below bust		£18	£40	£130	—
1707 Plumes in angles on rev.		£18	£40	£140	—
1708 Plain		£18	£35	£125	—
1708 E below bust		£18	£40	£140	—
1708 E* below bust		£24	£55	£175	—
1708 "Edinburgh" bust E* below		£24	£70	£185	—
1708 Plumes in angles on rev.		£24	£50	£150	—
1710 Roses & Plumes in angles on rev.		£24	£55	£180	—
1711 Plain		£15	£32	£100	—

GEORGE I (1714–27)

	F	VF	EF	UNC
*1717 Roses & Plumes in angles on rev.	£40	£100	£250	—
1720 —	£30	£80	£240	—
1723 SSC in angles on rev.	£10	£35	£110	—
1726 Small Roses & Plumes in angles on rev. .	£65	£160	£425	—

GEORGE II (1727–60)

	F	VF	EF	UNC
1728 Young head, Plain	£40	£100	£325	—
1728 — Proof	—	—	£1250	—
1728 — Plumes in angles on rev.	£25	£80	£250	—
1728 — Roses & Plumes in angles on rev.	£22	£70	£160	—
1731 — —	£22	£55	£150	—
*1732 — —	£22	£55	£150	—
1734 — —	£22	£60	£160	—
1735 — —	£22	£55	£150	—
1736 — —	£22	£55	£150	—
1739 — Roses in angles on rev.	£18	£45	£110	—
1741 —	£15	£45	£110	—
1743 Old head, Roses in angles on rev.	£12	£40	£100	—
1745 — —	£10	£35	£100	—
1745 — Plain, LIMA below bust	£12	£30	£75	—
1746 — —	£12	£30	£75	—
1746 — — Proof	—	—	£350	—
1750 — —	£12	£30	£90	—
1751 — —	£15	£35	£110	—
1757 — —	£10	£20	£50	—
1758 — —	£10	£20	£50	—

GEORGE III (1760–1820)

	F	VF	EF	UNC
1787 rev. no semée of hearts on 4th shield	£6	£14	£35	—
1787 rev. with semée of hearts	£6	£14	£32	—

NEW COINAGE

	MINTAGE	F	VF	EF	UNC
1816	—	£3	£9	£32	£55
1817	10,921,680	£3	£9	£32	£55
1818	4,284,720	£5	£12	£40	£70
1819	4,712,400	£3	£9	£32	£55
1820	1,488,960	£3	£9	£32	£60

DATE	MINTAGE	F	VF	EF	UNC

GEORGE IV (1820–30)

DATE	MINTAGE	F	VF	EF	UNC
*1821 First bust, first reverse	863,280	£8	£25	£60	£125
1821 — — Proof	incl. above	—	—	—	£350
1824 — Second (garter) reverse	633,600	£8	£25	£70	£125
1825 —	483,120	£8	£25	£70	£125
1826 — —	689,040	£15	£45	£110	£225
1826 Second bust, third (lion on crown) reverse	incl. above	£5	£18	£50	£90
1826 — — Proof	incl. above	—	—	—	£125
1827 — —	166,320	£10	£25	£90	£155
1828 — —	15,840	£10	£25	£90	£130
1829 — —	403,290	£10	£25	£90	£130

WILLIAM IV (1830–37)

DATE	MINTAGE	F	VF	EF	UNC
1831	1,340,195	£7	£22	£60	£100
1831 Proof	incl. above	—	—	£90	£175
*1834	5,892,480	£7	£22	£60	£100
1835	1,552,320	£7	£22	£60	£100
1836	1,987,920	£9	£30	£100	£160
1837	506,880	£9	£32	£110	£150

VICTORIA (1837–1901)

YOUNG HEAD ISSUES
First head

DATE	MINTAGE	F	VF	EF	UNC
1838	1,607,760	£6	£20	£45	£80
1839	3,310,560	£6	£20	£45	£85
1839 Proof	incl. above	—	—	—	£150
1840	2,098,800	£6	£20	£45	£110
1841	1,386,000	£6	£22	£50	£120
1842	601,920	£6	£20	£70	£110
1843	3,160,080	£6	£22	£50	£100
1844	3,975,840	£6	£20	£45	£90
1844 Large 44 in date	incl. above	£7	£25	£80	£130
1845	3,714,480	£6	£20	£45	£100
1846	4,226,880	£6	£20	£45	£100
1848	586,080	£18	£50	£125	£260
1850	498,960	£6	£20	£45	£100
1851	2,288,107	£6	£20	£45	£100
1852	904,586	£6	£20	£45	£100
1853	3,837,930	£6	£20	£45	£100
1853 Proof	incl above	—	—	—	£300
1854	840,116	£40	£100	£240	£350
1855	1,129,684	£6	£20	£45	£100
1856	2,779,920	£6	£20	£45	£100
1857	2,233,440	£6	£20	£45	£100
1858	1,932,480	£6	£20	£45	£100
1859	4,688,640	£6	£20	£45	£100
1860	1,100,880	£7	£22	£50	£110
1862	990,000	£20	£60	£130	£300
1863	491,040	£20	£60	£130	£300

Die no. added above date from 1864 to 1879

DATE	MINTAGE	F	VF	EF	UNC
1864	4,253,040	£6	£22	£50	£100
1865	1,631,520	£6	£22	£50	£100
1866	4,140,080	£6	£22	£50	£100
1866 no Die no.	incl. above	£15	£60	£150	£220

Second head

DATE	MINTAGE	F	VF	EF	UNC
1867	1,362,240	£6	£18	£45	£90
1868	1,069,200	£6	£18	£45	£90
1869	388,080	£6	£18	£45	£90
1870	479,613	£6	£18	£45	£85
1871	3,662,684	£6	£18	£45	£75
1871 no Die no.	incl. above	£6	£18	£45	£80
1872	3,382,048	£6	£18	£45	£80
1873	4,594,733	£6	£18	£45	£80
1874	4,225,726	£6	£18	£45	£80
1875	3,256,545	£6	£18	£45	£80

Victoria Jubilee Head

DATE	MINTAGE	F	VF	EF	UNC
1876	841,435	£6	£18	£50	£85
1877	4,066,486	£6	£18	£50	£85
1877 no Die no	incl. above	£6	£18	£50	£75
1878	2,624,525	£6	£18	£50	£75
1878 Dritanniar Error	incl. above	£50	£150	—	—
1879	3,326,313	£6	£18	£50	£75
1879 no Die no	incl. above	£5	£18	£50	£75
1880 no Die no	3,892,501	£5	£18	£50	£80
Third head					
1880	incl above	£4	£18	£40	£60
1881	6,239,447	£4	£18	£40	£50
1882	759,809	£5	£18	£60	£110
1883	4,986,558	£4	£16	£35	£55
1884	3,422,565	£4	£16	£35	£55
1885	4,652,771	£4	£16	£35	£55
1886	2,728,249	£4	£16	£35	£55
1887	3,675,607	£4	£16	£35	£60
JUBILEE HEAD ISSUES					
*1887 Shield reverse	incl. above	£3	£5	£9	£16
1887 — Proof	incl. above	—	—	—	£50
1887 Six Pence in wreath reverse	incl. above	£2	£4	£9	£16
1888	4,197,698	£3	£7	£20	£35
*1889 —	8,738,928	£3	£7	£24	£40
1890 —	9,386,955	£3	£7	£24	£40
1891 —	7,022,734	£3	£7	£24	£40
1892 —	6,245,746	£3	£8	£25	£45
1893 —	7,350,619	£175	£325	£800	£1500
OLD HEAD ISSUES					
1893	incl. above	£3	£7	£18	£32
1893 Proof	1,312	—	—	—	£60
1894	3,467,704	£6	£14	£40	£65
1895	7,024,631	£5	£12	£35	£50
1896	6,651,699	£4	£8	£30	£45
1897	5,031,498	£4	£8	£30	£45
1898	5,914,100	£4	£8	£30	£45
1899	7,996,80	£4	£8	£30	£45
1900	8,984,354	£4	£8	£30	£45
1901	5,108,757	£3	£8	£20	£35

Shield reverse

New reverse

EDWARD VII (1901–10)

1902	6,367,378	£1	£4	£20	£30
1902 "Matt Proof"	15,123	—	—	—	£20
1903	5,410,096	£3	£10	£35	£75
1904	4,487,098	£5	£20	£50	£100
1905	4,235,556	£4	£15	£40	£80
1906	7,641,146	£3	£8	£30	£60
1907	8,733,673	£3	£8	£30	£60
*1908	6,739,491	£4	£14	£35	£70
1909	6,584,017	£3	£10	£30	£60
1910	12,490,724	£1	£5	£15	£32

GEORGE V (1910–36)

First issue					
1911	9,155,310	£1	£3	£8	£20
1911 Proof	6,007	—	—	—	£30
1912	10,984,129	£1	£3	£16	£30
1913	7,499,833	£1	£6	£22	£40
1914	22,714,602	£1	£2	£8	£20
*1915	15,694,597	£1	£3	£10	£25
1916	22,207,178	£1	£2	£8	£20
1917	7,725,475	£2	£6	£22	£45
1918	27,553,743	£1	£2	£10	£22
1919	13,375,447	£1	£3	£12	£28
1920	14,136,287	£1	£3	£10	£25
Second issue—debased silver					
1920	incl. above	£1	£3	£10	£25
1921	30,339,741	£1	£3	£8	£25
1922	16,878,890	£1	£2	£10	£25

DATE	MINTAGE	F	VF	EF	UNC
1923	6,382,793	£1.50	£6	£25	£45
1924	17,444,218	£1	£5	£10	£20
1925	12,720,558	£1	£2	£10	£20
1925 Broad rim	incl. above	£1	£2	£10	£22
1926 —	21,809,621	£1	£2	£10	£22
Third issue—*Modified bust*					
1926	incl. above	£1	£2	£10	£25
1927	8,924,873	—	£1	£8	£25
Fourth issue—*New design (oakleaves)*					
1927 Proof only	15,000	—	—	—	£20
1928	23,123,384	—	£1	£6	£15
1929	28,319,326	—	£1	£6	£15
1930	16,990,289	—	£1	£6	£15
1931	16,873,268	—	£1	£6	£15
1932	9,406,117	—	£1	£6	£15
1933	22,185,083	—	£1	£6	£15
1934	9,304,009	£1	£2	£8	£20
1935	13,995,621	—	£1	£4	£8
*1936	24,380,171	—	£1	£4	£7

George V second reverse

GEORGE VI (1936–52)

	MINTAGE	F	VF	EF	UNC
First type					
1937	22,302,524	—	—	£1	£4
1937 Proof	26,402	—	—	—	£5
1938	13,402,701	—	£1	£3	£11
1939	28,670,304	—	—	£1	£5
1940	20,875,196	—	—	£1	£5
1941	23,086,616	—	—	£1	£5
1942	44,942,785	—	—	£1	£4
1943	46,927,111	—	—	£1	£4
1944	36,952,600	—	—	£1	£4
1945	39,939,259	—	—	£1	£3
1946	43,466,407	—	—	£1	£3
Cupro-nickel					
1947	29,993,263	—	—	£1	£3
1948	88,323,540	—	—	£1	£3
Second type—*new cypher on rev.*					
1949	41,335,515	—	—	£1	£3
1950	32,741,955	—	—	£1	£3
1950 Proof	17,513	—	—	—	£5
1951	40,399,491	—	—	£1	£3
1951 Proof	20,000	—	—	—	£5
1952	1,013,477	£2	£8	£15	£30

George VI first reverse

ELIZABETH II (1952–   )

	MINTAGE	F	VF	EF	UNC
1953	70,323,876	—	—	—	£2
1953 Proof	40,000	—	—	—	£4
1954	105,241,150	—	—	—	£3
1955	109,929,554	—	—	—	£1
1956	109,841,555	—	—	—	£1
1957	105,654,290	—	—	—	£1
1958	123,518,527	—	—	—	£3
1959	93,089,441	—	—	—	£1
1960	103,283,346	—	—	—	£2
1961	115,052,017	—	—	—	£2
1962	166,483,637	—	—	—	25p
1963	120,056,000	—	—	—	25p
1964	152,336,000	—	—	—	25p
1965	129,644,000	—	—	—	25p
1966	175,676,000	—	—	—	25p
1967	240,788,000	—	—	—	25p

George VI second reverse

GROATS OR FOURPENCES

DATE MINTAGE F VF EF UNC

WILLIAM IV (1831–37)

DATE	MINTAGE	F	VF	EF	UNC
*1836	—	£5	£12	£28	£50
1837	962,280	£5	£12	£28	£50

VICTORIA (1838–1901)

DATE	MINTAGE	F	VF	EF	UNC
1837	Extremely Rare Proofs or Patterns only				
1838	2,150,280	£5	£12	£30	£55
1839	1,461,240	£6	£14	£30	£55
1839 Proof	incl. above	—	—	—	£125
1840	1,496,880	£6	£12	£30	£55
1841	344,520	£6	£14	£35	£55
1842	724,680	£6	£14	£35	£55
1843	1,817640	£6	£14	£35	£55
1844	855,360	£6	£14	£35	£55
1845	914,760	£6	£14	£35	£55
1846	1,366,200	£6	£14	£35	£55
1847 7 over 6	225,720	£10	£25	£100	—
1848	712,800	£6	£14	£30	£50
1849	380,160	£6	£14	£30	£50
*1851	594,000	£18	£50	£160	£220
1852	31,300	£30	£85	£240	—
1853	11,880	£35	£100	£325	—
1853 Proof	incl. above	—	—	—	£300
1854	1,096,613	£6	£14	£35	£55
1855	646,041	£6	£14	£35	£55
1888 Jubilee Head	—	£6	£14	£35	£60

THREEPENCES

JAMES II (1685–88)

	F	VF	EF	
1685	£6	£16	£35	—
1686	£7	£16	£35	—
1687/6	£7	£16	£35	—
1688	£10	£20	£40	—

WILLIAM & MARY (1688–94)

	F	VF	EF	
*1689 First busts	£7	£16	£35	—
1690 —	£7	£16	£35	—
1691 —	£15	£30	£50	—
1691 Second busts	£10	£20	£45	—
1692 —	£10	£20	£45	—
1693 —	£8	£16	£40	—
1694 —	£10	£18	£35	—

WILLIAM III (1694–1702)

	F	VF	EF	
1698	£12	£28	£50	—
1699	£14	£30	£55	—
1700	£12	£28	£50	—
1701	£12	£22	£50	—

ANNE (1702–1714)

	F	VF	EF	
1703 First head	£10	£22	£45	—
1704 Second head	£7	£15	£33	—
1705 —	£7	£15	£33	—
1706 —	£8	£18	£40	—
1707 Third head	£7	£18	£40	—

DATE	MINTAGE	F	VF	EF	UNC
1708 Third head		£7	£18	£40	—
1708 —		£8	£18	£40	—
1709 —		£8	£18	£40	—
1710 —		£8	£18	£40	—
*1713 —		£8	£18	£40	—

GEORGE I (1714–27)

1717		£10	£22	£45	—
1721		£10	£22	£45	—
1723		£10	£25	£45	—
1727		£10	£25	£45	

GEORGE II (1727–60)

1729		£8	£16	£35	—
1731		£8	£16	£35	—
1732		£8	£16	£35	—
1735		£8	£16	£35	—
1737		£8	£16	£35	—
1739		£8	£16	£35	—
1740		£8	£16	£35	—
*1743		£8	£16	£35	—
1746		£8	£16	£35	—
1760		£8	£16	£35	—

GEORGE III (1760–1820)

1762		£5	£11	£22	—
1763		£5	£11	£22	—
1765		£100	£175	£450	—
1766		£5	£11	£25	—
1770		£6	£12	£25	—
1772		£5	£11	£25	—
1780		£5	£11	£25	—
1784		£5	£11	£25	—
1792		£12	£25	£40	—
1795		£5	£11	£25	—
1800		£5	£11	£25	—

WILLIAM IV (1830–37)

(issued for use in the West Indies)

1834		£6	£12	£35	£60
1835		£6	£12	£35	£60
1836		£6	£12	£35	£60
1837		£6	£12	£38	£65

VICTORIA (1837–1901)

YOUNG HEAD ISSUES

1838	—	£5	£18	£40	£60
1839	—	£5	£18	£45	£70
1940	—	£5	£18	£45	£70
1841	—	£5	£18	£50	£75
1842	—	£5	£18	£50	£75
1843	—	£5	£18	£35	£55
1844	—	£5	£18	£60	£80
*1845	1,314,720	£6	£18	£35	£60
1846	47,520	£6	£22	£70	£110
1849	126,720	£6	£18	£55	£90
1850	950,400	£5	£18	£40	£60
1851	479,065	£5	£18	£40	£60
1853	31,680	£15	£40	£80	£125
1854	1,467,246	£5	£18	£45	£60
1855	383,350	£5	£18	£45	£70
1856	1,013,760	£5	£18	£50	£70
1857	1,758,240	£5	£18	£50	£70
1858	1,441,440	£5	£18	£50	£60
1859	3,579,840	£5	£18	£40	£60

DATE	MINTAGE	F	VF	EF	UNC
1860	3,405,600	£5	£18	£35	£60
1861	3,294,720	£5	£18	£35	£60
1862	1,156,320	£5	£18	£40	£65
1863	950,400	£5	£18	£40	£75
1864	1,330,560	£5	£18	£35	£65
1865	1,742,400	£5	£18	£35	£80
1866	1,900,800	£5	£18	£30	£60
1867	712,800	£5	£18	£40	£70
1868	1,457,280	£	£18	£30	£65
1868 Rrittanniar error	incl. above	£50	£100	£225	—
1869	—	£20	£50	£100	£175
1870	1,283,218	£5	£15	£40	£55
1871	999,633	£5	£15	£35	£55
1872	1,293,271	£5	£15	£35	£55
1873	4,055,550	£5	£15	£35	£50
1874	4,427,031	£5	£15	£35	£50
1875	3,306,500	£5	£15	£35	£50
1876	1,834,389	£5	£15	£35	£50
1877	2,622,393	£5	£15	£35	£50
1878	2,419,975	£5	£15	£35	£50
1879	3,140,265	£5	£15	£35	£50
1880	1,610,069	£5	£15	£35	£50
1881	3,248,265	£5	£15	£35	£50
1882	472,965	£6	£20	£55	£100
1883	4,369,971	£5	£10	£28	£40
1884	3,322,424	£5	£10	£28	£40
1885	5,183,653	£5	£10	£28	£40
1886	6,152,669	£4	£8	£25	£40
1887	2,780,761	£4	£8	£25	£40

JUBILEE HEAD ISSUES

DATE	MINTAGE	F	VF	EF	UNC
1887	incl. above	£1	£3	£9	£18
1887 Proof	incl. above	—	—	—	£30
1888	518,199	£2	£5	£18	£35
*1889	4,587,010	£2	£5	£18	£35
1890	4,465,834	£2	£5	£18	£35
1891	6,323,027	£2	£5	£18	£35
1892	2,578,226	£2	£5	£18	£35
1893	3,067,243	£7	£24	£90	£140

OLD HEAD ISSUES

DATE	MINTAGE	F	VF	EF	UNC
1893	incl. above	£1	£3	£12	£25
1893 Proof	incl. above	—	—	—	£35
1894	1,608,603	£2	£6	£24	£40
1895	4,788,609	£1	£5	£20	£35
1896	4,598,442	£1	£5	£18	£30
1897	4,541,294	£1	£5	£18	£30
1898	4,567,177	£1	£5	£18	£30
*1899	6,246,281	£1	£5	£18	£30
1900	10,644,480	£1	£3	£16	£30
1901	6,098,400	£1	£3	£12	£25

EDWARD VII (1901–10)

DATE	MINTAGE	F	VF	EF	UNC
1902	8,268,480	£1	£2	£7	£15
1902 "Matt Proof"	incl. above	—	—	—	£15
1903	5,227,200	£1	£4	£20	£35
1904	3,627,360	£2	£7	£35	£70
1905	3,548,160	£1	£4	£25	£50
1906	3,152,160	£1	£4	£20	£45
1907	4,831,200	£1	£4	£20	£45
1908	8,157,600	£1	£2	£18	£30
1909	4,055,040	£1	£4	£20	£40
*1910	4,563,380	£1	£3	£14	£30

GEORGE V (1910–36)

First issue

DATE	MINTAGE	F	VF	EF	UNC
1911	5,841,084	—	—	£2	£8
1911 Proof	incl. above	—	—	—	£20
1912	8,932,825	—	—	£2	£8
1913	7,143,242	—	—	£2	£8
1914	6,733,584	—	—	£2	£8
1915	5,450,617	—	—	£2	£8
1916	18,555,201	—	—	£2	£7

DATE	MINTAGE	F	VF	EF	UNC
1917	21,662,490	—	—	£2	£7
7918	20,630,909	—	—	£2	£7
1919	16,845,687	—	—	£2	£7
1920	16,703,597	—	—	£2	£7
Second issue—*debased silver*					
1920	incl. above	—	—	£2	£7
1921	8,749,301	—	—	£2	£7
1922	7,979,998	—	—	£2	£7
1925	3,731,859	—	—	£5	£20
1926	4,107,910	—	—	£7	£20
Third issue—*Modified bust*					
1926	incl. above	—	—	£7	£18
Fourth issue—*new design (oakleaves)*					
1927 Proof only	15,022	—	—	—	£35
1928	1,302,106	£2	£6	£18	£40
1930	1,319,412	£1	£3	£8	£20
1931	6,251,936	—	—	£2	£5
1932	5,887,325	—	—	£2	£5
1933	5,578,541	—	—	£2	£5
1934	7,405,954	—	—	£2	£5
1935	7,027,654	—	—	£2	£5
1936	3,328,670	—	—	£2	£5

GEORGE VI (1936–52)

Silver

1937	8,148,156	—	—	£1	£3
1937 Proof	26,402	—	—	—	£5
1938	6,402,473	—	—	£1	£3
1939	1,355,860	—	—	£2	£6
1940	7,914,401	—	—	£1	£3
1941	7,979,411	—	—	£1	£3
1942	4,144,051	£2	£5	£12	£30
1943	1,397,220	£2	£5	£12	£30
1944	2,005,553	£4	£12	£35	£70
1945	Only one known				

Brass

1937	45,707,957	—	—	£1	£3
1937 Proof	26,402	—	—	—	£3
1938	14,532,332	—	—	£1	£8
1939	5,603,021	—	—	£2	£16
1940	12,636,018	—	—	£1	£6
1941	60,239,489	—	—	£1	£4
1942	103,214,400	—	—	£1	£5
1943	101,702,400	—	—	£1	£5
1944	69,760,000	—	—	£1	£6
1945	33,942,466	—	—	£1	£4
1946	620,734	£1.50	£10	£55	£150
1948	4,230,400	—	—	—	£6
1949	464,000	£2.50	£7	£50	£150
1950	1,600,000	—	£1	£7	£20
1950 Proof	17,513	—	—	—	£5
1951	1,184,000	—	£1	£7	£25
1951 Proof	20,000	—	—	—	£5
1952	25,494,400	—	—	—	£4

ELIZABETH II (1952–   )

1953	30,618,000	—	—	—	£1
1953 Proof	40,000	—	—	—	£5
1954	41,720,000	—	—	—	£4
1955	41,075,200	—	—	—	£4
1956	36,801,600	—	—	—	£4
1957	24,294,500	—	—	—	£3
1958	20,504,000	—	—	—	£6
1959	28,499,200	—	—	—	£3
1960	83,078,400	—	—	—	£2
1961	41,102,400	—	—	—	£1
1962	51,545,600	—	—	—	£1
1963	39,482,866	—	—	—	£1
1964	44,867,200	—	—	—	—
1965	27,160,000	—	—	—	—
1966	53,160,000	—	—	—	—
1967	151,780,800	—	—	—	—

TWO PENCE

DATE	F	VF	EF	UNC

CHARLES II (1660–85)

	F	VF	EF	UNC
1668	£20	£35	£85	—
1670	£15	£30	£55	—
1671	£15	£30	£55	—
1672	£15	£30	£55	—
1673	£15	£30	£55	—
1674	£15	£30	£55	—
1675	£15	£30	£55	—
1676	£15	£30	£55	—
1677	£15	£30	£55	—
1678	£15	£30	£55	—
1679	£15	£30	£55	—
1680	£15	£30	£55	—
1681	£15	£30	£55	—
1682	£15	£30	£55	—
1683	£15	£30	£55	—
1684	£15	£30	£55	—

JAMES II (1685–88)

	F	VF	EF	UNC
1686	£15	£30	£55	—
1687	£15	£30	£55	—
1687 ERA error on rev.	£22	£50	£100	—
1688	£15	£30	£55	—

WILLIAM & MARY (1688–94)

	F	VF	EF	UNC
1689	£15	£30	£55	—
1691	£15	£30	£55	—
1692	£15	£30	£55	—
1693	£15	£30	£55	—
1694	£20	£35	£75	—
1694 MARLA error on obv.	£22	£38	£85	—
1694 HI error on rev.	£22	£38	£85	—

WILLIAM III (1694–1702)

	F	VF	EF	UNC
1698	£20	£35	£65	—
1699	£20	£30	£60	—
1700	£20	£30	£60	—
1701	£20	£30	£60	—

ANNE (1702–14)

	F	VF	EF	UNC
1703 (pre-Union with Scotland)	£16	£30	£65	—
1704	£15	£25	£55	—
1705	£15	£25	£55	—
1706	£15	£25	£55	—
1707 (post-Union)	£15	£25	£55	—
1708	£16	£28	£60	—
1709	£16	£28	£60	—
1711	£15	£25	£55	—
1713	£15	£25	£55	—

GEORGE I (1714–27)

	F	VF	EF	UNC
1717	£15	£25	£50	—
1721	£15	£25	£50	—
1723	£16	£35	£65	—
1726	£15	£25	£50	—
1727	£15	£30	£55	—

DATE	F	VF	EF	UNC

GEORGE II (1727–60)

	F	VF	EF	UNC
1729	£12	£28	£45	—
1731	£15	£28	£45	—
1732	£15	£28	£45	—
1735	£15	£28	£45	—
1737	£15	£28	£45	—
1739	£15	£28	£45	—
1740	£15	£28	£45	—
1743	£15	£28	£45	—
1746	£15	£28	£45	—
1756	£15	£28	£45	—
1759	£15	£28	£45	—
1760	£15	£28	£45	—

GEORGE III (1760–1820)

	F	VF	EF	UNC
1763 Young Laureated bust	£18	£25	£48	—
1765 —	£80	£250	£600	—
1766 —	£15	£25	£40	—
1772 —	£15	£25	£40	—
1776 —	£15	£25	£40	—
1780 —	£15	£25	£40	—
1784 —	£15	£25	£40	—
1786 —	£15	£25	£40	—
1792 Small draped bust	£18	£36	£65	—
1795 —	£15	£18	£30	—

It is generally accepted that later issues were only produced for inclusion with the Maundy sets, q.v., except for those listed below

	F	VF	EF	UNC
1797 "Cartwheel"	£18	£37	£175	£500
1797 Copper Proof	—	—	—	£500

Proofs also exist in various other metals

VICTORIA (1837–1901)

For use in the Colonies

	F	VF	EF	UNC
1838	£4	£10	£18	£30
1848	£4	£12	£20	£35

THREE-HALFPENCE

WILLIAM IV (1830–37)

For use in the Colonies

	F	VF	EF	UNC
1834	£6	£14	£30	£70
1835 over 4	£6	£14	£30	£70
1836	£8	£16	£35	£75
1837	£12	£35	£100	£175

VICTORIA (1837–1901)

For use in the Colonies

	F	VF	EF	UNC
1838	£6	£15	£30	£55
1839	£6	£15	£30	£55
1840	£7	£18	£40	£75
1841	£6	£15	£30	£55
1842	£6	£18	£35	£70
1843	£6	£15	£30	£50
1860	£9	£20	£60	£100
1862	£9	£20	£60	£100

PENNIES

DATE	MINTAGE	F	VF	EF	UNC

CHARLES II (1660–85)

Silver up to 1781

DATE	MINTAGE	F	VF	EF	UNC
1670		£8	£18	£40	—
1671		£8	£18	£40	—
1672/1		£8	£18	£40	—
1673		£8	£18	£40	—
1674		£8	£18	£40	—
1675		£8	£18	£40	—
1676		£10	£20	£45	—
1677		£8	£18	£40	—
1678		£8	£18	£40	—
1679		£15	£30	£55	—
1680		£8	£18	£40	—
1681		£10	£20	£48	—
1682		£10	£20	£45	—
1683		£8	£18	£40	—
1684		£10	£20	£45	—

Charles II

James II

JAMES II (1685–88)

DATE	MINTAGE	F	VF	EF	UNC
1685		£7	£14	£35	—

WILLIAM & MARY (1688–94)

DATE	MINTAGE	F	VF	EF	UNC
1690		£8	£15	£35	—

George II

GEORGE I (1714–27)

DATE	MINTAGE	F	VF	EF	UNC
1716		£7	£18	£40	—
1718		£7	£18	£40	—
1720		£7	£18	£40	—
1725		£8	£20	£45	—
1726		£8	£20	£45	—

GEORGE II (1727–60)

DATE	MINTAGE	F	VF	EF	UNC
1750		£7	£15	£35	—
1752		£7	£15	£35	—
1753		£7	£15	£35	—
1754		£7	£15	£35	—
1755		£7	£15	£35	—
1756		£7	£15	£35	—
1757		£7	£15	£35	—
1758		£7	£15	£35	—
1759		£7	£15	£35	—

GEORGE III (1760–1820)

DATE	MINTAGE	F	VF	EF	UNC
1770		£6	£12	£30	
1776		£6	£12	£30	—
1779		£6	£12	£30	—
1781		£6	£12	£30	—

Copper

DATE	MINTAGE	F	VF	EF	UNC
*1797 "Cartwheel" Penny	8,601,600	£10	£25	£110	£325
1806 Third type	unknown	£4	£11	£55	£120
1807 —	unknown	£4	£11	£55	£125
1808 —				Only one known	

"Cartwheel" penny

DATE	MINTAGE	F	VF	EF	UNC

GEORGE IV (1820–30)

1825	1,075,200	£8	£30	£80	£220
*1826 (varieties)	5,913,600	£8	£30	£80	£220
1826 Proof	—	—	—	£90	£150
1827	1,451,520	£45	£130	£650	£1400

WILLIAM IV (1830–37)

1831(varieties)	806,400	£12	£30	£115	£250
1831 Proof	—	—	—	£100	£180
1834	322,560	£12	£32	£120	£270
1837	174,720	£12	£32	£120	£270

VICTORIA (1837–1901)

YOUNG HEAD ISSUES
Copper

1839 Proof	unrecorded	—	—	—	£175
*1841	913,920	£6	£12	£45	£100
1843	483,840	£20	£70	£200	£375
1844	215,040	£6	£15	£45	£110
1845	322,560	£7	£18	£75	£125
1846	483,840	£7	£18	£75	£125
1847	430,080	£5	£15	£60	£110
1848	161,280	£5	£15	£60	£95
1849	268,800	£30	£135	£320	£550
1851	268,800	£8	£18	£75	£150
1853	1,021,440	£4	£10	£40	£70
1853 Proof	—	—	—	—	£300
1854	6,720,000	£4	£10	£40	£70
1855	5,273,856	£4	£10	£40	£70
1856	1,212,288	£10	£35	£100	£170
1857	752,640	£4	£14	£40	£85
1858	1,599,040	£4	£12	£40	£80
1859	1,075,200	£5	£18	£50	£115
1860/59	32,256	£300	£475	£1200	—

Bronze

1860 Beaded border	5,053,440	£4	£8	£35	£60
1860 Toothed border	incl. above	£4	£10	£45	£80
1861	36,449,280	£3	£8	£35	£60
1862	50,534,400	£3	£7	£32	£60
1863	28,062,720	£3	£7	£30	£60
1864 Plain 4	3,440,640	£8	£35	£200	£300
1864 Crosslet 4	*incl. above*	£8	£35	£200	£300
1865	8,601,600	£4	£12	£35	£70
1866	9,999,360	£4	£12	£35	£70
1867	5,483,520	£4	£12	£35	£70
*1868	1,182,720	£8	£32	£100	£175
1869	2,580,480	£35	£110	£375	£625
1870	5,695,022	£6	£20	£80	£150
1871	1,290,318	£22	£90	£190	£450
1872	8,494,572	£5	£15	£40	£75
1873	8,494,200	£5	£15	£40	£75
1874	5,621,865	£5	£15	£40	£75
1874 H	6,666,240	£5	£15	£40	£75
1875	10,691,040	£5	£15	£40	£75
1875 H	752,640	£25	£80	£225	£425
1876 H	11,074,560	£5	£12	£45	£75
1877	9,624,747	£5	£14	£45	£75
1878	2,764,470	£5	£14	£45	£75
1879	7,666,476	£3	£12	£40	£70
1880	3,000,831	£4	£12	£35	£65

DATE	MINTAGE	F	VF	EF	UNC
1881	2,302,362	£5	£12	£40	£70
1881 H	3,763,200	£5	£12	£35	£60
1882 H	7,526,400	£5	£12	£35	£55
1882 No H			Extremely Rare		
1883	6,237,438	£5	£12	£35	£65
1884	11,702,802	£5	£12	£35	£75
1885	7,145,862	£4	£11	£40	£65
1886	6,087,759	£4	£11	£40	£65
1887	5,315,085	£4	£11	£40	£65
1888	5,125,020	£4	£11	£40	£65
1889	12,559,737	£4	£11	£40	£65
1890	15,330,840	£4	£11	£40	£65
1891	17,885,961	£4	£11	£40	£65
1892	10,501,671	£4	£11	£40	£65
1893	8,161,737	£4	£11	£40	£65
1894	3,883,452	£6	£18	£50	£95

OLD HEAD ISSUES

1895 Trident 2mm from (PENNY)	5,395,830	£4	£18	£70	£200
1895 Trident 1mm from P	incl. above	—	£2	£12	£35
1896	24,147,156	—	£2	£14	£33
*1897	20,756,620	—	£2	£14	£33
1898	14,296,836	—	£2	£15	£35
1899	26,441,069	—	£2	£12	£35
1900	31,778,109	—	£2	£12	£25
1901	22,205,568	—	£2	£7	£14

EDWARD VII (1901–10)

1902	26,976,768	—	£1	£8	£20
1902 "Low tide"	incl. above	—	£5	£20	£50
1903	21,415,296	—	£3	£12	£40
1904	12,913,152	—	£3	£12	£40
905	17,783,808	—	£3	£12	£40
1906	37,989,504	—	£3	£12	£40
1907	47,322,240	—	£3	£12	£40
*1908	31,506,048	—	£3	£12	£45
1909	19,617,024	—	£3	£15	£45
1910	29,549,184	—	£3	£12	£35

GEORGE V (1910–36)

1911	23,079,168	—	£3	£12	£32
1912	48,306,048	—	£3	£12	£32
*1912 H	16,800,000	—	£3	£25	£70
1913	65,497,812	—	£3	£12	£40
1914	50,820,997	—	£3	£12	£40
1915	47,310,807	—	£3	£12	£40
1916	86,411,165	—	£3	£12	£40
1917	107,905,436	—	£3	£12	£40
1918	84,227,372	—	£3	£12	£40
1918 H	3,660,800	£1	£8	£70	£240
1918 KN	incl. above	£7	£50	£225	£760
1919	113,761,090	—	£2	£12	£40
1919 H	5,209,600	£1	£10	£70	£240
1919 KN	incl. above	£8	£60	£240	£750
1920	124,693,485	—	£2	£12	£25
1921	129,717,693	—	£2	£12	£25
1922	16,346,711	—	£2	£12	£35
1926	4,498,519	—	£6	£20	£70
1926 Modified effigy	incl above	£7	£25	£300	£500
1927	60,989,561	—	£2	£8	£25
1928	50,178,00	—	£2	£8	£25
1929	49,132,800	—	£2	£8	£25
1930	29,097,600	—	£2	£12	£40

DATE	MINTAGE	F	VF	EF	UNC
1931	19,843,200	—	£2	£8	£30
1932	8,277,600	—	£2	£9	£30
1933			Only 7 examples known		
1934	13,965,600	—	£2	£8	£30
1935	56,070,000	—	—	£2	£9
1936	154,296,000	—	—	£2	£8

GEORGE VI (1936–52)

1937	88,896,000	—	—	—	£3
1937 Proof	26,402	—	—	—	£5
1938	121,560,00	—	—	—	£3
1939	55,560,000	—	—	—	£4
1940	42,284,400	—	—	—	£6
1944	42,600,000	—	—	—	£6
1945	79,531,200	—	—	—	£5
1946	66,855,600	—	—	—	£3
1947	52,220,400	—	—	—	£3
1948	63,961,200	—	—	—	£3
1949	14,324,400	—	—	—	£3
1950	240,000	£2.50	£6	£12	£18
1950 Proof	17,513	—	—	—	£14
1951	120,000	£5	£8	£16	£25
1951 Proof	20,000	—	—	—	£16

ELIZABETH II (1952–   )

*1953	1,308,400	—	—	£1	£4
1953 Proof	40,000	—	—	—	£6
1954			Only one known		
1961	48,313,400	—	—	—	£1
1962	143,308,600	—	—	—	50p
1963	125,235,600	—	—	—	50p
1964	153,294,000	—	—	—	50p
1965	121,310,400	—	—	—	50p
1966	165,739,200	—	—	—	50p
1967	654,564,000	—	—	—	—

Later issues are included in the Decimal section.

HALFPENNIES

CHARLES II (1660–85)

1672	£35	£110	£475	—
1673	£35	£110	£475	—
1675	£35	£90	£450	—

JAMES II (1685–88)

1685 (tin)	£100	£220	£1000	—
1686 (tin)	£110	£240	£1000	—
1687 (tin)	£100	£220	£1000	—

WILLIAM & MARY (1688–94)

1689 (tin) Small draped busts	£300	—	—	—
1690 (tin) Large cuirassed busts edge dated	£110	£265	£1000	—
1691 (tin) date on edge and in exergue	£110	£265	£1000	—
1692 (tin) —	£110	£265	£1000	—
*1694 (copper)	£28	£85	£625	—

DATE	F	VF	EF	UNC

WILLIAM III (1694–1702)

	F	VF	EF	UNC
1695 First issue (date in exergue)	£25	£80	£425	—
1696 —	£25	£90	£475	—
1697 —	£25	£80	£450	—
1698 —	£25	£80	£525	—
1698 Second issue (date in legend)	£28	£110	—	—
1699 —	£25	£80	£450	—
1699 Third issue (date in exergue)				
(Britannia r. hand on knee)	£25	£80	£450	—
1700 —	£25	£80	£425	—
1701 —	£25	£80	£425	—

GEORGE I (1714–27)

	F	VF	EF	UNC
*1717 "Dump" issue	£40	£110	£375	—
1718 —	£20	£55	£270	—
1719 Second issue	£20	£55	£270	—
1720 —	£20	£55	£270	—
1721 —	£20	£55	£270	—
1722 —	£20	£55	£270	—
1723 —	£20	£55	£270	—
1724 —	£20	£55	£270	—

GEORGE II (1727–60)

	F	VF	EF	UNC
1729 Young head	£18	£50	£160	—
1730 —	£15	£45	£150	—
1731 —	£15	£45	£150	—
1732 —	£15	£45	£150	—
1733 —	£15	£45	£150	—
1734 —	£15	£45	£150	—
1735 —	£15	£35	£150	—
1736 —	£15	£35	£135	—
1737 —	£15	£35	£135	—
1738 —	£15	£35	£135	—
1739 —	£15	£35	£135	—
1740 Old head	£10	£35	£135	—
1742 —	£10	£35	£135	—
1743 —	£10	£35	£135	—
1744 —	£10	£35	£135	—
1745 —	£10	£35	£135	—
1746 —	£10	£35	£135	—
1747 —	£10	£35	£135	—
1748 —	£10	£35	£135	—
1749 —	£10	£35	£135	—
1750 —	£10	£35	£135	—
1751 —	£10	£35	£135	—
1752 —	£10	£35	£135	—
1753 —	£10	£35	£135	—
1754 —	£8	£28	£130	—

GEORGE III (1760–1820)

First type—Royal Mint

	F	VF	EF	UNC
1770	£10	£25	£120	—
1771	£8	£24	£110	—
1772 Error Geor IVS	£35	£70	£160	—
1772	£8	£24	£110	—
1773	£8	£24	£110	—
1774	£8	£24	£110	—
*1775	£10	£28	£120	—

Second type—Soho Mint

DATE	MINTAGE	F	VF	EF	UNC
*1799		£2	£6	£30	£65
Third type					
1806		£2	£6	£30	£65
1807		£2	£6	£30	£66

GEORGE IV (1820–30)

1825	215,040	£8	£28	£70	£125
1826 (varieties)	9,031,630	£7	£24	£45	£90
1826 Proof	—	—	—	£80	£110
1827	5,376,000	£8	£25	£65	£110

WILLIAM IV (1830–37)

1831	806,400	£7	£22	£65	£120
1831 Proof	—	—	—	—	£125
1834	537,600	£7	£22	£65	£120
1837	349,440	£7	£22	£66	£120

VICTORIA (1837–1901)

YOUNG HEAD ISSUES
Copper

1838	456,960	£4	£14	£40	£70
1839 Proof	268,800	—	—	—	£120
1841	1,0745,200	£4	£14	£40	£70
1843	967,680	£8	£25	£65	£130
1844	1,075,200	£4	£15	£40	£70
1845	1,075,200	£22	£65	£200	£400
1846	860,160	£6	£15	£35	£65
1847	725,640	£6	£15	£35	£65
1848	322,560	£6	£15	£35	£65
1851	215,040	£5	£12	£35	£55
1852	637,056	£5	£12	£35	£55
1853	1,559,040	£4	£7	£20	£50
1853 over 2	*incl. above*	£4	£8	£20	£50
1853 Proof	—	—	—	—	£200
1854	12,354,048	£4	£8	£30	£50
1855	1,455,837	£4	£8	£30	£50
1856	1,942,080	£6	£14	£40	£75
1857	1,82,720	£5	£12	£30	£60
1858	2,472,960	£4	£10	£30	£55
1859	1,290,240	£5	£15	£35	£75
1860	*unrecorded*			Extremely rare	

Victoria copper halfpenny

Bronze

1860	6,630,400	£3	£9	£30	£50
1861	54,118,400	£3	£9	£30	£50
1862	61,107,200	£3	£9	£30	£50
1863	15,948,800	£3	£9	£30	£50
1864	537,600	£3	£9	£35	£60
1865	8,064,000	£4	£15	£50	£75
1866	2,508,800	£4	£9	£35	£60
1867	2,508,800	£5	£15	£45	£75
1868	3,046,400	£4	£10	£40	£70
1869	3,225,600	£7	£30	£60	£125
1870	4,350,739	£5	£15	£50	£90
1871	1,075,280	£25	£70	£140	£275
1872	4,659,410	£4	£10	£35	£60
1873	3,404,880	£4	£10	£35	£60
1874	1,347,655	£5	£20	£60	£110
1874 H	5,017,600	£3	£10	£30	£60
1875	5,430,815	£3	£8	£30	£60

Victoria bronze halfpenny

DATE	MINTAGE	F	VF	EF	UNC
1875 H	1,254,400	£4	£10	£35	£70
1876 H	5,809,600	£4	£10	£35	£65
1877	5,209,505	£3	£10	£30	£60
1878	1,425,535	£5	£18	£50	£90
1879	3,582,545	£3	£10	£30	£55
1880	2,423,465	£4	£12	£40	£70
1881	2,007,515	£4	£12	£35	£65
1881 H	1,792,000	£3	£10	£30	£45
1882 H	4,480,000	£3	£10	£30	£45
1883	3,000,725	£3	£10	£30	£45
1884	6,989,580	£3	£10	£30	£45
1885	8,600,574	£3	£10	£30	£45
1886	8,586,155	£3	£10	£25	£45
1887	10,701,305	£3	£10	£25	£45
1888	6,814,670	£3	£10	£25	£45
1889	7,748,234	£3	£10	£25	£45
1890	11,254,235	£3	£10	£25	£45
1891	13,192,260	£3	£10	£25	£45
1892	2,478,335	£3	£10	£25	£45
1893	7,229,344	£3	£10	£25	£45
1894	1,767,635	£5	£12	£30	£65

OLD HEAD ISSUES

1895	3,032,154	£1	£4	£15	£35
1896	9,142,500	£1	£4	£10	£30
1897	8,690,315	£1	£4	£10	£30
1898	8,595,180	£1	£4	£10	£30
1899	12,108,001	£1	£4	£10	£30
1900	13,805,190	£1	£4	£10	£25
1901	11,127,360	£1	£2	£6	£12

EDWARD VII (1901–10)

1902	13,672,960	£2	£4	£8	£20
1902 "Low tide"	*incl. above*	£5	£12	£40	£75
*1903	11,450,880	£2	£5	£18	£35
1904	8,131,200	£2	£5	£18	£35
1905	10,124,800	£2	£5	£18	£35
1906	16,849,280	£2	£5	£18	£35
1907	16,849,280	£2	£5	£18	£35
1908	16,620,800	£2	£5	£18	£35
1909	8,279,040	£2	£5	£18	£35
1910	10,769,920	£2	£5	£18	£35

GEORGE V (1910–36)

1911	12,570,880	—	£3	£12	£30
1912	21,185,920	—	£2	£12	£30
1913	17,476,480	—	£2	£14	£35
1914	20,289,111	—	£2	£12	£30
1915	21,563,040	£1	£3	£12	£30
1916	39,386,143	—	£2	£12	£30
1917	38,245,436	—	£2	£12	£30
1918	22,321,072	—	£2	£12	£30
1919	28,104,001	—	£2	£12	£30
1920	35,146,793	—	£2	£12	£30
1921	28,027,293	—	£2	£12	£30
*1922	10,734,964	—	£2	£14	£35
1923	12,266,282	—	£2	£12	£30
1924	13,971,038	—	£2	£10	£30
1925	12,216,123	—	£2	£10	£30
1925 Modified effigy	*incl. above*	£2	£5	£18	£40
1926	6,172,306	—	£2	£10	£30

DATE	MINTAGE	F	VF	EF	UNC
1927	15,589,622	—	£2	£10	£30
1928	20,935,200	—	£2	£8	£18
1929	25,680,000	—	£2	£8	£25
1930	12,532,800	—	£2	£8	£25
1931	16,137,600	—	£2	£8	£25
1932	14,448,000	—	£2	£8	£25
1933	10,560,000	—	£2	£8	£25
1934	7,704,000	—	£2	£12	£30
1935	12,180,000	—	£1	£6	£15
1936	23,008,800	—	£1	£5	£8

GEORGE VI (1936–52)

1937	24,504,000	—	—	£1	£2
1937 Proof	26,402	—	—	£1	£5
1938	40,320,000	—	—	£1	£4
1939	28,924,800	—	—	£1	£4
1940	32,162,400	—	—	£1	£5
1941	45,120,000	—	—	£1	£5
1942	71,908,800	—	—	£1	£3
1943	76,200,000	—	—	£1	£3
1944	81,840,000	—	—	£1	£3
1945	57,000,000	—	—	£1	£3
1946	22,725,600	—	—	£1	£5
1947	21,266,400	—	—	£1	£3
1948	26,947,200	—	—	£1	£2
*1949	24,744,000	—	—	£1	£2
1950	24,153,600	—	—	£1	£4
1950 Proof	17,513	—	—	£1	£5
1951	14,868,000	—	—	£1	£5
1951 Proof	20,000	—	—	£1	£5
1952	33,78,400	—	—	£1	£2

ELIZABETH II (1952–)

1953	8,926,366	—	—	—	£1
1953 Proof	40,000	—	—	—	£3
*1954	19,375,000	—	—	—	£3
1955	18,799,200	—	—	—	£3
1956	21,799,200	—	—	—	£3
1957	43,684,800	—	—	—	£1
1958	62,318,400	—	—	—	£1
1959	79,176,000	—	—	—	£1
1960	41,340,000	—	—	—	£1
1962	41,779,200	—	—	—	£1
1963	45,036,000	—	—	—	20p
1964	78,583,200	—	—	—	20p
1965	98,083,200	—	—	—	20p
1966	95,289,600	—	—	—	20p
1967	146,491,200	—	—	—	10p

Later issues are included in the Decimal section.

FARTHINGS

OLIVER CROMWELL

(copper) Draped bust, shield rev. (variations)
Undated .... Extremely rare

CHARLES II (1660–85)

1672 (copper) .... £20 £45 £220 —

DATE	MINTAGE	F	VF	EF	UNC
*1673 (copper)		£20	£45	£220	—
1674 (copper)		£20	£45	£220	—
1675 (copper)		£20	£45	£220	—
1679 (copper)		£25	£55	£270	—
1684 (tin) with date on edge		£150	£375	—	—
1685 (tin) —		£300	—	—	—

JAMES II (1685–88)

		F	VF	EF	UNC
1684 (tin) Cuirassed bust		£60	£220	£800	—
1685 (tin) —		£70	£202	£750	—
1686 (tin) —		£75	£220	£800	—
1687 (tin) —			Extremely rare		
1687 (tin) Draped bust		£150	£350	—	—

WILLIAM & MARY (1688–94)

		F	VF	EF	UNC
1689 (tin) Small draped busts		£300	—	—	—
1689 (tin) — with edge date 1690			Extremely rare		
1690 (tin) Large cuirassed busts		£100	£225	£850	—
1690 (tin) — with edge date 1689		£200	—	—	—
1691 (tin) —		£125	£325	—	—
1692 (tin) —		£100	£225	£900	—
1694 (copper) —		£24	£65	£500	—

WILLIAM III (1694–1702)

		F	VF	EF	UNC
1695 First issue (date in exergue)		£22	£75	£400	—
1696 —		£22	£75	£400	—
1697 —		£22	£77	£400	—
1698 —		£60	£150	—	—
1698 Second issue (date in legend)		£25	£90	£475	—
1699 First issue		£25	£85	£450	—
1699 Second issue		£25	£85	£475	—
1700 First issue		£25	£80	£425	—

ANNE (1702–14)

		F	VF	EF	UNC
*1714		£90	£240	£400	—

GEORGE I (1714–27)

		F	VF	EF	UNC
1717 First small "Dump" issue		£32	£110	£400	—
1719 Second issue		£20	£50	£220	—
1720 —		£20	£50	£220	—
1721 —		£20	£50	£200	—
1722 —		£20	£50	£200	—
1723 —		£20	£50	£200	—
1724 —		£20	£50	£200	—

GEORGE II (1727–60)

		F	VF	EF	UNC
1730 Young head		£14	£40	£160	—
1731 —		£14	£40	£160	—
1732 —		£14	£40	£160	—
1733 —		£14	£40	£160	—
1734 —		£10	£30	£150	—
1735 —		£10	£30	£140	—
1736 —		£10	£30	£150	—
1737 —		£9	£30	£150	—
1739 —		£9	£30	£140	—
1741 Old Head		£8	£30	£130	—
1744 —		£8	£30	£130	—

DATE	MINTAGE	F	VF	EF	UNC
1746 —		£8	£30	£130	—
1749 —		£8	£30	£130	—
1750 —		£8	£22	£125	—
1754 —		£7	£18	£120	—

GEORGE III (1760–1820)

1771 First (London) issue		£15	£35	£140	—
1773 —		£11	£25	£90	—
1774 —		£8	£25	£100	—
1775 —		£8	£25	£110	—
1797 Second (Soho Mint) issue			Patterns only		
*1799 Third (Soho Mint) issue		£2	£7	£30	£65
*1806 Fourth (Soho Mint) issue		£2	£7	£30	£60
1807 —		£2	£7	£30	£60

George III third Soho Mint issue

GEORGE IV (1820–30)

	MINTAGE	F	VF	EF	UNC
1821 First bust (laureate, draped), first reverse (date in exergue) .	2,688,000	£2	£8	£35	£60
*1822 —	5,924,350	£2	£8	£35	£60
1823 —	2,365,440	£2	£8	£35	£65
1825 —	4,300.800	£2	£8	£35	£65
1826 —	6,666,240	£2	£8	£35	£55
1826 Second bust (couped, date below), second reverse (ornament in exergue)	incl. above	£2	£8	£35	£75
1826 — Proof	—	—	—	£70	£120
1827 —	2,365,440	£2	£9	£35	£80
1828 —	2,365,440	£2	£9	£35	£80
1829 —	1,505,280	£2	£10	£40	£90
1830 —	2,365,440	£2	£8	£35	£80

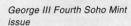

George III Fourth Soho Mint issue

WILLIAM IV (1830–37)

	MINTAGE	F	VF	EF	UNC
1831	2,688,000	£5	£12	£35	£80
1831 Proof	—	—	—	—	£100
1834	1,935,360	£5	£12	£35	£80
1835	1.720,320	£5	£12	£30	£75
1836	1,290.240	£5	£12	£40	£80
1837	3.010,560	£5	£12	£35	£80

VICTORIA (1837–1901)

YOUNG HEAD ISSUES

	MINTAGE	F	VF	EF	UNC
1838	591,360	£4	£12	£35	£60
1839	4,300,800	£4	£12	£35	£60
1839 Proof	—	—	—	—	£140
1840	3,010,560	£4	£12	£35	£50
1841	1,720,320	£4	£12	£35	£50
1842	1,290,240	£6	£18	£40	£85
1843	4,085,760	£4	£10	£35	£55
1844	430,080	£30	£75	£175	£450
1845	3,225,600	£4	£10	£35	£60
1846	2,580,480	£5	£16	£40	£75
*1847	3,879,720	£4	£10	£35	£60
1848	1,290,240	£4	£10	£35	£60
1849	645,120	£10	£30	£60	£125
1850	430,080	£4	£10	£35	£55
1851	1,935,360	£5	£15	£45	£75
1852	822,528	£5	£15	£40	£70
1853	1,028,628	£3	£7	£30	£45
1853 Proof	—	—	—	—	£250

DATE	MINTAGE	F	VF	EF	UNC
1854	6,504,960	£3	£8	£30	£45
1855	3,440,640	£3	£8	£30	£45
1856	1,771,392	£6	£12	£45	£75
1857	1,075,200	£3	£10	£35	£50
1858	1,720,320	£3	£8	£35	£45
1859	1,290,240	£6	£20	£55	£110
1860	*unrecorded*			Extremely	rare

YOUNG OR "BUN" HEAD (BRONZE) ISSUES

1860 Toothed border	2,867,200	£1	£5	£20	£40
1860 Beaded border	*incl. above*	£2	£5	£20	£40
1861	8,601,600	£1	£5	£20	£40
1862	14,336,000	£1	£5	£20	£40
1863	1,433,600	£18	£45	£130	£200
1864	2,508,800	£1	£5	£20	£40
1865	4,659,200	£1	£5	£20	£40
1866	3,584,000	£1	£5	£20	£40
1867	5,017,600	£1	£5	£20	£40
1868	4,851,210	£1	£5	£20	£40
1869	3,225,600	£1	£6	£25	£50
1872	2,150,400	£1	£5	£20	£40
1873	3,225,620	£1	£5	£20	£40
1874 H	3,584,000	£1	£5	£20	£40
1874 H both Gs over G	*incl. above*	£70	£150	£300	—
1875	712,760	£2	£8	£32	£60
1875 H	6,092,800	£1	£5	£20	£50
1876 H	1,175,200	£2	£9	£28	£65
*1878	4,008,540	£1	£4	£18	£40
1879	3,977,180	£1	£4	£18	£40
1880	1,842,710	£1	£4	£18	£40
1881	3,494,670	£1	£4	£18	£40
1881 H	1,792,000	£1	£4	£18	£35
1882 H	1,792,000	£1	£5	£18	£35
1883	1,128,680	£3	£12	£35	£55
1884	5,782,000	£1	£4	£16	£30
1885	5,442,308	£1	£4	£16	£30
1886	7.707,790	£1	£4	£16	£30
1887	1,340,800	£1	£4	£16	£30
1888	1,887,250	£1	£4	£16	£30
1890	2,133,070	£1	£4	£16	£30
1891	4,959,690	£1	£4	£16	£30
1892	887,240	£1	£7	£28	£50
1893	3,904,320	£1	£4	£16	£30
1894	2,396,770	£1	£4	£16	£30
1895	2,852,852	£10	£25	£60	£110

OLD HEAD ISSUES

1895 Bright finish	*incl. above*	£1	£2	£12	£18
1896 —	3,668,610	£1	£2	£12	£18
1897 —	4,579,800	£1	£2	£12	£18
1897 Dark finish	*incl. above*	£1	£2	£12	£18
1898 —	4,010,080	£1	£2	£12	£18
1899 —	3,864,616	£1	£2	£12	£18
1900 —	5,969,317	£1	£2	£12	£18
*1901 —	8,016,460	£1	£2	£6	£12

EDWARD VII (1901–10)

1902	5,125,120	50p	£1	£7	£12
1903	5,331,200	50p	£1	£7	£14
1904	3,628,800	£1	£2	£10	£20
1905	4,076,800	50p	£1	£7	£19
1906	5,340,160	50p	£1	£7	£14

DATE	MINTAGE	F	VF	EF	UNC
*1907	4,399,360	50p	£1	£7	£14
1908	4,264,960	50p	£1	£7	£14
1909	8,852,480	50p	£1	£7	£14
1910	2,298,400	£1	£6	£14	£40

GEORGE V (1910–36)

1911	5,196,800	25p	50p	£4	£10
1912	7,669,760	25p	50p	£4	£10
1913	4,184,320	25p	50p	£4	£10
1914	6,126,988	25p	50p	£4	£10
1915	7,129,255	25p	50p	£4	£10
1916	10,993,325	25p	50p	£4	£10
*1917	21,434,844	25p	50p	£4	£10
1918	19,362,818	25p	50p	£4	£10
1919	15,089,425	25p	50p	£4	£10
1920	11,480,536	25p	50p	£4	£8
1921	9,469,097	25p	50p	£4	£8
1922	9,956,983	25p	50p	£4	£8
1923	8,034,457	25p	50p	£4	£8
1924	8,733,414	25p	50p	£4	£8
1925	12,634,697	25p	50p	£4	£8
1926 Modified effigy	9,792,397	25p	50p	£4	£8
1927	7,868,355	25p	50p	£4	£8
1928	11,625,600	25p	50p	£4	£8
1929	8,419,200	25p	50p	£4	£8
1930	4,195,200	25p	50p	£4	£8
1931	6,595,200	25p	50p	£4	£8
1932	9,292,800	25p	50p	£4	£8
1933	4,560,000	25p	50p	£4	£8
1934	3,052,800	25p	50p	£4	£8
1935	2.227,200	£1	£2	£8	£20
1936	9,734,400	25p	50p	£3	£6

GEORGE VI (1936–52)

1937	8,131,200	—	—	50p	£1
1937 Proof	26,402	—	—	£1	£4
1938	7,449,600	—	—	£1	£5
1939	31,440,000	—	—	50p	£1
1940	18,360,000	—	—	50p	£1
1941	27,312,000	—	—	50p	£1
1942	28,857,600	—	—	50p	£1
1943	33,345,600	—	—	50p	£1
1944	25,137,600	—	—	50p	£1
1945	23,736,000	—	—	50p	£1
1946	24,364,800	—	—	50p	£1
1947	14,745,600	—	—	50p	£1
1948	16,622,400	—	—	50p	£1
*1949	8,424,000	—	—	50p	£1
1950	10,324,800	—	—	50p	£1
1950 Proof	17,513	—	—	50p	£3
1951	14,016,000	—	—	50p	£1
1951 Proof	20,000	—	—	50p	£3
1952	5,251,200	—	—	50p	£1

ELIZABETH II (1952–)

1953	6,131,037	—	—	—	£1
1953 Proof	40,000	—	—	—	£2
*1954	6,566,400	—	—	—	£1
1955	5,779,200	—	—	—	£1
1956	1,996,800	—	—	75p	£2

HALF FARTHING

DATE	MINTAGE	F	VF	EF	UNC

GEORGE IV (1820–30)

DATE	MINTAGE	F	VF	EF	UNC
1828 (two different obverses) (issued for Ceylon)	7,680,000	£7	£15	£35	£60
1830 (large or small date) (issued for Ceylon)	8,766,320	£7	£15	£35	£65

WILLIAM IV (1830–37)

DATE	MINTAGE	F	VF	EF	UNC
1837 (issued for Ceylon)	1,935,360	£15	£45	£100	£160

VICTORIA (1837–1901)

DATE	MINTAGE	F	VF	EF	UNC
1839	2,042,880	£5	£10	£25	£55
1842	unrecorded	£4	£7	£20	£45
1843	3,440,640	£3	£6	£16	£40
1844	6,451,200	£3	£6	£15	£40
1847	3,010,560	£6	£12	£30	£55
1851	unrecorded	£4	£12	£32	£55
1852	989,184	£4	£12	£40	£65
1853	955,224	£4	£12	£40	£75
1853 Proof	incl. above	—	—	—	£150
1854	677,376	£8	£20	£65	£120
1856	913,920	£8	£20	£65	£120

THIRD FARTHINGS

GEORGE IV (1820–30)

DATE	MINTAGE	F	VF	EF	UNC
1827 (issued for Malta)	unrecorded	£5	£12	£30	£55

WILLIAM IV (1830–37)

DATE	MINTAGE	F	VF	EF	UNC
1835 (issued for Malta)	unrecorded	£7	£16	£35	£65

VICTORIA (1837–1901)

DATE	MINTAGE	F	VF	EF	UNC
1844 (issued for Malta)	1,301,040	£8	£20	£60	£110
1866	576,000	£5	£12	£28	£55
1868	144,000	£5	£12	£28	£55
1876	162,000	£5	£12	£28	£55
1878	288,000	£5	£12	£28	£55
1881	144,000	£5	£12	£28	£50
1884	144,000	£5	£12	£28	£50
1885	288,000	£5	£12	£28	£50

EDWARD VII (1902–10)

DATE	MINTAGE	F	VF	EF	UNC
1902 (issued for Malta)	288,000	£3	£7	£20	£30

GEORGE V (1911–36)

DATE	MINTAGE	F	VF	EF	UNC
1913 (issued for Malta)	288,000	£3	£7	£20	£30

QUARTER FARTHINGS

VICTORIA (1837–1901)

DATE	MINTAGE	F	VF	EF	UNC
1839 (issued for Ceylon)	3,840,000	£10	£25	£50	£100
1851 (issued for Ceylon)	2,215,680	£10	£25	£50	£100
1852 (issued for Ceylon)	incl. above	£10	£25	£50	£100
1853 (issued for Ceylon)	incl. above	£10	£25	£50	£100
1853 Proof	incl. above	—	—	—	£240

EMERGENCY ISSUES

DATE	F	VF	EF	UNC

GEORGE III (1760–1820)

To alleviate the shortage of circulating coinage during the Napoleonic Wars the Bank of England firstly authorised the countermarking of other countries' coins, enabling them to pass as English currency. The coins, countermarked with punches depicting the head of George III, were mostly Spanish American 8 reales of Charles III. Although this had limited success it was later decided to completely overstrike the coins with a new English design on both sides—specimens that still show traces of the original host coin's date are avidly sought after by collectors. This overstriking continued for a number of years although all the known coins are dated 1804. Finally, in 1811 the Bank of England issued silver tokens which continued up to 1816 when a completely new regal coinage was introduced.

DOLLAR
Oval countermark of George III
On "Pillar" type 8 reales	£150	£600	£1000	—
*On "Portrait" type	£100	£275	£550	—

Octagonal countermark of George III
On "Portrait" type	£175	£500	£850	—

HALF DOLLAR
Oval countermark of George III
On "Portrait" type 4 reales .	£175	£350	£650	—

FIVE SHILLINGS OR ONE DOLLAR
These coins were overstruck on Spanish-American coins
*1804	£85	£175	£375	—

— With details of original coin still visible add from 10%.

BANK OF ENGLAND TOKENS
THREE SHILLINGS
1811 Draped bust	£25	£35	£75	—
1812 —	£25	£40	£100	—
1812 Laureate bust	£25	£35	£75	—
1813 —	£25	£35	£75	—
1814 —	£25	£35	£75	—
1815 —	£25	£35	£75	—
1816 —	£100	£200	£650	—

ONE SHILLING AND SIXPENCE
1811 Draped bust	£15	£30	£55	£120
1812 —	£15	£30	£55	£120
*1812 Laureate bust	£15	£30	£55	£120
1812 Proof in platinum				Unique
1813 —	£15	£30	£55	£120
1813 Proof in platinum				Unique
1814 —	£15	£30	£55	£120
1815 —	£15	£30	£55	£120
1816 —	£15	£30	£55	£120

NINEPENCE
1812 Pattern only	—	—	—	£1500

MAUNDY SETS

DATE	F	VF	EF	UNC

CHARLES II (1660–85)

DATE	F	VF	EF	UNC
Undated	£65	£120	£300	—
1670	£65	£100	£250	—
1671	£60	£90	£240	—
1672	£60	£90	£240	—
1673	£60	£90	£240	—
1674	£62	£95	£240	—
1675	£60	£90	£240	—
1676	£65	£95	£240	—
1677	£60	£90	£240	—
1678	£100	£140	£300	—
1679	£70	£110	£250	—
1680	£60	£90	£240	—
1681	£80	£110	£275	—
1682	£65	£95	£250	—
1683	£65	£100	£250	—
1684	£100	£150	£300	—

JAMES II (1685–88)

DATE	F	VF	EF	UNC
1686	£55	£100	£250	—
1687	£55	£100	£240	—
1688	£80	£125	£280	—

WILLIAM & MARY (1688–94)

DATE	F	VF	EF	UNC
1689	£250	£400	£650	—
1691	£100	£175	£350	—
1692	£135	£200	£400	—
1693	£125	£190	£375	—
1694	£100	£175	£325	—

WILLIAM III (1694–1702)

DATE	F	VF	EF	UNC
1698	£75	£125	£275	—
1699	£120	£185	£350	—
1700	£95	£150	£325	—
1701	£80	£140	£285	—

ANNE (1702–114)

DATE	F	VF	EF	UNC
1703	£75	£145	£285	—
1705	£70	£130	£260	—
1706	£70	£130	£260	—
1708	£120	£185	£300	—
1709	£85	£140	£275	—
1710	£100	£155	£300	—
1713	£80	£140	£275	—

GEORGE I (1714–27)

DATE	F	VF	EF	UNC
1723	£75	£135	£285	—
1727	£70	£130	£260	—

GEORGE II (1727–60)

DATE	F	VF	EF	UNC
1729	£60	£100	£220	—
1731	£60	£100	£220	—
1732	£50	£90	£185	—
1735	£50	£90	£185	—
1737	£50	£90	£185	—
1739	£50	£90	£185	—

DATE	MINTAGE	F	VF	EF	UNC
1740		£50	£90	£185	—
1743		£60	£100	£200	—
1746		£50	£90	£175	—
1760		£55	£90	£185	—

GEORGE III (1760–1820)

DATE	MINTAGE	F	VF	EF	UNC
1763		£50	£70	£145	—
1766		£50	£70	£145	—
1772		£50	£70	£150	—
1780		£50	£70	£145	—
1784		£50	£70	£145	—
1786		£50	£70	£150	—
1792 Wire		£110	£160	£270	—
1795		£45	£65	£115	—
1800		£45	£65	£100	—
New Coinage					
1817		£40	£60	£100	£155
1818		£40	£60	£100	£155
1820		£40	£60	£100	£155

GEORGE IV (1820–30)

DATE	MINTAGE	F	VF	EF	UNC
1822		—	£50	£110	£170
1823		—	£50	£110	£170
1824		—	£50	£110	£170
1825		—	—	£100	£160
1826		—	£50	£100	£160
1827		—	—	£100	£160
1828		—	£50	£100	£160
1829		—	£50	£100	£160
1830		—	£50	£100	£160

WILLIAM IV (1830–37)

DATE	MINTAGE	F	VF	EF	UNC
1831		—	£50	£90	£165
1831 Proof		—	£50	—	£275
1832		—	£50	£90	£165
1833		—	£50	£90	£165
1834		—	£50	£90	£165
1835		—	£50	£90	£165
1836		—	£50	£90	£165

VICTORIA (1837–1901)

YOUNG HEAD ISSUES

DATE	MINTAGE	F	VF	EF	UNC
1838	4,158	—	—	£70	£110
1839	4,125	—	—	£75	£125
1839 Proof	unrecorded	—	—	£100	£250
1840	4,125	—	—	£90	£145
1841	2,574	—	—	£95	£145
1842	4,125	—	—	£90	£145
1843	4,158	—	—	£65	£110
1844	4,158	—	—	£75	£120
1845	4,158	—	—	£60	£95
1846	4,158	—	—	£85	£130
1847	4,158	—	—	£110	£160
1848	4,158	—	—	£110	£160
1849	4,158	—	—	£90	£140
1850	4,158	—	—	£70	£110
1851	4,158	—	—	£70	£110

DATE	MINTAGE	EF	UNC
1852 4,158	—	—	£115 £170
1853 4,158	£120	£180
1853 Proof .... unrecorded	—	£400
1854 4,158	£65	£100
1855 4,158	£65	£100
1856 4,158	£60	£90
1857 4,158	£60	£90
1858 4,158	£60	£90
1859 4,158	£55	£85
1860 4,158	£60	£90
1861 4,158	£55	£85
1862 4,158	£60	£90
1863 4,158	£60	£90
1864 4,158	£55	£85
1865 4,158	£60	£90
1866 4,158	£55	£85
1867 4,158	£60	£90
1868 4,158	£55	£85
1869 4,158	£65	£95
1870 4,458	£60	£80
1871 4,488	£50	£75
1872 4,328	£50	£75
1873 4,162	£50	£75
1874 4,488	£50	£75
1875 4,154	£50	£75
1876 4,488	£50	£75
1877 4,488	£50	£75
1878 4,488	£50	£75
1879 4,488	£50	£75
1880 4,488	£50	£75
1881 4,488	£50	£75
1882 4,146	£55	£80
1883 4,488	£50	£70
1884 4,488	£50	£70
1885 4,488	£50	£70
1886 4,488	£50	£70
1887 4,488	£50	£80

JUBILEE HEAD ISSUES

DATE	MINTAGE	EF	UNC
1888 4,488	£50	£70
1889 4,488	£50	£70
1890 4,488	£50	£70
1891 4,488	£50	£70
1892 4,488	£50	£70

OLD HEAD ISSUES

DATE	MINTAGE	EF	UNC
1893 8,976	£45	£55
1893 Proof .... unrecorded	—	£120
1894 .... 8.976	£45	£65
1895 .... 8.976	£45	£65
1897 .... 8.976	£45	£65
1898 .... 8.976	£45	£65
1899 .... 8.976	£45	£65
1900 .... 8.976	£45	£65
1901 8,976	£45	£65

EDWARD VII (1902–110)

DATE	MINTAGE	EF	UNC
1902 8,976	£30	£40
1902 Matt proof 15,123	—	£45
1903 8,976	£30	£40
1904 8,976	£30	£45
1905 8,976	£30	£45
1906 8,800	£30	£42
1907 .... 8.760	£30	£40
1908 8,769	£30	£40
1909 1,983	£45	£70
1910 1,440	£50	£80

GEORGE V (1911–136)

DATE	MINTAGE	EF	UNC
1911 1,786	£40	£60
1911 Proof 6,007	—	£60

DATE	MINTAGE	EF	UNC
1912 1,246	£40	£60
1913 1,228	£45	£65
1914 982	£45	£60
1915 1,293	£40	£55
1916 1,128	£40	£55
1917 1,237	£40	£55
1918 1,375	£40	£55
1919 1,258	£40	£55
1920 1,399	£40	£55
1921 1,386	£40	£55
1922 1,373	£40	£55
1923 1,430	£45	£60
1924 1,515	£45	£60
1925 1,438	£40	£55
1926 1,504	£40	£55
1927 1,647	£45	£60
1928 1,642	£45	£60
1929 1,761	£45	£60
1930 1,724	£40	£55
1931 1,759	£40	£55
1932 1,835	£40	£55
1933 1,872	£40	£55
1934 1,887	£40	£55
1935 1,928	£40	£60
1936 1,323	£55	£75

GEORGE VI (1936–52)

DATE	MINTAGE	EF	UNC
1937 1,325	£40	£50
1937 Proof 20,900	£40	£50
1938 1,275	£40	£55
1939 1,234	£40	£55
1940 1,277	£40	£55
1941 1,253	£40	£55
1942 1,231	£40	£55
1943 1,239	£40	£55
1944 1,259	£40	£55
1945 1,355	£40	£55
1946 1,365	£40	£55
1947 1,375	£40	£60
1948 1,385	£45	£60
1949 1,395	£45	£60
1950 1,405	£45	£65
1951 1,468	£45	£65
1952 1,012	£50	£75

ELIZABETH II (1952–   )

DATE	MINTAGE	EF	UNC
1953 1,025	—	£250
1954 1,020	—	£60
1955 1,036	—	£60
1956 1,088	—	£60
1957 1,094	—	£60
1958 1,100	—	£60
1959 1,106	—	£60
1960 1,112	—	£60
1961 1,118	—	£60
1962 1,125	—	£60
1963 1,131	—	£60
1964 1,137	—	£60
1965 1,143	—	£60
1966 1,206	—	£60
1967 986	—	£60
1968 964	—	£65
1969 1,002	—	£60
1970 980	—	£60

Later issues are listed in the Decimal section.

MAUNDY ODDMENTS/SMALL SILVER

DATE	F	VF	EF

FOUR PENCE

CHARLES II

DATE	F	VF	EF
Undated	£20	£35	£75
1670	£30	£45	£85
1671	£17	£28	£65
1672	£17	£28	£65
1673	£17	£28	£65
1674	£17	£28	£65
1675	£17	£26	£65
1676	£17	£28	£65
1677	£16	£25	£65
1678	£17	£28	£65
1679	£15	£24	£50
1680	£16	£27	£50
1681	£17	£28	£65
1682	£16	£28	£70
1683	£17	£28	£75
1684	£16	£27	£80

JAMES II

DATE	F	VF	EF
1686	£18	£32	£70
1687	£25	£40	£85
1688	£16	£29	£65

WILLIAM & MARY

DATE	F	VF	EF
1689	£18	£30	£75
1690	£25	£38	£80
1691	£25	£40	£85
1692	£38	£42	£85
1693	£32	£45	£90
1694	£25	£40	£80

WILLIAM III

DATE	F	VF	EF
1698	£25	£35	£70
1699	£27	£35	£75
1700	£25	£35	£70
1701	£28	£38	£75
1702	£22	£30	£65

ANNE

DATE	F	VF	EF
1703	£25	£40	£80
1704	£17	£30	£65
1705	£25	£38	£65
1706	£20	£35	£60
1708	£17	£30	£65
1709	£20	£30	£65
1710	£15	£22	£45
1713	£18	£27	£60

GEORGE I

DATE	F	VF	EF
1717	£20	£35	£60
1721	£18	£35	£55
1723	£25	£40	£70
1727	£20	£35	£70

GEORGE II

DATE	F	VF	EF
1729	£20	£35	£50
1731	£16	£30	£45
1732	£16	£30	£45
1735	£18	£35	£48
1737	£16	£25	£40
1739	£16	£25	£40
1740	£18	£28	£42
1743	£25	£40	£65
1746	£17	£28	£45
1760	£17	£25	£40

GEORGE III

DATE	F	VF	EF
1763	£12	£22	£35
1765	£225	£450	£700
1766	£15	£25	£45
1770	£35	£55	£85
1772	£20	£30	£55
1780	£15	£25	£45
1784	£15	£25	£42
1786	£15	£25	£50
1792	£25	£38	£70
1795	£14	£25	£35
1800	£10	£20	£30
1817	£15	£20	£30
1818	£15	£20	£30
1820	£16	£22	£33

THREEPENCE

CHARLES II

DATE	F	VF	EF
Undated	£18	£29	£70
1670	£16	£28	£60
1671	£15	£25	£60
1672	£15	£25	£60
1673	£15	£25	£60
1674	£15	£25	£60
1675	£17	£28	£65
1676	£17	£28	£65
1677	£15	£25	£60
1678	£16	£27	£65
1679	£13	£22	£50
1680	£15	£25	£60
1681	£17	£28	£65
1682	£17	£28	£65
1683	£17	£28	£65
1684	£17	£28	£65

JAMES II

DATE	F	VF	EF
1685	£17	£28	£60
1686	£18	£30	£65
1687	£12	£19	£50
1688	£22	£45	£85

WILLIAM & MARY

DATE	F	VF	EF
1689	£17	£28	£60
1690	£20	£33	£75
1691	£45	£62	£115
1692	£25	£35	£75
1693	£65	£100	£150
1694	£25	£42	£75

WILLIAM III

DATE	F	VF	EF
1698	£25	£35	£65
1699	£25	£37	£70
1700	£25	£38	£70
1701	£20	£30	£60

DATE	F	VF	EF

ANNE

DATE	F	VF	EF
1703	£20	£30	£65
1704	£15	£26	£50
1705	£18	£30	£55
1706	£18	£30	£55
1707	£15	£25	£50
1708	£17	£28	£55
1709	£17	£29	£55
1710	£15	£25	£52
1713	£16	£30	£55

GEORGE I

DATE	F	VF	EF
1717	£18	£30	£55
1721	£20	£30	£55
1723	£25	£35	£65
1727	£20	£35	£65

GEORGE II

DATE	F	VF	EF
1729	£18	£28	£45
1731	£18	£28	£45
1732	£18	£28	£45
1735	£18	£30	£45
1737	£18	£30	£45
1739	£17	£28	£45
1740	£18	£30	£45
1743	£16	£25	£42
1746	£16	£25	£40
1760	£18	£28	£40

GEORGE III

DATE	F	VF	EF
1762	£7	£15	£25
1763	£7	£15	£25
1765	£150	£250	£450
1766	£15	£22	£45
1770	£17	£25	£45
1772	£15	£22	£40
1780	£15	£22	£40
1784	£16	£27	£45
1786	£15	£22	£40
1792	£22	£35	£65
1795	£12	£22	£30
1800	£10	£20	£30
1817	£12	£20	£30
1818	£12	£20	£30
1820	£14	£22	£33

TWOPENCE
CHARLES II

DATE	F	VF	EF
Undated	£17	£28	£60
1668	£18	£32	£75
1670	£15	£25	£50
1671	£15	£25	£50
1672	£15	£25	£50
1673	£17	£28	£58
1671	£15	£25	£50
1675	£17	£27	£58
1676	£15	£25	£50
1677	£15	£25	£50
1678	£16	£25	£50
1679	£13	£20	£40
1680	£15	£22	£50
1681	£15	£22	£50
1682	£15	£22	£50
1683	£15	£22	£50
1684	£18	£26	£50

JAMES II

DATE	F	VF	EF
1686	£17	£27	£60
1687	£22	£33	£75
1688	£16	£28	60

WILLIAM & MARY

DATE	F	VF	EF
1689	£15	£25	£55
1691	£17	£28	£60
1692	£40	£60	£100
1693	£18	£32	£65
1694	£17	£30	£60

WILLIAM III

DATE	F	VF	EF
1698	£27	£38	£75
1699	£20	£35	£65
1700	£20	£32	£65
1701	£20	£35	£70

ANNE

DATE	F	VF	EF
1703	£20	£33	£60
1704	£15	£25	£48
1705	£20	£30	£55
1706	£20	£32	£60
1707	£15	£25	£45
1708	£17	£28	£50
1709	£22	£35	£70
1710	£12	£22	£48
1713	£25	£40	£70

GEORGE I

DATE	F	VF	EF
1717	£17	£27	£50
1721	£12	£20	£38
1723	£25	£45	£70
1726	£12	£22	£40
1727	£20	£32	£60

GEORGE II

DATE	F	VF	EF
1729	£12	£20	£30
1731	£12	£20	£30
1732	£12	£20	£30
1735	£12	£20	£30
1737	£12	£20	£30
1739	£15	£22	£32
1740	£15	£23	£35
1743	£13	£25	£40
1746	£12	£25	£35
1756	£12	£16	£25
1759	£12	£16	£25
1760	£18	£25	£37

GEORGE III

DATE	F	VF	EF
1763	£12	£20	£35
1765	£175	£300	£550
1766	£12	£20	£30
1772	£12	£20	£27
1780	£12	£20	£27
1784	£12	£20	£27
1786	£10	£18	£25
1792	£20	£28	£45
1795	£10	£15	£20
1800	£8	£14	£18
1817	£8	£13	£17
1818	£8	£13	£17
1820	9	£14	£18

PENNY

DATE	F	VF	EF
CHARLES II			
Undated	£20	£32	£70
1670	£17	£30	£65
1671	£17	£30	£65
1672	£17	£30	£65
1673	£17	£30	£65
1674	£17	£30	£65
1675	£17	£30	£65
1676	£20	£35	£70
1677	£17	£30	£65
1678	£70	£120	£160
1679	£30	£45	£85
1680	£17	£30	£65
1681	£40	£65	£110
1682	£20	£35	£70
1683	£20	£35	£70
1684	£60	£90	£150
JAMES II			
1685	£20	£30	£65
1686	£20	£35	£70
1687	£25	£37	£75
1688	£16	£30	£60
WILLIAM & MARY			
1689	£175	£250	£400
1690	£25	£37	£70
1691	£27	£40	£80
1692	£50	£80	£140
1693	£28	£35	£70
1694	£25	£35	£70
WILLIAM III			
1698	£25	£35	£65
1699	£70	£110	£150
1700	£30	£42	£75
1701	£25	£38	£60
ANNE			
1703	£20	£32	£65
1705	£22	£35	£70
1706	£20	£28	£60
1708	£80	£120	£160
1709	£18	£28	£65
1710	£60	£100	£145
1713	£20	£35	£65

DATE	F	VF	EF
GEORGE I			
1716	£10	£18	£30
1718	£10	£18	£30
1720	£10	£18	£30
1723	£20	£30	£60
1725	£12	£20	£32
1726	£12	£20	£32
1727	£18	£30	£45
GEORGE II			
1729	£20	£35	£50
1731	£15	£30	£40
1732	£12	£20	£35
1735	£12	£22	£32
1737	£12	£22	£32
1739	£12	£22	£32
1740	£12	£22	£32
1743	£12	£20	£30
1746	£15	£30	£40
1750	£10	£15	£22
1752	£10	£15	£22
1753	£10	£15	£22
1754	£10	£15	£22
1755	£10	£15	£22
1756	£10	£15	£22
1757	£10	£15	£22
1758	£10	£15	£22
1759	£10	£15	£22
1760	£15	£20	£30
GEORGE III			
1762	£15	£22	£35
1765	£10	£15	£22
1766	£10	£15	£22
1772	£12	£17	£25
1780	£10	£15	£22
1781	£10	£15	£22
1784	£10	£15	£22
1786	£10	£15	£22
1792	£14	£20	£30
1795	£10	£15	£20
1800	£7	£10	£14
1817	£7	£12	£14
1818	£7	£12	£13
1820	£7	£12	£14

Sets in contemporary dated boxes are usually worth a higher premium. For example approximately £10 can be added to sets from Victoria to George VI in contemporary undated boxes and £15 for dated boxes.

DECIMAL COINAGE

Since the initial introduction of the Decimal system in the UK, the majority of coins have been issued in vast quantities, although in some years certain denominations have either not been struck at all or only limited numbers are available to collectors so, surprisingly, there are a number of potential scarcities worth looking out for—this scarcity is reflected in the prices quoted. In this section it has been decided to only include the mintage figures of coins struck in precious metals where these are available. Where dates are available in uncirculated grade at, or just above, face value no price has been quoted.

Proof issues of circulation coinage (£1–½ pence) of the decimal series were only issued as part of the appropriate year sets, but over the passage of time many of these sets have been broken up and the individual coins are now appearing on the market, hence the decision to include these coins in the appropriate sections.

A new portrait of Her Majesty the Queen, executed by Ian Rank-Broadley, FRBS, FSNAD, was introduced on the British coinage in 1998, making it the fourth portrait of Her Majesty to appear on the coins and the third since the introduction of decimal coinage in 1968.

FIVE POUNDS

DATE	Mintage	UNC
ST. GEORGE REVERSE—GOLD		
1980 Proof only	10,000	£450
1981 Proof only	5,400	£450
1982 Proof only	2,500	£475
1984 Proof	905	£460
1984 with U in circle	15,104	£400
1985 New portrait Proof	6,130	£475
1985 with U in circle	13,626	£400
1986 with U in circle	7,723	£400
1987 with U in circle	5,694	£400
*1988 with U in circle	3,315	£400
1990 Proof	1,721	£500
1990 with U in circle	1,226	£400
1991 Proof	1,336	£550
1991 with U in circle	976	£400
1992 Proof	1,165	£550
1992 with U in circle	797	£400
1993 Proof	1,078	£550
1993 with U in circle	906	£400
1994 Proof	918	£550
1994 with U in circle	1,000	£400
1995 Proof	1,250	£550
1995 with U in circle	1,000	£400
1996 Proof	1,250	£550
1996 with U in circle	1,000	£400
1997 Proof	1,000	£600
1997 with U in circle	1,000	£400
1998 Proof	1,500	£650
1998 with U in circle	1,000	£425
1999 Proof	1,000	£650
1999 with U in circle	1,000	£425

The obverse of the 1989 gold coins portray HM the Queen enthroned

COMMEMORATIVE		
*1989 500th Anniversary of the Sovereign, Gold	2,937	£500
1989 — Proof	5,000	£600
1990 Queen Mother's 90th Birthday. Crown. Cupro-nickel) ..	48,477	£8
1990 — in Presentation folder	incl. above	£10
1990 — Silver Proof	56,800	£32
1990 — Gold Proof	2,500	£525
1993 40th Anniversary of the Coronation. Crown. Cu-Ni	—	£8
1993 — in Presentation folder	—	£10
1993 — Proof	—	£15
1993 — Silver Proof	100,000	£30
1993 — Gold Proof	2,500	£525
*1996 Her Majesty the Queen's 70th Birthday. Crown. Cu-Ni	—	£8
1996 — in Presentation folder	—	£10
1996 — Proof	—	£15
1996 — Silver Proof	70,000	£32
1996 — Gold Proof	2,750	£650
*1997 Golden Wedding Anniversary of Her Majesty the Queen and Prince Philip. Crown. Cu-Ni	—	£7
1997 — in Presentation folder	—	£9
1997 — — with £5 note	5,000	£50
1997 — Proof	—	£22
1997 — Silver Proof	75,000	£35
1997 — Gold Proof	2,750	£650
1998 50th birthday of the Prince of Wales. Crown. Cu-Ni	—	£7
1998 — in Presentation folder	—	£12
1998 — Proof	—	£20
1998 — Silver Proof	—	£40
1998 — Gold Proof	—	£650

The obverse of the 1997 £5 crown shows the conjoined portraits of HM the Queen and Prince Philip

DATE	Mintage	UNC
1999 Princess of Wales Memorial. Cu-Ni	—	£7
1999 — in Presentation folder	—	£12
1999 — Proof	—	£20
1999 — Silver Proof	350,000	£40
1999 — Gold Proof	7,500	£650
1999 Millennium. Cu-Ni	—	£8
1999 — in Presentation folder	—	£15
1999 — Proof	—	£20
1999 — Silver Proof	100,000	£40
1999 — Gold Proof	2,500	£600
*2000 Millennium. Cu-Ni	—	£8
2000 — with special Dome mintmark	—	£12
2000 — in Presentation folder	—	£15
2000 — Proof	—	£22
2000 — Silver Proof with gold highlight	50,000	£40
2000 — Gold Proof	2,500	£500
2000 Queen Mother Centenary. Cu-Ni	—	£7
2000 — in Presentation folder	—	£12
2000 — Proof	—	£20
2000 — Silver Proof	100,000	£40
2000 — Gold Proof	3,000	£500

In addition the later cu-ni crowns are available in attractive philanumismatic covers.

TWO POUNDS

ST GEORGE REVERSE—*Gold*

1980 Proof only	10,000	£200
1982 Proof only	2,500	£200
1983 Proof only	12,500	£180
1985 Proof only	5,849	£200
1986 Proof only	15,777	£200
1987 Proof only	14,301	£200
1988 Proof only	12,743	£200
1989 Proof only	14,936	£200
*1990 Proof only	4,374	£200
1991 Proof only	3,108	£200
1992 Proof only	2,608	£210
1993 Proof only	2,155	£210
1996 Proof only	3,167	£210
1998 Proof only	4,500	£220
1999 Proof only	2,250	£300

COMMEMORATIVE

*1986 Commonwealth Games. Nickel-brass		£6
1986 — in Presentation folder		£7
1986 — Proof		£10
1986 — Silver		£15
1986 — Silver Proof		£18
1986 — Gold Proof		£250
*1989 300th Anniversary of Bill of Rights. Nickel-brass		£6
1989 — in Presentation folder		£8
1989 — Proof		£12
1989 — Silver Proof		£25
1989 — Silver Proof Piedfort		£48
*1989 300th Anniversary of Claim of Right. Nickel-brass		£12
1989 — in Presentation folder		£15
1989 — Proof		£18
1989 — Silver Proof		£28
1989 — Silver Proof Piedfort		£50
1989 500th Anniversary of the Sovereign. Gold Proof		£265

DATE	MINTAGE	UNC
1994 Tercentenary of the Bank of England. Nickel-brass		£5
1994 — in Presentation folder		£7
1994 — Proof		£10
1994 — Silver Proof		£27
1994 — Silver Proof Piedfort		£65
1994 — Gold Proof		£400
1994 — — obverse error (no denomination, as standard £2)		£575
1995 50th Anniversary of End of WW2. Nickel-brass		£4
1994 — in Presentation folder		£6
1995 — Proof		£10
1995 — Silver Proof		£32
1995 — Silver Proof Piedfort		£55
1995 — Gold Proof		£450
1995 50th Anniversary of The United Nations. Nickel-brass		£5
1994 — in Presentation folder		£6
1995 — Silver Proof		£35
1995 — Silver Proof Piedfort		£60
1995 — Gold Proof		£450
*1996 European Football Championships. Nickel-brass		£4
1996 — in Presentation folder		£5
1996 — Proof		£8
1996 — Silver Proof		£32
1996 — Silver Proof Piedfort		£55
1996 — Gold Proof		£450
*1999 Rugby World Cup. Bi-metallic		£3
1999 — Silver Proof		£32
1999 — Silver Proof Piedfort with Hologram		£85
1999 — Gold Proof		£350

CIRCULATING COINAGE

	MINTAGE	UNC
*1997 First Bi-metallic currency		£4
1997 — in Presentation folder		£8
1997 — Proof		£12
1997 — Silver Proof		£35
1997 — Gold (two types) Proof		£355
1998 Bi-metallic currency. New effigy		£3
1998 — in Presentation folder		£7
1998 — Proof		£10
1998 — Silver Proof		£32
1998 — Gold Proof		£355
1999 —		£3
1999 — Proof		£10
1999 — Silver Proof		£32
1999 — Gold Proof		£355
2000 —		£3
2000 — Proof		£10
2000 — Silver Proof		£30
2000 — Gold Proof		£355

SOVEREIGN

DATE	MINTAGE	UNC
1974	—	£60
1976	—	£60
1978	—	£60
1979	—	£60
1979 Proof	50,000	£75
1980	—	£60
1980 Proof	91,200	£75
1981	—	£60
1981 Proof	32,960	£75
1982	—	£60
1982 Proof	22,500	£75
1983 Proof only	21,250	£75
1984 Proof only	19,975	£75
1985 New portrait Proof only	17,242	£80
1986 Proof only	17,579	£80
1987 Proof only	22,479	£80
1988 Proof only	18,862	£80
1989 500th Anniversary of the Sovereign Proof only	23,471	£150
1990 Proof only	8,425	£100
1991 Proof only	7,201	£100
1992 Proof only	6,854	£100
1993 Proof only	6,090	£100
1994 Proof only	7,165	£100
1995 Proof only	9,500	£100
1996 Proof only	10,000	£100
1997 Proof only	9,750	£110
1998 Proof only	13,500	£120
1999	—	£60
1999 Proof	12,250	£145
2000	—	£60
2000 Proof	12,250	£125

HALF SOVEREIGN

DATE	MINTAGE	UNC
1980 Proof only	86,700	£50
1982	—	£50
1982 Proof	21,590	£60
1983 Proof only	19,710	£60
1984 Proof only	19,505	£60
1985 New portrait Proof only	15,800	£45
1986 Proof only	17,075	£45
1987 Proof only	20,687	£45
1988 Proof only	18,266	£50
1989 500th Anniversary of the Sovereign Proof only	21,824	£80
1990 Proof only	7,889	£50
1991 Proof only	6,076	£55
1992 Proof only	5,915	£65
1993 Proof only	4,651	£65
1994 Proof only	7,167	£75
1995 Proof only	7,500	£75
1996 Proof only	10,500	£75
1997 Proof only	9,750	£75
1998 Proof only	11,000	£75
1999 Proof only	9,750	£75
2000 Proof only	9,750	£70

ONE POUND

DATE	UNC
1983 Royal Arms Nickel-brass	£5
1983 — in Presentation folder	£6
1983 — Proof	£10
1983 — Silver Proof	£28
1983 — Silver Piedfort Proof	£120
1984 Scottish Thistle Nickel-brass	£4
1984 — in Presentation folder	£6
1984 — Proof	£7
1984 — Silver Proof	£30
1984 — Silver Piedfort Proof	£65
1985 Welsh Leek Nickel-brass	£4
1985 — in Presentation folder	£5
1985 — Proof	£7
1985 — Silver Proof	£30
1985 — Silver Piedfort Proof	£60
1986 Northern Ireland Flax Nickel-brass	£4
1986 — in Presentation folder	£5
1986 — Proof	£7
1986 — Silver Proof	£30
1986 — Silver Piedfort Proof	£62
1987 English Oak Nickel-brass	£4
1987 — in Presentation folder	£5
1987 — Proof	£7
1987 — Silver Proof	£28
1987 — Silver Piedfort Proof	£60
1988 Royal Shield Nickel-brass	£4
1988 — in Presentation folder	£5
1988 — Proof	£8
1988 — Silver Proof	£30
1988 — Silver Piedfort Proof	£65
1989 Scottish Thistle Nickel-brass	£4
1989 — Proof	£7
1989 — Silver Proof	£28
1989 — Silver Piedfort Proof	£60
1990 Welsh Leek Nickel-brass	£4
1990 — Proof	£7
1990 — Silver Proof	£28
1991 Northern Ireland Flax Nickel-brass	£4
1991 — Proof	£7
1991 — Silver Proof	£32
1992 English Oak Nickel-brass	£4
1992 — Proof	£7
1992 — Silver Proof	£32
1993 Royal Arms Nickel-brass	£4
1993 — Proof	£7
1993 — Silver Proof	£32
1993 — Silver Piedfort Proof	£75
1994 Scottish Lion Nickel-brass	£3
1994 — in Presentation folder	£5
1994 — Proof	£7
1994 — Silver Proof	£32
1994 — Silver Piedfort Proof	£68
1995 Welsh Heraldic Dragon Nickel-brass	£3
1995 — in Presentation folder (English)	£6
1995 — — (Welsh)	£7
1995 — Proof	£8
1995 — Silver Proof	£32
1995 — Silver Piedfort Proof	£68
1996 Northern Ireland Celtic Nickel-brass	£3
1996 — in Presentation folder	£4
1996 — Proof	£7
1996 — Silver Proof	£33
1996 — Silver Piedfort Proof	£68

1983, 1993, 1998

1984, 1989

1985, 1990

1986, 1991

1987, 1992

1994, 1999

1995, 2000

DATE	UNC
1997 English Lions. Nickel-brass	£4
1997 — in Presentation folder	£5
1997 — Proof	£7
1997 — Silver Proof	£32
1997 — Silver Piedfort Proof	£70
1998 New portrait. Royal Arms. Nickel-brass (from Year sets only)	£4
1998 — in Presentation folder	£5
1998 — Proof	£8
1998 — Silver Proof	£30
1998 — Silver Piedfort Proof	£65
1999 Scottish Lion. Nickel-brass (from Year sets only)	£4
1999 — in Presentation folder	£6
1999 — Proof	£8
1999 — Silver Proof	£35
1999 — Silver Piedfort Proof	£75
2000 Welsh Dragon. Nickel-brass	£2
2000 — in Presentation folder	£5
2000 — Proof	£8
2000 — Silver Proof	£35
2000 — Silver Piedfort Proof	£55

1996

1997

FIFTY PENCE

1969	£3
1970	£4
1971 Proof	£8
1972 Proof	£8
1973 Accession to EEC	£3
1973 — Proof	£5
1974 Proof	£5
1975 Proof	£5
1976	£3
1976 Proof	£5
1977	£3
1977 Proof	£5
1978	£3
1978 Proof	£5
1979	£3
1979 Proof	£5
1980	£3
1980 Proof	£5
1981	£2
1981 Proof	£5
1982 Legend changed to FIFTY PENCE	£3
1982 Proof	£5
1983	£3
1983 Proof	£5
1984	£3
1984 Proof	£5
1985 New portrait	£3
1985 Proof	£5
1986	£4
1986 Proof	£5
1987	£4
1987 Proof	£5
1988	£4
1988 Proof	£5
1989	£4
1989 Proof	£5
1990	£4
1990 Proof	£5
1991	£5
1991 Proof	£6

DATE	UNC
*1992 Presidency of EC Council and completion of Single Market	£5
1992 — in Presentation folder with Britannia	£7
1992 — Proof	£6
1992 — Silver Proof	£30
1992 — Silver Proof Piedfort	£50
1992 — Gold Proof	£400
1993	£2
*1994 Anniversary of the Normandy Landings	£3
1994 — in Presentation folder	£4
1994 — Proof	£6
1994 — Silver Proof	£30
1994 — Silver Proof Piedfort	£60
1994 — Gold Proof	£425
1995	£5
1995 Proof	£8
1996	£4
1996 Proof	£6
1996 Silver Proof	£22
1997	£4
1997 Proof	£6
1997 Silver Proof	£28
1997 *new reduced size*	£3
1997 Proof	£5
1997 Silver Proof	£28
1997 Silver Proof Piedfort	£65
1998 New portrait	£2
1998 Proof	£5
1998 Silver Proof	£25
1998 Silver Proof Piedfort	£65
*1998 Presidency and 25th anniversary of entry into the EU	£2
1998 — Proof	£5
1998 — Silver Proof	£25
1998 — Silver Proof Piedfort	£75
•1998 50th Anniversary of the National Health Service	£2
1998 — Proof	£5
1998 — Silver Proof	£25
1998 — Silver Proof Piedfort	£75
1999	£2
1999 Proof	£5
1999 Silver Proof	£25
1999 Silver Proof Piedfort	£75
2000	—
2000 — Proof	£5
2000 — Silver Proof	£30
2000 — Silver Proof Piedfort	£85
•2000 150th Anniversary of Public Libraries	£2
2000 — Proof	£5
2000 — Silver Proof	£30
1998 — Gold proof	£250

TWENTY-FIVE PENCE (CROWN)

1972 Royal Silver Wedding Cu-Ni	£1
1972 — Proof	£6
1972 — Silver Proof	£20
1977 Silver Jubilee Cu-Ni	£1
1977 — in Presentation folder	£3
1977 — Proof	£5
1977 — Silver Proof	£12
1980 Queen Mother 80th Birthday Cu-Ni	£1
1980 — in Presentation folder	£3
1980 — Silver Proof	£28
1981 Royal Wedding Cu-Ni	£2
1981 — in Presentation folder	£3
1981 — Silver Proof	£25

TWENTY PENCE

DATE	UNC	DATE	UNC
		1989 Proof	£3
		1990	£1
		1990 Proof	£3
		1991	£1
		1991 Proof	£3
		1992	£1
		1992 Proof	£3
		1993	£1
1982	£2	1993 Proof	£3
1982 Proof	£4	1994	£1
1982 Silver Piedfort Proof	£50	1994 Proof	£3
1983	£2	1995	£1
1983 Proof	£4	1995 Proof	£3
1984	£2	1996	£1
1984 Proof	£4	1996 Proof	£3
1985 New portrait	£1	1996 Silver Proof	£15
1985 Proof	£3	1997	£1
1986	£2	1997 Proof	£3
1986 Proof	£4	1998 New portrait	£1
1987	£1	1998 Proof	£3
1987 Proof	£3	1999	£1
1988	£1	1999 Proof	£3
1988 Proof	£3	2000	—
1989	£1	2000 Proof	£3

TEN PENCE

DATE	UNC	DATE	UNC
		1984 Proof	£3
		1985 New portrait	£4
		1985 Proof	£3
		1986	£4
		1986 Proof	£3
		1987	£4
		1987 Proof	£5
		1988	£4
		1988 Proof	£5
		1989	£6
		1989 Proof	£5
1968	£1	1990	£6
1969	£2	1990 Proof	£5
1970	£2	1991	£6
1971	£2	1991 Proof	£5
1971 Proof	£2	1992	£5
1972 Proof	£3	1992 Proof	£6
1973	£2	1992 Silver Proof	£17
1973 Proof	£4	1992 *Size reduced to 24.5mm*	£1
1974	£2	1992 Proof	£4
1974 Proof	£4	1992 Silver Proof	£17
1975	£2	1992 Silver Proof piedfort	£40
1975 Proof	£4	1993	£1
1976	£2	1993 Proof	£2
1976 Proof	£4	1994	£1
1977	£2	1994 Proof	£2
1977 Proof	£4	1995	£1
1978 Proof	£5	1995 Proof	£2
1979	£2	1996	£1
1979 Proof	£4	1996 Proof	£2
1980	£2	1996 Silver Proof	£22
1980 Proof	£3	1997	£1
1981	£2	1997 Proof	£2
1981 Proof	£3	1998 New portrait (from Year sets only)	£2
1982 Legend changed to TEN PENCE	£4	1998 Proof	£2
1982 Proof	£5	1999 (from Year sets only)	£2
1983	£3	1999 Proof	£2
1983 Proof	£2	2000	—
1984	£2	2000 Proof	£3

FIVE PENCE

DATE	UNC	DATE	UNC
1968	50p	1986 Proof	£2
1969	50p	1987	£1
1970	55p	1987 Proof	£3
1971	50p	1988	£1
1971 Proof	£4	1988 Proof	£2
1972 Proof	£4	1989	50p
1973 Proof	£4	1989 Proof	£3
1974 Proof	£4	1990	£2
1975	50p	1990 Proof	£4
1975 Proof	£2	1990 Silver Proof	£15
1976 Proof	£4	1990 *Size reduced to 18mm*	£1
1977	50p	1990 Proof	£2
1977 Proof	£3	1990 Silver Proof	£15
1978	50p	1990 Silver Proof Piedfort	£30
1978 Proof	£2	1991	50p
1979	50p	1991 Proof	£3
1979 Proof	£2	1992	50p
1980	50p	1992 Proof	£3
1980 Proof	£2	1993	50p
1981 Proof	£3	1993 Proof	£4
1982 Legend changed to FIVE PENCE	£3	1994	50p
1982 Proof	£3	1994 Proof	£2
1983	£4	1995	50p
1983 Proof	£3	1995 Proof	£2
1984	£3	1996	—
1984 Proof	£2	1996 Proof	£2
1985 New portrait	£2	1996 Silver proof	£15
1985 Proof	£2	1997	—
1986	£2	1997 Proof	£2
		1998	—
		1998 Proof	£2
		1999	—
		1999 Proof	—
		2000	—
		2000 Proof	—

TWO PENCE

Bronze

DATE	UNC	DATE	UNC
1971	50p	1976	50p
1971 Proof	£2	1976 Proof	£1
1972 Proof	£2	1977	50p
1973 Proof	£2	1977 Proof	£1
1974 Proof	£2	1978	50p
1975	50p	1978 Proof	£1
1975 Proof	£1	1979	50p
		1979 Proof	£1
		1980	50p
		1980 Proof	£1
		1981	50p
		1981 Proof	£1
		1982 Legend changed to TWO PENCE	£2
		1982 Proof	£1
		1983	£1
		1983 Proof	£1
		1983 Error reverse as New Pence	Rare

DATE	UNC	DATE	UNC
1984	£1	1993 Proof	£1
1984 Proof	£1	1994	—
1985 New portrait	50p	1994 Proof	£1
1985 Proof	£1	1995	—
1986	25p	1995 Proof	£1
1986 Proof	£1	1996	—
1987	25p	1996 Proof	£1
1987 Proof	£1	1996 Silver Proof	£16
1988	25p	1997	—
1988 Proof	£1	1997 Proof	£1
1989	25p	1998 New portrait	50p
1989 Proof	£1	1998 Proof	£2
1990	25p	1998 *Bronze*	—
1990 Proof	£1	1998 *Bronze* Proof	£1
1991	25p	1999	—
1991 Proof	£1	1999 Proof	£1
1992	25p	1999 *Bronze*	—
1992 Proof	£1	1999 *Bronze* Proof	£1
Copper-plated steel		2000	—
1992	—	2000 Proof	£1
1993	—		

ONE PENNY

Bronze

1971	25p	1986	25p
1971 Proof	£1	1986 Proof	£1
1972 Proof	£2	1987	25p
1973	30p	1987 Proof	£1
1973 Proof	£1	1988	25p
1974	30p	1988 Proof	£1
1974 Proof	£1	1989	25p
1975	20p	1989 Proof	£1
1975 Proof	£1	1990	25p
1976	20p	1990 Proof	£1
1976 Proof	£1	1991	25p
1977	20p	1991 Proof	£1
1977 Proof	£1	1992	25p
1978	40p	1992 Proof	£1
1978 Proof	£1	*Copper-plated steel*	
1979	20p	1992	—
1979 Proof	£1	1993	—
1980	15p	1993 Proof	£1
1980 Proof	£1	1994	—
1981	15p	1994 Proof	£1
1981 Proof	£1	1995	—
1982 Legend changed to ONE PENNY	25p	1995 Proof	£1
1982 Proof	£2	1996	—
1983	25p	1996 Proof	£1
1983 Proof	£1	1996 Silver Proof	£15
1984	£1	1997	—
1984 Proof	£1	1997 Proof	£1
1985 New portrait	25p	1998 New portrait	50p
1985 Proof	£1	1998 Proof	£2
		1998 *Bronze*	—
		1998 *Bronze* Proof	£1
		1999	—
		1999 Proof	£2
		1999 *Bronze*	—
		1999 *Bronze* Proof	£1
		2000	—
		2000 Proof	—

It would appear that 1998 and 1999 year sets *mostly* include bronze 2p and 1p coins whereas those put into general circulation are copper-plated steel. However, early in 1998 a number of 1998-dated 2ps in bronze were also put into circulation.

HALF PENNY

DATE	UNC	DATE	UNC
		1977	50p
		1977 Proof	£2
		1978	75p
		1978 Proof	£2
		1979	£1
1971	25p	1979 Proof	£2
1971 Proof	£1	1980	50p
1972 Proof	£5	1980 Proof	£1
1973	50p	1981	£1
1973 Proof	£3	1981 Proof	£1
1974	50p	1982 Legend changed to HALF PENNY	50p
1974 Proof	£2	1982 Proof	£1
1975	50p	1983	£1
1975 Proof	£2	1983 Proof	£1
1976	50p	1984 (only issued in Unc. year sets)	£3
1976 Proof	£2	1984 Proof	£2

MAUNDY SETS

DATE AND PLACE OF ISSUE	MINTAGE	UNC
1971 Tewkesbury Abbey	1,108	£60
1972 York Minster	1,026	£65
1973 Westminster Abbey	1,004	£60
1974 Salisbury Cathedral	1,042	£60
1975 Peterborough Cathedral	1,050	£60
1976 Hereford Cathedral	1,158	£65
1977 Westminster Abbey	1,138	£70
1978 Carlisle Cathedral	1,178	£60
1979 Winchester Cathedral	1,188	£60
1980 Worcester Cathedral	1,198	£65
1981 Westminster Abbey	1,178	£65
1982 St David's Cathedral	1,218	£65
1983 Exeter Cathedral	1,228	£65
1984 Southwell Minster	1,238	£65
1985 Ripon Cathedral	1,248	£65
1986 Chichester Cathedral	1,378	£65
1987 Ely Cathedral	1,390	£70
1988 Lichfield Cathedral	1,402	£70
1989 Birmingham Cathedral	1,353	£70
1990 Newcastle Cathedral	1,523	£75
1991 Westminster Abbey	1,384	£80
1992 Chester Cathedral	1,424	£85
1993 Wells Cathedral	1,440	£85
1994 Truro Cathedral	1,433	£85
1995 Coventry Cathedral	1,466	£90
1996 Norwich Cathedral	1,485	£95
1997 Birmingham Cathedral	1,486	£100
1998 Portsmouth Cathedral	1,488	£100
1999 Bristol Cathedral		£100
2000 Lincoln Cathedral		£100

In keeping with ancient tradition the Royal Maundy sets are made up of four silver coins of 4p, 3p, 2p and 1p. The designs for the reverse of the coins are a crowned numeral in a wreath of oak leaves—basically the same design that has been used for Maundy coins since Charles II.

PROOF AND SPECIMEN SETS

DATE	FDC

GEORGE IV
1826 £5–farthing (11 coins) £18,000

WILLIAM IV
1831 Coronation £2–farthing (14 coins) £15,500

VICTORIA
1839 "Una and the Lion" £5–farthing (15 coins) £30,000
1853 Sovereign–quarter farthing, including "Gothic"crown (16 coins) £27,500
1887 Golden Jubilee £5– 3d (11 coins) £6,500
1887 Golden Jubilee Crown–3d (7 coins) £1,250
1893 £5–3d (10 coins) £7,500
1893 Crown–3d (6 coins) £1,250

EDWARD VII
1902 Coronation £5–Maundy penny matt proofs (13 coins) £1,550
1902 Coronation Sovereign–Maundy penny matt proofs (11 coins) £550

GEORGE V
1911 Coronation £5–Maundy penny (12 coins) £2,550
1911 Sovereign–Maundy penny (10 coins) £800
1911 Coronation Halfcrown–Maundy penny (8 coins) £400
1927 New types Crown–3d (6 coins) £300

GEORGE VI
1937 Coronation £5–half sovereign (4 coins) £1,550
1937 Coronation Crown–farthing including Maundy money (15 coins) £125
1950 Mid-century Halfcrown–farthing (9 coins) £55
1951 Festival of Britain, Crown–farthing (10 coins) £75

ELIZABETH II
1953 Coronation Crown–farthing (10 coins) £55
1953 Coronation Currency (plastic) set halfcrown–farthing (9 coins) £12
1968 Specimen decimal set 10p, 5p, 1971 2p, 1p, ½p in wallet (5 coins) £2.50
1970 Last £sd coins (sets issued 1971–73) Halfcrown– halfpenny (8 coins) £18
1971 Proof (issued 1973), 50p–½p (6 coins) £12
1972 Proof 50p–½p, Silver Wedding crown (7 coins) £15
1973 Proof 50p–½p (6 coins) £12
1974 Proof 50p–½p (6 coins) £16
1975 Proof 50p–½p (6 coins) £16
1976 Proof 50p–½p (6 coins) £16
1977 Proof 50p–½p, Jubilee crown (7 coins) £15
1978 Proof 50p–½p (6 coins) £14
1979 Proof 50p–½p (6 coins) £16
1980 Proof 50p–½p (6 coins) £14
1980 Proof gold £5–half sovereign (4 coins) £775
1981 Commemorative Proof £5–sovereign, Royal Wedding Silver crown, 50p–½p (9 coins) £675
1981 Proof 50p–½p (6 coins) £16
1982 Proof gold £5–half sovereign (4 coins) £775
1982 Proof 50p–½p (7 coins) £16
1982 Uncirculated 50p–½p (7 coins) £12
1983 Proof gold £2–half sovereign (3 coins) £355
1983 Proof £1–½p (8 coins) £20
1983 Uncirculated £1–½p (8 coins) £16
1984 Proof gold £5–half sovereign (3 coins) £650
1984 Proof £1 (Scottish rev.)–½p (8 coins) £16
1984 Uncirculated £1 (Scottish rev.)–½p (8 coins) £15
1985 Proof Gold new portrait £5–half sovereign (4 coins) £775

DATE	FDC
1985 Proof new portrait £1 (Welsh rev.)–1p in de luxe case (7 coins)	£25
1985 Proof as above, in standard case	£18
1985 Uncirculated £1 (Welsh rev.)–1p (7 coins)	£15
1986 Proof Gold Commonwealth Games £2–half sovereign (3 coins)	£425
1986 Proof Commonwealth Games £2, Northern Ireland £1, 50p–1p in de luxe case (8 coins)	£25
1986 Proof as above in standard case (8 coins)	£23
1986 Uncirculated as above in folder (8 coins)	£15
1987 Proof gold Britannia set 1 oz.–1/10 oz. (4 coins)	£775
1987 Proof gold Britannia ¼ oz., 1/10 oz. (2 coins)	£155
1987 Proof gold £2–half sovereign (3 coins)	£365
1987 Proof £1 (English rev.)–1p in de luxe case (7 coins)	£28
1987 Proof £1 (English rev.)–1p in standard case (7 coins)	£18
1987 Uncirculated as above in folder (7 coins)	£11
1988 Proof gold Britannia set 1 oz.–1/10 oz. (4 coins)	£755
1988 Proof gold Britannia ¼ oz., 1/10 oz. (2 coins)	£155
1988 Proof gold £2–half sovereign (3 coins)	£310
1988 Proof £1 (Royal Arms rev.)–1p in de luxe case (7 coins)	£30
1988 Proof as above in standard case (7 coins)	£25
1988 Uncirculated as above in folder (7 coins)	£12
1989 Proof gold Britannia set 1 oz.–1/10 oz. (4 coins)	£760
1989 Proof gold Britannia ¼ oz., 1/10 oz. (2 coins)	£165
1989 Proof gold 500th anniversary of the sovereign. £5–half sovereign (4 coins)	£950
1989 Proof gold 500th anniversary of the sovereign. £2–half sovereign (3 coins)	£450
1989 Proof Bill of Rights £2, Claim of Right £2 (2 coins)	£42
1989 Proof silver piedfort as above (2 coins)	£85
1989 Uncirculated £2 as above in folder (2 coins)	£14
1989 Proof Bill of Rights £2, Claim of Right £2, £1 (Scottish rev.)–1p in de luxe case (9 coins)	£32
1989 Proof as above in standard case (9 coins)	£30
1989 Uncirculated £1 (Scottish rev.)–1p (7 coins)	£18
1990 Proof gold Britannia set 1 oz.–1/10 oz. (4 coins)	£800
1990 Proof gold £5–half sovereign (4 coins)	£875
1990 Proof gold £2–half sovereign (3 coins)	£355
1990 Proof silver 5p, 2 sizes (2 coins)	£25
1990 Proof £1 (Welsh rev.)–1p, two sizes of 5p, in de luxe case (8 coins)	£32
1990 Proof as above in standard case (8 coins)	£25
1990 Uncirculated as above (8 coins)	£16
1991 Proof gold Britannia set 1 oz.–1/10 oz. (4 coins)	£775
1991 Proof gold £5–half sovereign (4 coins)	£1,250
1991 Proof gold £2–half sovereign (3 coins)	£450
1991 Proof £1 (Irish rev.)–1p in de luxe case (7 coins)	£30
1991 Proof as above in standard case (7 coins)	£25
1991 Uncirculated as above (7 coins)	£16
1992 Proof gold Britannia set 1 oz.–1/10 oz. (4 coins)	£775
1992 Proof gold £5–half sovereign (4 coins)	£950
1992 Proof gold £2–half sovereign (3 coins)	£450
1992 Proof £1 (English rev.)–1p (2x10p and 2x50p) in de luxe case (9 coins)	£35
1992 Proof as above in standard case (9 coins)	£30
1992 Uncirculated as above (9 coins)	£15
1993 Proof gold Britannia set 1 oz.–1/10 oz. (4 coins)	£900
1993 Proof gold £5–half sovereign plus silver Pistrucci medal (4 coins + medal)	£1,200
1993 Proof gold £2–half sovereign (3 coins)	£520
1993 Proof £1–1p plus Coronation anniversary £5 in red leather case (8 coins)	£38
1993 Proof as above in standard case (8 coins)	£35
1993 Uncirculated £1–1p plus European Community 50p (8 coins)	£14
1994 Proof gold Britannia set 1 oz.–1/10 oz. (4 coins)	£825
1994 Proof gold £5–half sovereign (4 coins)	£1,250
1993 Proof gold £2–half sovereign (3 coins)	£550
1994 Proof Bank of England Tercentenary £2–1p in red leather case (8 coins)	£35
1994 Proof as above in standard case (8 coins)	£32
1994 Uncirculated £1–1p including Normandy Landings 50p (7 coins)	£16
1995 Proof gold Britannia set 1 oz.–1/10 oz. (4 coins)	£810
1995 Proof gold £5–half sovereign (4 coins)	£1,250
1995 Proof gold £2–half sovereign (3 coins)	£525
1995 Proof "Peace" £2–1p in red leather case (8 coins)	£35
1995 Proof as above in standard case (8 coins)	£32
1995 Uncirculated "Peace" £2–1p (8 coins)	£14
1996 Proof gold Britannia set 1oz–¼oz (4 coins)	£950

DATE	FDC
1996 Proof gold £5–half sovereign (4 coins)	£1,250
1996 Proof gold £2–half sovereign (3 coins)	£525
1996 Proof "Royal 70th Birthday" £5–1p in red leather case (9 coins)	£42
1996 Proof as above in standard case (9 coins)	£36
1996 Uncirculated "Football" £2–1p (8 coins)	£14
1996 Proof silver 25th Anniversary of Decimal currency £1–1p (7 coins)	£125
1997 Proof gold £5–half sovereign (4 coins)	£1,250
1997 Proof gold £2–half sovereign (3 coins)	£520
1997 Proof Royal Golden Wedding £5 in cupro-nickel, Bi-metallic £2, "English" £1, 50p–1p in red leather case (10 coins)	£50
1997 Proof as above in standard case (10 coins)	£38
1997 Uncirculated "Royal Golden Wedding" £5–1p (10 coins)	£15
1997 Proof silver 50p—two sizes (2 coins)	£52
1997 Proof silver Britannia set £2–20p	£100
1998 Proof gold Britannia set (4 coins)	£1,150
1998 Proof gold £5–half sovereign (4 coins)	£1,250
1998 Proof gold £2–half sovereign (3 coins)	£500
1998 Proof silver Britannia set £2–20p	£95
1998 Proof Prince of Wales Birthday £5–1p (10 coins) in leather case	£42
1998 Proof as above in standard case (10 coins)	£36
1998 Uncirculated "Prince's Birthday" £5–1p (10 coins)	£15
1999 Proof gold Britannia set (4 coins)	£1,250
1999 Proof gold £5–half sovereign incl. £2 Rugby World Cup (4 coins)	£1,265
1999 Proof £2 Rugby World Cup–half sovereign (3 coins)	£500
1999 Proof Diana £5–1p (9 coins)	£45
1999 Proof as above in standard case (9 coins)	£35
1999 Uncirculated set £2–1p , no £5 (8 coins)	£14
2000 Proof gold Britannia set (4 coins)	£1,250
2000 Proof gold £5–half sovereign (4 coins)	£1,265
2000 Proof £2–half sovereign (3 coins)	£500
2000 Proof Millennium £5–1p in de-luxe "shaped" pack (10 coins)	£48
2000 Proof as above in standard pack (10 coins)	£35
2000 Uncirculated set £2–1p , no £5 (9 coins)	£12
2000 Millennium Time capsule (9 coins)	£25

In addition to the above the Royal Mint also produce special Wedding and "Baby" gift packs each year.

A 1911 Proof set—a superb example of the minter's art and worthy of pride of place in any collection.

The coins illustrated are pennies representative of the reign, unless otherwise stated.

DAVID I (1124–53)

Berwick, Carlisle, Edinburgh and Roxburgh Mints

	F	VF
Penny	£550	£1300

HENRY (1136–52)

Bamborough, Carlisle and Corbridge Mints for the Earl of Huntingdon and
Northumberland

	F	VF
Penny	£1200	£3000

David I

MALCOLM IV (1153–65)

Berwick and Roxburgh Mints

	F	VF
Penny (5 different types)	£3500	£9500

WILLIAM THE LION (1165–1214)

Berwick, Edinburgh, Dun (Dunbar?), Perth and
Roxburgh Mints

	F	VF
Penny	£75	£155

Henry

ALEXANDER II (1214–49)

Berwick and Roxburgh Mints

	F	VF
Penny	£750	£1500

ALEXANDER III (1249–86)

William the Lion

FIRST COINAGE (1250–80)
Pennies struck at the Mints at

	F	VF
Aberdeen	£78	£230
Ayr	£90	£290
Berwick	£55	£135
"Dun" (Dumfries?)	£125	£350
Edinburgh	£45	£125
Forfar	£125	£375
Forres	£135	£350
Glasgow	£140	£400
Inverness	£135	£380
Kinghorn	£160	£400
Lanark	£125	£350
Montrose	£255	£500
Perth	£55	£160
Renfrew	£175	£500
Roxburgh	£60	£175
St Andrews	£85	£225
Sterling	£130	£350

Alexander II

SECOND COINAGE (1280–86)

	F	VF
Penny	£30	£70
Halfpenny	£80	£190
Farthing	£155	£425

Alexander III

JOHN BALIOL (1292–1306)

FIRST COINAGE *(Rough Surface issue)*

	F	VF
Penny	£110	£255
Halfpenny	*Extremely rare*	

SECOND COINAGE *(Smooth Surface issue)*

	F	VF
Penny	£160	£350
Halfpenny	£225	£500

John Baliol

ROBERT BRUCE (1306–29)

	F	VF
Berwick Mint		
*Penny	£250	£600
Halfpenny	£350	£750
Farthing		Extremely Rare

Robert Bruce

DAVID II (1329–71)

Aberdeen and Edinburgh Mints		
Noble		Extremely Rare
Groat	£70	£205
Halfgroat	£65	£185
Penny	£50	£90
Halfpenny	£155	£350
Farthing	£500	£1500

David II

ROBERT II (1371–90)

Dundee, Edinburgh and Perth Mints		
Groat	£60	£190
Halfgroat	£90	£210
Penny	£75	£165
Halfpenny	£125	£400

Robert II

ROBERT III (1390–1406)

Aberdeen, Dumbarton, Edinburgh, Perth Mints		
*Lion or crown	£430	£900
Demy lion or halfcrown	£350	£800
Groat	£60	£155
Halfgroat	£105	£300
Penny	£155	£325
Halfpenny	£300	£1000

JAMES I (1406–37)

Aberdeen, Edinburgh, Inverness, Linlithgow, Perth, Stirling Mints		
Demy	£350	£600
Half demy	£450	£800
Groat	£125	£265
Penny	£90	£255
Halfpenny	£112	£400

JAMES II (1437–60)

Robert III Lion

Aberdeen, Edinburgh, Linlithgow, Perth, Roxburgh, Stirling Mints		
Demy	£375	£800
Lion	£450	£1400
Half lion		Extremely rare
*Groat	£155	£500
Halfgroat	£385	£850
Penny (billon)	£180	£500

JAMES III (1460–88)

Aberdeen, Berwick and Edinburgh Mints		
Rider	£700	£1700
Half rider	£900	£2000
Quarter rider	£900	£2000
Unicorn	£750	£1700
Groat	£155	£355
Halfgroat	£330	£850
Penny (silver)	£100	£350
Plack (billon)	£60	£160
Half plack		Extremely rare
Penny (billon)	£70	£175
Farthing (copper)	£155	£325

James III Groat, Berwick Mint

	F	VF

JAMES IV (1488–1513)

Edinburgh Mint

	F	VF
Unicorn	£675	£1500
Half unicorn	£550	£1100
Lion or crown	£800	£1750
Half lion	£1500	£3500
Groat	£310	£750
Halfgroat	£310	£650
Penny (silver)	£400	£1000
Plack	£35	£85
Half plack	£78	£185
*Penny (billon)	£47	£108

James IV

JAMES V (1513–42)

Edinburgh Mint

	F	VF
Unicorn	£750	£1800
Half Unicorn	£1450	£4000
Crown	£500	£1250
Ducat or Bonnet piece	£1450	£3100
Two-thirds ducat	£1850	£3200
One -third ducat	£2000	£4000
*Groat	£87	£205
One-third groat	£145	£358
Plack	£35	£105
Bawbee	£27	£88
Half bawbee	£73	£158
Quarter bawbee	*Extremely rare*	

James V Edinburgh Groat

MARY (1542–67)

Edinburgh and Stirling Mints
FIRST PERIOD (1542–58)

	F	VF
Crown	£850	£2350
Twenty shillings	£1750	£3000
Lions (Forty-four shillings)	£800	£1950
Half lions (Twenty-two shillings)	£450	£1500
Ryals (Three pounds)	£1750	£4500
Half ryal	£2750	£6000
Portrait testoon	£1000	£4000
*Non-portrait testoon	£153	£453
Half testoon	£153	£390
Bawbee	£37	£83
Half bawbee	£69	£178
Penny (facing bust)	£175	£500
Penny (no bust)	*Extremely rare*	
Lion	£30	£79
Plack	£30	£79

SECOND PERIOD (Francis and Mary, 1558–60)

	F	VF
Ducat (Sixty shillings)	*Extremely rare*	
Non-portrait testoon	£158	£405
Half testoon	£158	£455
12 penny groat	£87	£200
Lion	£30	£80

Mary First Period Testoon

THIRD PERIOD (Widowhood, 1560–65)

	F	VF
Portrait testoon	£750	£2500
Half testoon	£800	£1850

FOURTH PERIOD (Henry and Mary, 1565–67)

	F	VF
Portrait ryal	*Extremely rare*	
Non-portrait ryal	£180	£500
Two-third ryal	£180	£550

	F	VF
One-third ryal	£420	£1000
Testoon	£208	£800

FIFTH PERIOD (Second widowhood, 1567)

Non-portrait ryal	£188	£550
Two thirds ryal	£205	£525
One-third ryal	£205	£500

JAMES VI
(Before accession to the English throne)
(1567–1603)

FIRST COINAGE (1567–71)

Ryal	£183	£488
Two-third ryal	£179	£457
One-third ryal	£185	£485

SECOND COINAGE (1571–80)

Twenty pounds		*Extremely rare*
Noble	£78	£350
Half noble	£78	£215
Two merks or Thistle dollar	£900	£1700
Merk	£850	—

THIRD COINAGE (1580–81)

Ducat		*Extremely rare*
Sixteen shillings	£900	£2500
Eight shillings	£850	£2200
Four shillings		*Extremely rare*
Two shillings		*Extremely rare*

James VI Fourth coinage thirty shillings

FOURTH COINAGE (1582–88)

Lion noble	£2000	£6000
Two-third lion noble	£2500	£6500
One-third lion noble	£3000	£7750
Forty shillings	£2500	£7600
*Thirty shillings	£180	£750
Twenty shillings	£128	£400
Ten shillings	£110	£279

FIFTH COINAGE (1588)

Thistle noble	£1200	£3000

SIXTH COINAGE (1591–93)

"Hat" piece	£2500	£6000
"Balance" half merk	£175	£400
"Balance" quarter merk	£258	£577

SEVENTH COINAGE (1594–1601)

Rider	£425	£900
Half rider	£350	£750
Ten shillings	£88	£275
Five shillings	£95	£300
Thirty pence	£80	£250
Twelve pence	£65	£250

EIGHTH COINAGE (1601–04)

Sword and sceptre piece	£269	£500
Half sword and sceptre piece	£215	£375
Thistle-merk	£48	£178
Half thistle-merk	£38	£136
Quarter thistle-merk	£38	£136
Eighth thistle-merk	£40	£165

	F	VF
Billon and copper issues		
Plack	£30	£93
Half plack	£880	£400
Hardhead	£28	£80
Saltire plack	£98	£500
Twopence		*Very rare*
Penny		*Very rare*

JAMES VI
(After accession to the English throne)
(1603–25)

	F	VF
Unit	£378	£750
Double crown	£450	£1200
British crown	£325	£1000
Halfcrown	£275	£500
Thistle crown	£265	£500
Sixty shillings	£278	£650
*Thirty shillings	£80	£200
Twelve shillings	£69	£175
Six shillings	£120	£550
Two shillings	£50	£250
One shilling	£70	£300
Copper twopence	£30	£60
Copper penny	£30	£75

James VI after accession thirty shillings

CHARLES I (1625–49)

FIRST COINAGE (1625–36)

	F	VF
Unit	£450	£850
Double crown	£1200	£2500
British crown		*Extremely rare*
Sixty shillings	£258	£750
Thirty shillings	£65	£250
Twelve shillings	£60	£180
Six shillings	£103	£400
Two shillings	£75	£325
One shilling		*Extremely rare*

SECOND COINAGE (1636)

	F	VF
Half merk	£50	£178
Forty penny piece	£43	£150
Twenty penny piece	£45	£300

THIRD COINAGE (1637–42)

	F	VF
Unit	£425	£950
Half unit	£550	£1750
British crown	£400	£1200
British half crown	£350	£1000
Sixty shillings	£275	£800
*Thirty shillings	£58	£150
Twelve shillings	£58	£165
Six shillings	£58	£145
Half merk	£47	£140
Forty pence	£28	£85
Twenty pence	£22	£60
Three shillings	£45	£125
Two shillings	£45	£130
Twopence (copper)	£22	£75
Penny		*Extremely rare*
Twopence (CR crowned)	£18	£65
Twopence (Stirling turner)	£18	£55

Charles I Third coinage thirty shillings

	F	VF

CHARLES II (1660–85)

FIRST COINAGE
Four merks

	F	VF
1664 Thistle above bust	£258	£600
1664 Thistle below bust	£277	£700
1665		*Extremely rare*
1670	£183	£550
1673	£183	£550
1674 F below bust	£295	£750
1675	£180	£500

Two merks

	F	VF
1664 Thistle above bust	£188	£500
1664 Thistle below bust	£188	£600
1670	£153	£450
1673	£153	£450
1673 F below bust	£254	£900
1674	£250	£900
1674 F below bust	£200	£800
1675	£155	£450

Merk

	F	VF
1664	£38	£150
1665	£38	£150
1666	£80	£350
1668	£43	£155
1669	£43	£155
1670	£70	£225
1671	£65	£180
1672	£65	£175
1673	£65	£180
1674	£53	£200
1674 F Below bust	£53	£200
*1675 F below bust	£53	£200
1675	£85	£275

Half merk

	F	VF
1664	£58	£185
1665	£58	£185
1666	£70	£195
1667	£55	£180
1668	£55	£180
1669	£78	£200
1670	£100	£350
1671	£60	£155
1672	£60	£155
1673	£50	£150
1675 F below bust	£42	£145
1675	£52	£200

SECOND COINAGE
Dollar

	F	VF
1676	£184	£430
1679	£177	£400
1680	£233	£1000
1681	£150	£450
1682	£142	£300

Half Dollar

	F	VF
1675	£165	£430
1676	£185	£475
1681	£170	£440

Quarter Dollar

	F	VF
1675	£68	£200
1676	£76	£240
1677	£95	£325

Charles II two merks

	F	VF
1679	£73	£325
1680	£65	£265
1681	£78	£350
1682	£95	£250
Eighth Dollar		
1676	£55	£155
1677	£55	£155
1678/7		*Rare*
1679	£154	£600
1680	£75	£175
1682	£103	£500
Sixteenth Dollar		
1677	£38	£110
1678/7	£77	£175
1679/7		*Rare*
1680	£78	£200
1681	£43	£135
Twopence CR[II] crowned	£28	£100
Bawbees	£38	£110
Turners	£28	£110

James VII ten shillings

JAMES VII 1685–9

	F	VF
Sixty shillings		
1688 proof only	—	£1000
Forty shillings		
1687	£88	£325
1688	£153	£400
Ten shillings		
*1687	£86	£275
1688	£100	£300

WILLIAM & MARY 1689–94

	F	VF
Sixty shillings		
1691	£155	£555
1692	£140	£500
Forty shillings		
1689	£100	£295
1690	£87	£285
1691	£75	£205
1692	£85	£285
1693	£110	£405
1694	£100	£405
Twenty shillings		
1693	£100	£385
1694	£200	£500
Ten shillings		
1689		*Extremely rare*
1690	£98	£275
*1691	£75	£220
1692	£47	£120
1694	£163	£400
Five shillings		
1691	£705	£265
1694	£68	£220
Bawbee		
1691–94	£45	£120
Bodle		
1691–94	£38	£85

William & Mary ten shillings

	F	VF

WILLIAM II 1694–1702

Pistole	£1550	£4000
Half pistole	£1405	£3500

Forty shillings

1695	£78	£300
1696	£55	£250
1697	£80	£350
1698	£55	£255
1699	£107	£600
1700	£200	£800

Twenty shillings

1695	£48	£180
1696	£48	£180
1697	£100	—
1698	£88	£320
1699	£85	£320

Ten shillings

*1695	£76	£250
1696	£80	£280
1697	£80	£300
1698	£80	£300
1699	£105	£350

Five shillings

1695	£60	£250
1696	£60	£250
1697	£37	£115
1699	£50	£228
1700	£50	£220
1701	£55	£250
1702	£68	£280

Bawbee

1695–97	£32	£100

Bodle

1695–97	£35	£150

William II ten shillings

ANNE 1702–14

PRE-UNION 1702–7

Ten shillings

1705	£68	£186
1706	£110	£360

Five shillings

1705	£27	£68
*1706	£32	£105

Anne five shillings

POST-UNION 1707–14
See listing in English section.

JAMES VIII 1688–1766 (The Old Pretender)

A number of Guineas and Crowns in various metals were struck in 1828 using original dies prepared by Norbert Roettiers, all bearing the date 1716. These coins are extremely rare and are keenly sought after.

ISLE OF MAN

DATE	F	VF	EF	UNC
PENNY				
*1709 Cast	£18	£58	£155	—
1709 Silver cast Proof	—	—	—	£1210
1709 Brass	£25	£78	£155	—
*1733 "Quocunque"	£14	£32	£128	£205
1733 "Ouocunuoe"	£19	£42	£168	£355
1733 Bath metal "Quocunque"	£10	£18	£112	—
1733 Silver Proof	—	—	—	£428
1733 Bronze Proof	—	—	—	£268
1733 Proof	—	—	—	£400
1733 Cap frosted	£10	£25	£130	£190
1733 Brass, cap frosted	£18	£38	£155	£322
1733 Silver Proof cap frosted	—	—	—	£355
1733 Bronze annulets instead of pellets	£28	£55	£210	£455
1758	£12	£30	£117	£228
1758 Proof	—	—	—	£310
1758 Silver Proof	—	—	—	£610
*1786 Engrailed edge	£10	£25	£108	£280
1786 Engrailed edge Proof	—	—	—	£310
1786 Plain edge Proof	—	—	—	£610
1786 Pellet below bust	£12	£42	£152	£310
*1798	£14	£38	£92	£188
1798 Proof	—	—	—	£210
1798 Bronze Proof	—	—	—	£210
1798 Copper-gilt Proof	—	—	—	£1000
1798 Silver Proof	—	—	—	£1500
1813	£12	£28	£88	£179
1813 Proof	—	—	—	£200
1813 Bronze Proof	—	—	—	£165
1813 Copper-gilt Proof	—	—	—	£1500
1839	£8	£25	£68	£130
1839 Proof	—	—	—	£228

DATE	F	VF	EF	UNC

HALF PENCE

*1709 Cast	£30	£45	£130	—
1709 Brass	£34	£129	£310	—
1723 Silver	£510	£1000	£2000	—
1723 Copper	£225	£455	£1100	£1600
1733 Copper	£14	£32	£130	£188
1733 Bronze	£18	£34	£130	£200
1733 Silver Proof plain cap	—	—	—	£300
1733 Silver Proof frosted cap	—	—	—	—
1733 Bronze Proof	—	—	—	£255
1733 Bath metal plain cap	£18	£25	£108	—
1733 Bath metal frosted cap	£18	£30	£122	—
*1758	£16	£34	£132	£188
1758 Proof	—	—	—	£452
1786 Engrailed edge	£10	£22	£60	£165
1786 Proof engrailed edge	—	—	—	£205
1786 Plain edge	£20	£42	£138	£188
1786 Proof plain edge	—	—	—	£400
1786 Bronze Proof	—	—	—	£205
1798	£10	£22	£58	£152
1798 Proof	—	—	—	£200
1798 Bronze Proof	—	—	—	£185
1798 Copper-gilt Proof	—	—	—	£700
1798 Silver Proof	—	—	—	£1000
1813	£9	£19	£60	£128
1813 Proof	—	—	—	£200
1813 Bronze Proof	—	—	—	£180
1813 Copper-gilt Proof	—	—	—	£750
1839	£9	£19	£38	£78
1839 Bronze Proof	—	—	—	£152

FARTHING

*1839 Copper	£9	£19	£45	£78
1839 Bronze Proof	—	—	—	£200
1839 Copper-gilt Proof	—	—	—	£1500

The last issue of coins made in the Isle of Man had been in 1839 but in 1970 Spink & Son Ltd was commissioned to produce a modern coinage for the Isle of Man Government which was struck at the Royal Mint. From 1973 onwards the Pobjoy Mint took over the contract and has been a very prolific producer of definitive and commemorative issues. It is not proposed to give a complete listing of all these coins but the Crown and 25p, which from the collector's point of view are the most interesting in the series, have been selected.

The listings that follow are of the ordinary uncirculated cupro-nickel coins. The Island has also issued most of the coins listed in other metals, including silver, gold and platinum in non proof and proof form and in 1984 some were also issued in silver clad cupro-nickel in proof form.

DATE	UNC
1970 Manx Cat	£2.75
1972 Royal Silver Wedding	£2.75
1974 Centenary of Churchill's birth	£1.57
1975 Manx Cat	£2.75
1976 Bi-Centenary of American Independence	£1.75
1976 Centenary of the Horse Drawn Tram	£1.75
1977 Silver Jubilee	£1.75
1977 Silver Jubilee Appeal	£1.75
1978 25th Anniversary of the Coronation	£1.75
1979 300th Anniversary of Manx Coinage	£1.75
1979 Millennium of Tynwald (5 coins)	£7.00
1980 Winter Olympics	£1.75
1980 Derby Bicentennial	£1.75
1980 22nd Olympics (3 coins)	£6
1980 80th Birthday of Queen Mother	£1.75
1981 Duke of Edinburgh Award Scheme (4 coins)	£5.75
1981 Year of Disabled (4 coins)	£5.75
1981 Prince of Wales' Wedding (2 coins)	£2.75
1982 12th World Cup—Spain (4 coins)	£8
1982 Maritime Heritage (4 coins)	£8
1983 Manned Flight (4 coins)	£8
1984 23rd Olympics (4 coins)	£8
1984 Quincentenary of College of Arms (4 coins)	£8
1984 Commonwealth Parliamentary Conference (4 coins)	£8
1985 Queen Mother (6 coins)	£8
1986 13th World Cup—Mexico (6 coins)	£8
1986 Prince Andrew Wedding (2 coins)	£6
1987 200th Anniversary of the United States Constitution	£1.55
1987 America's Cup Races (5 coins)	£9
1988 Bicentenary of Steam Navigation (6 coins)	£9
1988 Australia Bicentennial (6 coins)	£8.75
1988 Manx Cat	£2.75
1989 Royal Visit	£3
1989 Bicentenary of the Mutiny on the Bounty (4 coins)	£8
1989 Persian Cat	£4
1989 Bicentenary of Washington's Inauguration (4 coins)	£9
1990 150th Anniversary of the Penny Black	£6.75
1990 World Cup—Italy (4 coins)	£8
1990 25th Anniversary of Churchill's Death (2 coins)	£5
1990 Alley Cat	£4
1990 Queen Mother's 90th Birthday	£4
1991 Norwegian Forest Cat	£4
1991 Centenary of the American Numismatic Association	£2.75
1991 1992 America's Cup	£3.75
1991 10th Anniversary of Prince of Wales' Wedding (2 coins)	£5.75
1992 Discovery of America (4 coins)	£12
1992 Siamese Cat	£5
1992 1992 America's Cup	£2.75
1993 Maine Coon Cat	£2.75

DATE	UNC
1993 Preserve Planet Earth—Dinosaurs (2 coins)	£7
1994 Preserve Planet Earth—Mammoth	£3.75
1994 Year of the Dog	£3.75
1994 World Football Cup (6 coins)	£22
1994 Japanese Bobtail Cat	£3.75
1994 Normandy Landings (8 coins)	£29
1994 Preserve Planet Earth—Endangered Animals (3 coins)	£13
1995 Man in Flight—Series i (8 coins)	£48
1995 Man in Flight—Series ii (8 coins)	£48
1995 Queen Mother's 95th Birthday	£4
1995 Year of the Pig	£4
1995 Turkish Cat	£4
1995 Preserve Planet Earth—Egret and Otter	£8
1995 America's Cup	£4.50
1995 Aircraft of World War II (19 coins)	£78
1995 Famous World Inventions—Series i (12 coins)	£48
1996 Year of the Rat	£5
1996 70th Birthday of HM the Queen	£8
1996 The Flower Fairies—Series i (4 coins)	£28
1996 Famous World Inventions—Series ii (6 coins)	£28
1996 Olympic Games (6 coins)	£24
1996 Preserve Planet Earth—Killer Whale and Razorbill	£8
1996 Burmese Cat	£6
1996 Robert Burns (4 coins)	£17
1996 King Arthur & the Knights of the Round Table (5 coins)	£24
1996 European Football Championships (8 coins)	£38
1996 Football Championships Winner	£8
1996 Explorers (2 coins)	£12
1997 Year of the Ox	£8
1997 The Flower Fairies—Series ii (4 coins)	£19
1997 Royal Golden Wedding (2 coins)	£10
1997 Explorers—Eriksson and Nansen (2 coins)	£10
1997 Long-haired Smoke Cat	£6
1997 10th Anniversary of the "Cats on Coins" series (silver only)	£29
1997 90th Anniversary of the TT Races (4 coins)	£22
1998 The Millennium (16 coins to be issued in the next 3 years)	—
1998 Year of the Tiger	£8
1998 FIFA World Cup (4 coins)	£19
1998 Birman Cat	£8
1998 The Flower Fairies—Series iii (4 coins)	£22
1998 18th Winter Olympics, Nagano (4 coins)	£23
1998 Explorers—Vasco da Gama and Marco Polo (2 coins)	£12
1998 125th Anniversary of Steam Railway (8 coins)	£48
1998 International Year of the Oceans (4 coins)	£26
1999 50th Birthday of HRH the Prince of Wales	£6
1999 Year of the Rabbit	£6
1999 27th Olympics in Sydney (5 coins)	£28
1999 Rugby World Cup (6 coins)	£32
1999 Wedding of HRH Prince Edward and Sophie Rhys-Jones	£7
1999 Queen Mother's 100th Birthday (4 coins)	£20
1999 The Millennium (4 coins)	£20
1999 Titanium Millennium crown	£5
*2000 Year of the Dragon	£5
2000 Scottish Fold cat	£5
2000 Millennium—own a piece of time	£5
2000 Explorers, Francisco Piarro and Wilem Brents (2 coins) ...	£10
2000 Life and times of the Queen Mother (4 coins)	£20
2000 Queen Mother's 100th Birthday	£5
2000 60th Anniversary of the Battle of Britain	£5
*2000 BT Global Challenge	£5
2000 18th Birthday of H.R.H. Prince William	£5

GUERNSEY

DATE	F	VF	EF	UNC

TEN SHILLINGS

	F	VF	EF	UNC
*1966	—	£1	£1	£1.60
1966 Proof	—	—	—	£4

THREEPENCE

	F	VF	EF	UNC
1956	15p	25p	50p	£1
1956 Proof	—	—	—	£4
1959	15p	25p	50p	£1
1966 Proof	—	—	—	£3

EIGHT DOUBLES

	F	VF	EF	UNC
1834	£2	£4	£25	£88
*1858 5 berries	£2	£4	£26	£88
1858 4 berries	£2	£4	£26	£88
1864 1 stalk	£1	£2	£12	£42
1864 3 stalks	£1	£2	£14	£45
1868	£3	£6	£15	£38
1874	£2	£3	£6	£32
1885H	£2	£3	£5	£22
1889H	£1	£2	£4	£19
1893H small date	£1	£2	£4	£19
1893H large date	£1	£2	£4	£19
1902H	£1	£2	£3	£17
1903H	£1	£2	£4	£17
1910	£1	£2	£5	£19
1911H	£2	£3	£6	£22
1914H	25p	£1	£3	£14
1918H	25p	£1	£3	£12
1920H	25p	£1	£2	£12
1934H	30p	£1	£3	£17
1934H Proof	—	—	—	£82
1938H	30p	£1	£2	£9
1945H	25p	50p	£1	£6
1947H	20p	50p	£1	£6
1949H	20p	50p	£1	£6
1956	15p	25p	75p	£4
1956	15p	25p	75p	£4
1959	15p	25p	75p	£4
1966 Proof	—	—	—	£8

FOUR DOUBLES

	F	VF	EF	UNC
1830	£1	£3	£25	£62
1830 Mule with obv. St Helena ½d	—	£650	—	—
1858	£3	£6	£32	£62
1864 Single stalk	50p	£2	£8	£32
1864 3 stalks	50p	£2	£8	£38
1868	£1	£2	£14	£48
1874	50p	£1	£12	£48
1885H	50p	£1	£8	£19
1889H	50p	£1	£6	£17
1893H	50p	£1	£6	£17
1902H	50p	£1	£4	£14
1903H	50p	£1	£6	£16
1906H	50p	£1.50	£4	£14
1908H	50p	£1	£4	£14
1910H	50p	£1	£4	£14
1911H	50p	£1	£3	£9
1914H	50p	£1	£6	£18
1918H	50p	£1	£6	£18
1920H	50p	£1	£4	£14
1945H	50p	£1	£4	£9
1949H	£1	£2	£6	£18
1956	25p	50p	£2	£4
1966 Proof	—	—	—	£4

DATE	F	VF	EF	UNC

TWO DOUBLES

1858	£2	£5	£29	£99
1868 Single stick	£3	£6	£32	£99
1868 3 stalks	£5	£10	£52	£110
1874	£2	£4	£27	£65
1885H	£1	£2	£6	£18
1889H	£1	£2	£5	£14
1899H	£1	£2.50	£8	£22
1902H	£1	£2	£8	£18
1902H	£1	£2	£9	£19
1906H	£1	£2	£9	£22
1908H	£1	£2	£9	£22
1911H	£1	£2	£12	£24
1914H	£1	£2	£12	£24
1917H	£5	£15	£42	£87
1918H	75p	£2	£6	£14
*1920H	75p	£2	£6	£14
1929H	50p	£1	£4	£8

ONE DOUBLE

*1830	£1	£2	£12	£22
1868	£4	£8	£22	£58
1868/30	£3	£5	£19	£49
1885H	50p	£1	£3	£8
1889H	25p	50p	£2	£8
1893H	25p	50p	£2	£8
1899H	25p	50p	£2	£8
1902	25p	50p	£2	£8
1903H	25p	50p	£2	£8
1911H	25p	£1	£4	£9
1911 (new shield)	25p	50p	£2	£8
1914H	25p	£1	£4	£9
1929H	25p	50p	£2	£8
1933H	25p	50p	£2	£8
1938H	25p	50p	£2	£8

DECIMAL COINAGE

Ordinary circulating coinage from 1986 onwards is usually available in uncirculated condition at a small premium above face value thus it is not listed here. The coins listed are cupro-nickel unless otherwise stated.

TWENTY-FIVE POUNDS—*Gold*

1994 50th Anniversary of Normandy Landings	£1785
1995 Queen Mother's 95th Birthday. Proof	£210
1996 HM the Queen's 70th birthday. Proof	£210
1996 European Football Championships. Proof	£210
1997 Royal Golden Wedding. Proof	£210
1998 Royal Air Force. Proof	£210
1999 Wedding of HRH Prince Edward and Sophie Rhys-Jones. Proof ..	£210
1999 Queen Mother. Proof	£210

TEN POUNDS—*Silver*

1997 Royal Golden Wedding. Proof	£160
1999 Millennium	£360

FIVE POUNDS

1995 Queen Mother's 95th birthday	£14
1995 — Silver proof	£40
1996 HM the Queen's 70th birthday	£14
1996 — Silver proof	£40
1996 European Football Championships	£14
1996 — Silver proof	£40
1997 Royal Golden Wedding	£14
1997 — Silver proof	£40
1997 — Small size Gold. BU	£52
1997 Castles of the British Isles—Castle Cornet, Guernsey	£12
1997 — Silver proof	£42
1997 Castles of the British Isles—Caernarfon Castle. Silver proof only .	£42

DATE   UNC

1997 Castles of the British Isles—Leeds Castle. Silver proof only £42
1998 Royal Air Force. Silver proof £42
1999 Millennium £12
1999 — Silver proof £32
1999 Wedding of HRH Prince Edward and Sophie Rhys-Jones £13
1999 — Silver proof £48
1999 Queen Mother £13
1999 — Silver proof £48

TWO POUNDS
1985 40th anniversary of Liberation, crown size £8
1985 — Silver proof £28
1986 Commonwealth Games, in plastic case £8
1986 — in special folder £8
1986 — .500 Silver £17
1986 — .925 Silver proof £28
*1987 900th anniv. of death of William the Conqueror, in special folder . £7
1987 — Silver proof £28
1987 — Gold proof £910
1988 William II, in presentation folder £7
1988 — Silver proof £28
1989 Henry I, in presentation folder £7
1989 — Silver proof £28
1989 Royal Visit £7
1989 — Silver proof £28
1990 Queen Mother's 90th birthday £7
1990 — Silver proof £32
1991 Henry II, in presentation folder £7
1991 — Silver proof £32
1993 40th Anniversary of the Coronation £7
1993 — Silver proof £32
*1994 Anniversary of the Normandy Landings £7
1994 — Silver proof £32
1995 50th Anniversary of Liberation £7
1995 — Silver proof £32
1995 — Silver Piedfort proof £64

ONE POUND
1981 .... £4
1981 Gold proof £87
1981 Gold piedfort £255
1983 New specification, new reverse £4
1985 New design (in folder) £4
1995 Queen Mother's 95th Birthday. Silver proof £28
1996 Queen's 70th Birthday. Silver proof £28
1997 Royal Golden Wedding. Silver BU £12
1997 — Silver proof £28
1997 Castles of the British Isles—Tower of London. Silver proof only £22
1998 Royal Air Force. Silver proof £24
1999 Millennium. Silver proof (gold plated) £32
1999 Wedding of Prince Edward and Sophie Rhys-Jones. Silver proof .. £28
1999 Queen Mother. Silver proof £28

FIFTY PENCE
1969 .... £2
1970 .... £4
1971 Proof £6
1981 .... £2
1982 .... £2
1985 New design .... —
2000 60th Anniversary of the Battle of Britain gold proof £210
*2000 60th Anniversary of the Battle of Britain silver proof £32

TWENTY-FIVE PENCE
1972 Royal Silver Wedding £6
1972 — Silver proof £14
1977 Royal Silver Jubilee £1.75
1977 — Silver proof £14
1978 Royal Visit £1.75
1978 — Silver proof £12
1980 Queen Mother's 80th birthday £3
1980 — Silver proof £14

JERSEY

DATE	F	VF	EF	UNC
FIVE SHILLINGS				
1966	—	£1	£1	£3
1966 Proof	—	£1	£2	£8
ONE QUARTER OF A SHILLING				
1957	—	50p	£1	£3
1960 Proof	—	—	—	£6
1964	—	—	50p	£2
1966	—	—	50p	£2
ONE TWELFTH OF A SHILLING				
1877H	50p	£1	£8	£32
1877H Proof in nickel	—	—	—	£1000
1877 Proof only	—	—	—	£355
1877 Proof in nickel	—	—	—	£1000
1881	£1	£2	£10	£42
1888	50p	£1	£8	£32
1894	50p	£1	£8	£32
1909	50p	£1	£10	£22
1911	50p	£1	£4	£19
1913	50p	£1	£4	£19
1923 Spade shield	50p	£1	£4	£19
1923 Square shield	50p	£1	£4	£17
1926	50p	£1	£5	£28
1931	50p	£1	£2	£7
1933	50p	£1	£2	£7
1935	50p	£1	£2	£7
1937	50p	£1	£2	£7
1946	50p	£1	£2	£5
1947	25p	£1	£2	£5
"1945" GVI	10p	25p	50p	£3
"1945" QE2	10p	25p	50p	£3
1957	10p	20p	40p	£2
*1960 1660–1960 300th anniversary	10p	15p	30p	£1
1960 Mule	—	—	—	£78
1966 "1066–1966"	—	—	50p	£1
ONE THIRTEENTH OF A SHILLING				
1841	£2	£6	£28	£105
1844	£2	£7	£32	£125
1851	£3	£10	£42	£105
1858	£2	£7	£32	£105
1861	£3	£10	£42	£105
1865 Proof only	—	—	—	£555
1866 with LCW	£1	£3	£22	£60
1866 without LCW Proof only	—	—	—	£278
1870	£2	£6	£28	£58
1871	£2	£6	£28	£58
ONE TWENTY-FOURTH OF A SHILLING				
1877H	£1	£2	£6	£28
1877 Proof only	—	—	—	£210
1888	£1	£2	£6	£22
1894	£1	£2	£6	£22
1909	£1	£2	£6	£20
1911	75p	£1.50	£4	£18
1913	75p	£1.50	£4	£18

DATE	F	VF	EF	UNC
1923 Spade shield	£1	£2	£5	£20
1923 Square shield	£1	£2	£4	£20
1926	£1	£2	£4	£14
1931	75p	£1.50	£3	£14
*1933	75p	£1.50	£3	£12
1935	75p	£1.50	£3	£12
1937	50p	£1	£2	£8
1946	50p	£1	£2	£8
1947	50p	£1	£2	£8

ONE TWENTY-SIXTH OF A SHILLING

1841	£3	£6	£22	£58
1844	£3	£6	£18	£52
1851	£2.50	£5	£16	£52
1858	£3	£7	£38	£105
1861	£2.50	£5	£16	£48
*1866	£2	£4	£16	£58
1870	£2	£4	£14	£38
1871	£2	£4	£14	£38

ONE FORTY-EIGHTH OF A SHILLING

1877H	£5	£10	£38	£78
1877 Proof only	—	—	—	£255

ONE FIFTY-SECOND OF A SHILLING

1841	£6	£17	£48	£105
1861 Proof only	—	—	—	£478

DECIMAL COINAGE
Ordinary circulating coinage from 1986 onwards is usually available in uncirculated condition at a small premium above face value thus it is not listed here.

ONE HUNDRED POUNDS
1995 50th Anniversary of Liberation. Gold Proof £405

FIFTY POUNDS
1995 50th Anniversary of Liberation. Gold Proof £312

TWENTY-FIVE POUNDS
1995 50th Anniversary of Liberation. Gold Proof £205

TEN POUNDS
*1990 50th Anniversary of the Battle of Britain. Gold Proof £160
1995 50th Anniversary of Liberation. Gold Proof £160

FIVE POUNDS
*1990 50th Anniversary of the Battle of Britain. Silver Proof (5 ounces) £90
1997 Royal Golden Wedding £12
1997 — Silver proof £40
*1999 Millennium £48

(Reduced)

TWO POUNDS FIFTY PENCE
1972 Royal Silver Wedding £9
1972 — Silver proof £18

TWO POUNDS
(note all modern Proof coins have frosted relief)
1972 Royal Silver Wedding £8
1972 — Silver proof £12
1981 Royal Wedding, nickel silver (crown size) £5
1981— in presentation pack £8
1981 — Silver proof £18
1981 — Gold proof £305
1985 40th Anniversary of Liberation (crown size) £5
1985 — in presentation pack £6
1985 — Silver proof £25

(Enlarged)

DATE	UNC
1985 — Gold proof	£955
1986 Commonwealth Games	£6
1986 — in presentation case	£6
1986 — .500 silver	£18
1986 — .925 silver proof	£25
1987 World Wildlife Fund 25th Anniversary	£6
1987 — Silver proof	£25
1989 Royal Visit	£6
1989 — Silver proof	£25
1990 Queen Mother's 90th Birthday	£6
1990 — Silver proof	£38
1990 — Gold proof	£404
1990 50th Anniversary of the Battle of Britain, silver proof	£34
1993 40th Anniversary of the Coronation	£6
1993 — Silver proof	£38
*1995 50th Anniversary of Liberation	£6
1995 — Silver Proof	£38
1996 HM the Queen's 70th Birthday	£6
1996 — Silver proof	£34
1997 Bimetal	£6
1997 — Silver proof	£28
1997 — new portrait	£6

ONE POUND

1972 Royal Silver Wedding	£5
1972 — Silver proof	£6
1981	£4
1981 Silver proof	£12
1981 Gold proof	£164
1983 New designs and specifications on presentation card (St Helier)	£4
1983 — Silver proof	£18
1983 — gold proof	£355
1984 Presentation wallet (St Saviour)	£5
1984 — Silver proof	£24
1984 — Gold proof	£355
1984 Presentation wallet (St Brelade)	£4
1984 — Silver proof	£24
1984 — Gold proof	£355
1985 Presentation wallet (St Clement)	£4
1985 — Silver proof	£24
1985 — Gold proof	£355
1985 Presentation wallet (St Lawrence)	£4
1985 — Silver proof	£24
1985 — Gold proof	£355
1986 Presentation wallet (St Peter)	£4
1986 — Silver proof	£24
1986 — Gold proof	£355
1986 Presentation wallet (Grouville)	£4
1986 — Silver proof	£24
1986 — Gold proof	£355
1987 Presentation wallet (St Martin)	£4
1987 — Silver proof	£4
1987 — Gold proof	£355
1987 Presentation wallet (St Ouen)	£3
1987 — Silver proof	£24
1987 — Gold proof	£354
1988 Presentation wallet (Trinity)	£5
1988 — Silver proof	£24
1988 — Gold proof	£355
1988 Presentation wallet (St John)	£4
1988 — Silver proof	£24
1988 — Gold proof	£355
1989 Presentation wallet (St Mary)	£4
1989 — Silver proof	£24
1989 — Gold proof	£355

DATE	UNC
1991 Ship Building in Jersey Series	
1991 "Tickler" Silver proof	£38
1991 — Gold proof	£358
1991 "Percy Douglas" Silver proof	£29
1991 — Gold proof	£358
1992 "The Hebe" Silver proof	£24
1992 — Gold proof	£323
1992 "Coat of Arms" Silver proof	£24
1992 — Gold proof	£323
1993 "The Gemini" Silver proof	£24
1993 — Gold proof	£355
1993 "The Century" Silver proof	£24
1993 — Gold proof	£355
*1994 "Resolute" Silver proof	£28
1994 — Gold proof	£355

FIFTY PENCE

1969	£1.70
1972 Royal Silver Wedding	£4
1972 — Silver proof	£4
1983 New design	£1.75
1985 40th Anniversary of Liberation	£4

TWENTY-FIVE PENCE

1977 Royal Jubilee	£1.75
1977 — Silver proof	£14

TWENTY PENCE

1982 Date on rocks on rev. (cased)	£2
1982 — Silver proof piedfort	£38
1983 New obv. with date, rev. no date on rocks	—

SOVEREIGN

*1999 The Millennium	£95

ALDERNEY

DATE   UNC

ONE HUNDRED POUNDS
1994 50th Anniversary of D-Day Landings gold proof £460

FIFTY POUNDS
1994 50th Anniversary of D–Day Landing gold proof £255

TWENTY FIVE POUNDS
1993 40th Anniversary of Coronation gold proof £165
1994 50th Anniversary of D-Day Landings gold proof £182
1997 Royal Golden Wedding gold proof £210
*2000 60th Anniversary of the Battle of Britain gold proof £195

TEN POUNDS
1994 50th Anniversary of D–Day Landing gold proof £58

FIVE POUNDS
1995 Queen Mother Cupro-Nickel Crown £10
1995 — Silver proof £33
1995 — Silver piedfort £62
1995 — Gold proof £812
1996 HM the Queen's 70th Birthday £10
1996 — Silver proof £33
1996 — Silver piedfort £62
1996 — Gold proof £812
*1999 — Eclipse of the Sun. Silver proof with colour centre .... —
2000 60th Anniversary of the Battle of Britain £8

TWO POUNDS
1989 Royal Visit Cupro-Nickel Crown £6
1989 — Silver proof £28
1989 — Silver piedfort £58
1989 — Gold proof £912
*1990 Queen Mother's 90th Birthday £6
1990 — Silver proof £29
1990 — Silver piedfort £62
1990 — Gold proof £912
*1992 40th Anniversary of Accession £6
1992 — Silver proof £29
1992 — Silver piedfort £63
1992 — Gold proof £912
1993 40th Anniversary of Coronation £6
1993 — Silver proof £29
1993 — Silver piedfort £62
1994 50th Anniversary of D-Day Landings £6
1994 — Silver proof £32
1994 — Silver piedfort £62
1995 50th Anniversary of Return of Islanders £6
1995 — Silver proof £38
1995 — Silver piedfort £63
1995 — Gold proof £810
*1997 WWF Puffin £8
1997 — Silver proof £38
1997 Royal Golden Wedding £5
1997 — Silver proof £39

ONE POUND
1993 40th Anniversary of Coronation Silver proof £32
*1995 50th Anniversary of VE Day Silver proof £24
1995 — Gold proof £312

IRELAND

DATE	F	VF	EF	UNC

All copper unless otherwise stated

PENNIES

	F	VF	EF	UNC
1805	£5	£15	£75	£150
1805 Proof	—	—	—	£150
1805 in Bronze Proof	—	—	—	£135
1805 in Copper Gilt Proof	—	—	—	£200
1805 in Silver Proof (restrike)	—	—	—	£1250
1822	£8	£18	£100	£205
1822 Proof	—	—	—	£300
1823	£5	£15	£95	£200
1823 Proof	—	—	—	£305

HALFPENNIES

	F	VF	EF	UNC
1722 Holding Harp Left	£32	£88	£205	£500
1722 Holding Harp Right	£27	£80	£205	£400
1723/2 Harp Right	£27	£80	£205	£500
1723 Harp right	£10	£50	£100	£250
1723 Silver Proof	—	—	—	£1500
1723 Obv. R's altered from B's	£15	£63	£155	—
1723 No stop after date	£12	£6	£150	£250
1724 Rev. legend divided	£22	£70	£180	—
1724 Rev. legend continuous	£22	£70	£180	—
*1736	£12	£45	£105	£200
1736 Proof	—	—	—	£250
1736 Silver Proof	—	—	—	£600
1737	£12	£32	£102	—
1738	£18	£42	£120	—
1741	£18	£42	£120	—
1742	£18	£42	£120	—
1743	£18	£42	£120	—
1744/3	£18	£38	£105	—
1744	£18	£45	£125	—
1746	£18	£40	£120	—
1747	£18	£40	£120	—
1748	£18	£40	£120	—
1749	£18	£40	£120	—
1750	£18	£40	£120	—
1751	£18	£40	£120	—
1752	£18	£40	£120	—
1753	£18	£40	£120	—
1755	£20	£70	£200	—
*1760	£10	£35	£85	—
1766	£10	£35	£85	—
1769	£10	£35	£85	—
1769 Longer bust	£20	£50	£120	—
1774 Pattern only Proof	—	—	—	£900
1775	£12	£33	£105	—
1775 Proof	—	—	—	£300
1776	£28	£85	£200	—
1781	£18	£32	£78	£180
1782	£18	£32	£78	£180
1805	£5	£7	£32	£85
1805 Copper Proof	—	—	—	£100
1805 in Bronze	—	—	—	£80
1805 in Gilt Copper	—	—	—	£150
1805 in Silver (restrike)	—	—	—	£750

DATE	F	VF	EF	UNC
1822	£8	£12	£48	£145
1822 Proof	—	—	—	£255
1823	£8	£12	£48	£135
1823	—	—	—	£250

NB Prooflike Unirculated Pennies and Halfpennies of 1822/23 are often misdescribed as Proofs. The true Proofs are rare. Some are on heavier, thicker flans.

FARTHINGS

	F	VF	EF	UNC
1722 D.G. Rex Harp to left (Pattern)	£500	£1000	£1500	—
1723 D.G. Rex Harp to right	£68	£100	£250	—
1723 Dei Gratia Rex Harp to right	£15	£43	£100	£220
1723 — Silver Proof	—	—	—	£1000
1724 Dei Gratia Rex Harp to right	£43	£80	£200	£460
1737	£18	£38	£78	£165
1737 Proof	—	—	—	£200
1737 Silver Proof	—	—	—	£400
1738	£18	£38	£90	£185
1744	£18	£38	£90	£185
1760	£10	£18	£55	£125
*1806	£6	£13	£38	£75
1806 Copper Proof	—	—	—	£100
1806 Bronzed Copper Proof	—	—	—	£65
1806 Copper Gilt Proof	—	—	—	£100
1806 Silver Proof (restrike)	—	—	—	£500
1822 George IV (Pattern) Proof	—	—	—	£700

TOKEN ISSUES BY THE BANK OF IRELAND

FIVE PENCE IN SILVER

	F	VF	EF	UNC
1805	£8	£18	£36	£98
1806	£14	£32	£83	£155
1806/5	£28	£78	£230	£500

TEN PENCE IN SILVER

	F	VF	EF	UNC
1805	£9	£18	£36	£122
1806	£12	£33	£84	£150
*1813	£8	£18	£36	£104
1813 Proof	—	—	—	£250

THIRTY PENCE IN SILVER

	F	VF	EF	UNC
1808	£17	£49	£127	£255

SIX SHILLINGS

	F	VF	EF	UNC
*1804 in Silver	£68	£127	£253	£750
1804 Proof	—	—	—	£800
1804 in Copper (restrike)	—	—	—	£450
1804 Copper Gilt	—	—	—	£900
1804 in Gilt Silver	—	—	—	£1500

In this series fully struck specimens, with sharp hair curls, etc., are worth appreciably more than the prices quoted.

DATE	F	VF	EF	UNC

TEN SHILLINGS

	F	VF	EF	UNC
*1966 Easter Rising	—	£4	£6	£10
1966 Cased Proof	—	—	—	£12
1966 special double case	—	—	—	£35

HALF CROWNS

	F	VF	EF	UNC
1928	£2	£5	£20	£35
1928 Proof	—	—	—	£35
1930	£5	£12	£80	£225
1931	£5	£20	£110	£280
1933	£5	£12	£100	£230
1934	£5	£7	£30	£95
1937	£35	£90	£325	£800
*1939	£2	£4	£14	£40
1939 Proof	—	—	—	£400
1940	£2	£4	£14	£38
1941	£3	£8	£16	£48
1942	£3	£5	£14	£35
1943	£60	£120	£500	£1200
1951	£1	£2	£5	£20
1951 Proof	—	—	—	£300
1954	£1	£2	£5	£20
1954 Proof	—	—	—	£300
1955	£1	£2	£4	£16
1955	—	—	—	£400
1959	£1	£2	£4	£12
1961	£1	£2	£10	£25
1961 Obv as 1928, rev. as 1951	£10	£15	£135	—
1962	£1	£2	£4	£10
1963	£1	£2	£3	£7
1964	£1	£2	£3	£5
1966	£1	£2	£3	£5
1967	£1	£2	£3	£5

FLORINS

	F	VF	EF	UNC
1928	£2	£4	£10	£30
1928 Proof	—	—	—	£35
1930	£3	£10	£75	£225
1930 Proof				Unique
1931	£4	£15	£100	£275
1933	£3	£10	£75	£250
1934	£5	£80	£150	£400
1934 Proof	—	—	—	£1800
1935	£2	£9	£40	£100
1937	£5	£15	£85	£250
1939	£1	£3	£12	£20
1939 Proof	—	—	—	£400
1940	£2	£4	£14	£32
1941	£2	£4	£15	£35
1941 Proof	—	—	—	£500
1942	£3	£8	£16	£35
1943	£500	£1000	£2000	£4000
1951	50p	£1	£5	£14
1951 Proof	—	—	—	£300
1954	50p	£1	£4	£15
1954 Proof	—	—	—	£250
1955	—	50p	£3	£12

DATE	F	VF	EF	UNC
1955 Proof	—	—	—	£250
1959	35p	£1	£4	£10
1961	50p	£2	£8	£25
1962	35p	£1	£3	£10
1963	25p	£1	£2	£7
1964	25p	£1	£2	£5
1965	25p	£1	£2	£5
1966	25p	£1	£2	£4
1968	25p	£1	£2	£4

SHILLINGS

	F	VF	EF	UNC
1928	£1	£3	£6	£17
1928 Proof	—	—	—	£16
1930	£2	£10	£60	£175
1930 Proof	—	—	—	£600
1931	£2	£10	£60	£115
1933	£2	£10	£60	£150
1935	£2	£5	£25	£75
1937	£4	£40	£150	£700
1939	£1	£3	£10	£25
1939 Proof	—	—	—	£400
1940	£1	£3	£12	£24
1941	£2	£4	£15	£32
1942	£2	£3	£8	£22
1951	50p	£1	£4	£10
1951 Proof	—	—	—	£275
1954	50p	£1	£3	£8
1954 Proof	—	—	—	£300
1955	50p	£1	£4	£10
1959	50p	£1	£4	£15
1962	25p	£1	£2	£6
1963	25p	£1	£2	£4
1964	25p	£1	£2	£3
1966	25p	£1	£2	£3
1968	25p	£1	£2	£3

SIXPENCES

	F	VF	EF	UNC
1928	50p	£1	£5	£14
1928 Proof	—	—	—	£15
1934	50p	£2	£10	£55
1935	75p	£2	£18	£75
1939	50p	£1	£5	£32
1939 Proof	—	—	—	£400
1940	50p	£1	£5	£32
1942	50p	£1	£8	£34
1945	£1p	£3	£22	£68
1946	£1	£3	£45	£230
1947	£1	£2	£20	£55
1948	50p	£2	£10	£38
1949	50p	£1	£6	£27
1950	50p	£2	£18	£70
1952	50p	£1	£3	£15
1953	50p	£1	£3	£15
1953 Proof	—	—	—	£75
1955	50p	£1	£3	£15
1956	50p	£1	£2	£12
1956 Proof	—	—	—	£80
1958	£1	£2	£10	£42
1958 Proof	—	—	—	£250
1959	25p	50p	£2	£8
1960	25p	50p	£1	£5
1961	25p	50p	£1	£5

DATE	F	VF	EF	UNC
1962	£1	£3	£15	£40
1963	25p	£2	£5	£7
1964	25p	50p	£3	£5
1966	25p	50p	£3	£5
1967	25p	50p	£1	£3
1968	25p	50p	£1	£3
1969	£1	£2	£5	£8

THREEPENCES

	F	VF	EF	UNC
1928	£1	£2	£6	£10
1928 Proof	—	—	—	£15
1933	£2	£5	£40	£185
1934	50p	£1	£5	£35
1935	£1	£3	£12	£100
1939	£2	£6	£45	£225
1939 Proof	—	—	—	£725
1940	50p	£1	£5	£35
1942	25p	75p	£4	£25
1943	£1	£2	£8	£48
1946	25p	75p	£5	£24
1946 Proof	—	—	—	£155
1948	£1	£2	£18	£55
1949	25p	£1	£2	£20
1949 Proof	—	—	—	£155
1950	25p	£1	£2	£6
1950 Proof	—	—	—	£155
1953	25p	£1	£2	£7
1956	25p	£1	£2	£5
1961	25p	50p	£1	£3
1962	25p	50p	£1	£5
1963	25p	50p	£1	£5
1964	20p	50p	£1	£3
1965	20p	50p	£1	£2
1966	20p	50p	£1	£2
1967	20p	50p	£1	£2
1968	20p	40p	£1	£2

PENNIES

	F	VF	EF	UNC
1928	£1	£2	£6	£14
1928 Proof	—	—	—	£20
1931	£1	£3	£20	£70
1931 Proof	—	—	—	£750
1933	£1	£3	£25	£90
1935	50p	£1	£10	£30
1937	75p	£1	£15	£65
1937 Proof	—	—	—	£700
1938				Unique
1940	£2	£10	£80	—
1941	50p	£1	£5	£16
1942	25p	50p	£2	£10
1943	25p	£1	£3	£14
1946	25p	£1	£2	£9
1948	25p	£1	£2	£9
1949	25p	£1	£2	£9
1949 Proof	—	—	—	£250
1950	25p	75p	£2	£12
1952	25p	50p	£2	£4
1962	30p	75p	£2	£6
1962 Proof	—	—	—	£80
1963	10p	25p	£1	£3
1963 Proof	—	—	—	£70
1964	—	20p	50p	£2

DATE	F	VF	EF	UNC
1965	—	25p	50p	£3
1966	—	25p	50p	£3
1967	—	15p	25p	£2
1968	—	15p	25p	£2
1968 Proof	—	—	—	£155

HALFPENNIES

	F	VF	EF	UNC
1928	50p	£1	£5	£15
1928 Proof	—	—	—	£15
1933	£3	£10	£45	£320
1935	£2	£4	£20	£100
1937	£1	£3	£10	£45
1939	£2	£5	£25	£100
1939 Proof	—	—	—	£550
1940	50p	£2	£18	£100
1941	20p	50p	£3	£18
1942	20p	50p	£3	£18
1943	20p	50p	£5	£20
1946	50p	£1	£14	£50
1949	20p	50p	£4	£18
1953	10p	25p	£1	£6
1953 Proof	—	—	—	£350
1964	—	25p	50p	£2
1965	—	30p	75p	£3
1966	—	25p	50p	£2
1967	—	25p	50p	£2

FARTHINGS

	F	VF	EF	UNC
1928	50p	£1	£3	£6
1928 Proof	—	—	—	£12
1930	50p	£1	£4	£12
1931	£1	£2	£10	£20
1931 Proof	—	—	—	£550
1932	£1	£3	£12	£22
1933	50p	£1	£3	£10
1935	£1	£3	£10	£22
1936	£1	£3	£9	£20
1937	50p	£1	£3	£10
1939	50p	£1	£2	£4
1939 Proof	—	—	—	£400
1940	£1	£2	£5	£12
1941	50p	£1	£2	£5
1943	50p	£1	£2	£5
1944	50p	£1	£3	£7
1946	50p	£1	£2	£5
1949	£1	£2	£5	£12
1949 Proof	—	—	—	£250
1953	25p	50p	£1	£3
1953 Proof	—	—	—	£180
1959	50p	£1	£2	£3
1966	—	50p	£1.50	£3

For the 1928–50 coppper issues it is worth noting that UNC means UNC with some lustre. BU examples with full lustre are extremely elusive and are worth much more than the quoted prices.

Decimal issues are not included in this publication but it should be noted that many dates are virtually impossible to find in uncirculated grade. An example is the 1986 set which was sold exclusively through souvenir shops and included the only specimens of the ½p for that year.

Official and semi-official commemorative
Medals

It is probably a strong love of history, rather than the strict disciplines of coin collecting that make collectors turn to commemorative medals. The link between the two is intertwined, and it is to be hoped that collectors will be encouraged to venture into the wider world of medallions, encouraged by this brief guide, supplied by courtesy of Daniel Fearon, acknowledged expert and author of the *Catalogue of British Commemorative Medals*.

DATE	VF	EF
JAMES I		
1603 Coronation *(possibly by*		
C. Anthony), 29mm, Silver	£325	£750
QUEEN ANNE		
1603 Coronation,29mm, AR	£375	£750
CHARLES I		
1626 Coronation *(by N. Briot)*, 30mm, Silver	£200	£600
1633 Scottish Coronation *(by N. Briot)*, 28mm,		
Silver	£150	£300
1649 Memorial *(by J. Roettier)*. Struck after the		
Restoration, 50mm, Bronze	£65	£200
CHARLES II		
1651 Scottish Coronation, in exile *(from design*		
by Sir J. Balfour), 32mm, Silver	£365	£800
CROMWELL		
1651 Lord Protector *(by T. Simon)*, 38mm,		
Silver	£325	£750
— Cast examples	£85	£175
CHARLES II		
1661 Coronation *(by T. Simon)*, 29mm		
— Gold	£800	£1500
— Silver	£85	£200
1685 Death *(by N. Roettier)*, 39mm, Bronze	£75	£175

James I Coronation, 1603

Charles II Coronation, 1661

DATE	VF	EF

JAMES II
1685 Coronation *(by J. Roettier)*, 34mm
— Gold £850 £1600
— Silver £175 £300

MARY
1685 Coronation *(by J. Roettier)*, 34mm
— Gold £850 £1700
— Silver £135 £300

WILLIAM & MARY
1689 Coronation *(by J. Roettier)*, 32mm
— Gold £750 £1600
— Silver £100 £225
1689 Coronation,"Perseus" *(by G. Bower)*,
   38mm, Gold £650 £1500

MARY
1694 Death *(by N. Roettier)*, 39mm,Bronze £50 £150

WILLIAM III
1697 "The State of Britain" *(by J. Croker)*, 69mm,
   Silver £350 £800

ANNE

Charles II Coronation, 1661

1702 Accession, "Entirely English" *(by J. Croker)*, 34mm
— Gold £650 £1500
— Silver £75 £175
1702 Coronation *(by J. Croker)*, 36mm
— Gold £550 £1500
— Silver £75 £175
1707 Union with Scotland *(by J. Croker, rev. by S. Bull)*, 34mm
— Gold £500 £850
— Silver £65 £125
1713 Peace of Utrecht *(by J. Croker—issued in gold to Members
of Parliament)*, 34mm
— Gold £450 £900
— Silver £65 £125

GEORGE I
1714 Coronation*(by J. Croker)*, 34mm
— Gold £650 £1650
— Silver £80 £160
1727 Death *(by J. Dassier)*, 31mm, Silver £65 £125

GEORGE II
1727Coronation *(by J. Croker)*, 34mm
— Gold £600 £1600
— Silver £85 £165

QUEEN CAROLINE
1727 Coronation *(by J. Croker)*, 34mm
— Gold £600 £1650
— Silver £80 £160
1732 The Royal Family *(by J. Croker)*, 70mm
— Silver £150 £350
— Bronze £75 £175

George III, Coronation, 1761

DATE	VF	EF

GEORGE III
1761 Coronation *(by L. Natter)*, 34mm

— Gold	£650	£1800
— Silver	£120	£275
— Bronze	£50	£120

QUEEN CHARLOTTE
1761 Coronation *(by L. Natter)*, 34mm

— Gold	£650	£1850
— Silver	£120	£275
— Bronze	£50	£120
1810 Golden Jubilee, "Frogmore", 48mm, Silver	£80	£175
— Bronze	£50	£120

GEORGE IV
1821 Coronation *(by B. Pistrucci)*, 35mm

— Gold	£400	£750
— Silver	£50	£100
— Bronze	£35	£75

WILLIAM IV
1831 Coronation *(by W. Wyon; rev.shows
Queen Adelaide)*, 33mm

— Gold	£375	£750
— Silver	£50	£100
— Bronze	£35	£75

QUEEN VICTORIA
1838 Coronation *(by B. Pistrucci)*, 37mm

— Gold	£385	£850
— Silver	£65	£150
— Bronze	£25	£65

George IV Coronation, 1841

Queen Victoria Coronation, 1838

Queen Victoria Diamond Jubilee 1897

DATE	VF	EF

1887 Golden Jubilee *(by J. E. Boehm, rev. by Lord Leighton)*

— Gold, 58mm	£775	£1100
— Silver, 78mm	£85	£185
— Bronze, 78mm	£40	£100

1897 Diamond Jubilee *(by T. Brock),*

— Gold, 56mm	£750	£1000
— Silver, 56mm	£35	£75
— Bronze, 56mm	£20	£35
— Gold, 21mm	£125	£165
— Silver, 21mm	£15	£30

EDWARD VII

1902 Coronation (August 9) *(by G. W. de Saulles)*

— Gold, 56mm	£750	£1000
— Silver, 56mm	£35	£75
— Bronze, 56mm	£15	£30
— Gold, 31mm	£130	£175
— Silver, 31mm	£15	£30

Some rare examples of the official medal show the date as June 26, the original date set for the Coronation which was postponed because the King developed appendicitis.

GEORGE V

1911 Coronation *(by B. Mackennal)*

— Gold, 51mm	£750	£1000
— Silver, 51mm	£25	£75
— Bronze, 51mm	£14	£28
— Gold, 31mm	£135	£180
— Silver, 31mm	£15	£30

1935 Silver Jubilee *(by P. Metcalfe)*

— Gold, 58mm	£750	£1000
— Silver, 58mm	£25	£65
— Gold, 32mm	£120	£160
— Silver, 32mm	£15	£30

PRINCE EDWARD

1911 Investiture as Prince of Wales *(by W. Goscombe John)*

— Gold, 31mm	£250	£450
— Silver, 31mm	£30	£50

EDWARD VIII

1936 Abdication *(by L. E. Pinches), 35mm*

— Gold	£350	£650
— Silver	£35	£65
— Bronze	£15	£35

GEORGE VI

1937 Coronation *(by P. Metcalfe)*

— Gold, 58mm	£800	£1100
— Silver, 58mm	£25	£70
— Gold, 32mm	£145	£175
— Silver, 32mm	£10	£20
— Bronze, 32mm	£5	£12

George V Silver Jubilee, 1937

Edward, Prince of Wales, 1911

DATE	VF	EF

ELIZABETH II
1953 Coronation *(by Spink & Son)*

— Gold, 57mm	£750	£950
— Silver, 57mm	£25	£60
— Bronze, 57mm	£15	£25
— Gold, 32mm	£140	£175
— Silver, 32mm	£15	£25
— Bronze, 32mm	£10	£15

*The gold medals are priced for 18ct—they can also be found as 22ct and 9ct, and prices should be adjusted accordingly.

PRNCE CHARLES
1969 Investiture as Prince of Wales *(by M. Rizello)*

— Silver, 57mm	—	£35
— Bronze gilt, 57mm	—	£25
— Silver, 45mm	—	£20
— Gold, 32mm	—	£100
— Silver, 32mm	—	£20
— Bronze, 32mm	—	£12

1977 Silver Jubilee *(by A. Machin)*

— Silver, 57mm		£30
Silver, 44mm		£25

QUEEN ELIZABETH THE QUEEN MOTHER
1980 80th Birthday *(by L. Durbin)*

Edward VIII Abdication, 1936

— Silver, 57mm	—	£30
— Silver, 38mm	—	£20
— Bronze, 38mm	—	£15

N.B.—Official Medals usually command a premium when still in their original cases of issue.

English
Banknote
price guide

This price guide, supplied by courtesy of Pam West of British Notes, is by no means definitive. It is possible to buy notes for less than listed here, just as some may cost more. The prices quoted are for VF to EF up to the end of Peppiatt and EF and Uncirculated from O'Brien, which is usually considered to be the start of the modern period. Obviously notes in current circulation can be obtained at face value and it is always a good idea to put an uncirculated note away occasionally. Sometimes they may have "half moon" machine cutting marks, though they have never been circulated. More detailed information, as well as prices for the bank notes of Scotland, Channel Islands, Isle of Man, Northern Ireland and the Republic of Ireland, is available in the BANKNOTE YEARBOOK.

TREASURY NOTES

ISSUE	VF	EF	ISSUE	VF	EF
1st ISSUE			T16 with Anchor on rev. A1/B1 prefix	£150	£450
T1 Bradbury £1	£900	£1650	T17 Bradbury 10/-	£170	£300
T2 Bradbury £1	£900	£1650	T18 Bradbury 10/-	£140	£300
T3 Bradbury £1 5/6 digit	£250	£550	T19 Bradbury 10/-	£950	£1500
T4 Bradbury £1	£550	£1150	T20 Bradbury 10/-	£95	£195
T5 Bradbury £1	£650	£1350			
T6 Bradbury £1	£400	£950	**1st ISSUE**		
T7 Bradbury £1	—	—	T24 Fisher £1	£35	£70
T8 Bradbury 10/-	£400	£950	T25 Fisher 10/-	£65	£170
T9 Bradbury 10/-	£190	£450	T26 Fisher 10/-	£55	£145
T10 Bradbury 10/-	£650	£1250			
			2nd ISSUE		
2nd ISSUE			T30 Fisher 10/-	£60	£145
T11 Bradbury £1	£120	£340	T31 Fisher £1	£45	£85
T12 Bradbury 10/-	£95	£250	T32 Fisher £1	£65	£1165
T13 Bradbury 10/-	£100	£275			
T14 Bradbury £1 Dardenelles	£2100	£4500	**3rd ISSUE (NORTHERN IRELAND)**		
T15 Bradbury 10/- Dardenelles	£450	£1000	T33 Fisher 10/-	£65	£135
			T34 Fisher £1	£40	£85
3rd ISSUE			T35 Fisher £1	£70	£165
T16 Bradbury £1	£60	£125			

BANK OF ENGLAND WHITE £5 NOTES

ISSUE	EF	ISSUE	EF
B208b Nairne	£300	B255 Peppiatt	£80
B209a Harvey	£200	B264 Peppiatt	£90
B215 Mahon	£160	B270 Beale	£75
B228 Catterns	£190	B275 O'Brien	£75
B241 Peppiatt	£110	B276 O'Brien	£80

White notes in better grades are becoming difficult to obtain thus earlier rarer dates and notes in exceptional condition should command a premium.

BANK OF ENGLAND ISSUES

SERIES A—BRITANNIA

	VF	EF
B210 Mahon 10/-	£55	£90
B212 Mahon £1	£20	£65
B223 Catterns 10/-	£20	£50
B223 Catterns 10/- V prefix	£30	£80
B225 Catterns £1 LNN	£10	£25
B226 Catterns £1 NNL	£50	£100

1st PERIOD

	VF	EF
B235 Peppiatt 10/- LNN	£12	£35
B235 Peppiatt 10/- LNN J Prefix	£18	£50
B236 Peppiatt 10/- NNL	£15	£50
B238 Peppiatt £1 NNL	£12	£25
B239 Peppiatt £1 LNNL	£10	£20

2nd PERIOD

	VF	EF
B248 Peppiatt £1 Blue	£5	£20
B249 Peppiatt £1 Blue	£3	£9
B251 Peppiatt 10/- Mauve	£12	£25

3rd PERIOD

	VF	EF
B256 Peppiatt 10/-	£20	£60
B258 Peppiatt £1	£8	£15
B258 Peppiatt £1 S--A	£10	£30

4th PERIOD (THREADED)

	VF	EF
B260 Peppiatt £1	£3	£8
B261 Peppiatt £1 ®	£35	£140
B262 Peppiatt 10/-	£8	£30
B263 Peppiatt 10/- ® 01A	£350	£650
B265 Beale 10/- NNL	£10	£25
B266 Beale 10/- LNNL	£10	£18
B267 Beale 10/- ® 05A	£60	£105
B268 Beale £1	£3	£8
B269 Beale £1 ®	£20	£35
B271 O'Brien 10/-	£8	£15
B272 O'Brien 10/- ®	£45	£70
B273 O'Brien £1	£3	£6
B274 O'Brien £1 ®	£20	£35
B274 O'Brien £1 ® S--T	£20	£40

SERIES B—HELMETED BRITANNIA

	EF	UNC
B277 O'Brien £5 Shaded Symbol	£20	£40
— A01 (first)	£70	£190
B280 O'Brien £5 White Symbol	£20	£35

SERIES C—PORTRAIT

	EF	UNC
B281 O'Brien £1 LNN	£3	£5
B282 O'Brien £1 LNNL	£3	£5
B283 O'Brien £1 "R" EXP LNNL	£130	£280
B284 O'Brien £1 LNNL	£10	£20
B285 O'Brien £1 ®	£10	£30
B286 O'Brien 10/-	£3	£6
B287 O'Brien 10/- ®	£12	£30
B288 Hollom £1 LNNL	£2	£5
B289 Hollom £1 R LNN	£15	£30
B290 Hollom £1 R NNL	£12	£20
B291 Hollom £1 R LNNL	£20	£95
B292 Hollom £1 G	£2	£6
B293 Hollom £1 G ®	£14	£40
B294 Hollom 10/- LNN	£2	£5
B295 Hollom 10/- NNL	£2	£4

	EF	UNC
B296 Hollom 10/- ®	£20	£35
B297 Hollom £5	£12	£20
B298 Hollom £5 ®	£60	£150
B299 Hollom £10	£15	£30
B301 Fforde £1	£3	£6
B302 Fforde £1 R	£20	£40
B303 Fforde £1 G	£4	£8
B304 Fforde £1 G ®	£20	£45
B305 Fforde £1	£2	£5
B306 Fforde £1 ®	£14	£20 (types)
— R01M (first)	£65	£250
— Mid	£8	£15
— S01M (first)	£65	£200
B307 Fforde £1 G	£3	£10
B308 Fforde £1 G ®	£15	£40
B308 — T--M G	£60	£180
B309 Fforde 10/- LLN	£2	£5
B310 Fforde 10/- LNNL	£2	£4
B311 Fforde 10/- R	£4	£10
B312 Fforde £5 LNN	£12	£22
B313 Fforde £5 ®	£60	£110
B314 Fforde £5 NNL	£12	£30
B315 Fforde £5 ®	£70	£150
B316 Fforde £10	£18	£35
B318 Fforde £20	£90	£180
B319 Fforde £20 ®	£100	£250
B320 Page £1 LNNL	£2	£4
B321 Page £1 ®	£10	£20
B322 Page £1 LLNN	£2	£4
B323 Page ® (Some types rarer)	£5	£20
B324 Page £5	£20	£35
B325 Page £5 ®	£80	£150
B326 Page £10	£18	£35
B327 Page £10 ®	£28	£40

SERIES D—PICTORIAL

	EF	UNC
B328 Page £20	£28	£60
B329 Page £20 ®	£50	£90
B330 Page £10	£20	£32
B331 Page £10 ®	£55	£95
B332 Page £5 LNN no "L" on reverse	£15	£20
B333 Page £5 ®	£80	£130
B334 Page £5 NNL	£14	£20
B335 Page £5 ®	£70	£130
B336 Page £5 LLNN	£8	£15
B337 Page £1 LNN	£2	£4
B338 Page £1 ®	£170	£250
B339 Page £1 NNL	£2	£4
B339a Page £1 8l .. various	£120	£200
B340 Page £1 LNNL	£4	£8
B341 Somerset £1 W	£3	£4
B342 Somerset £1 EXP	£350	£650
B343 Somerset £5	£10	£18

The B343 series starts DN01 and runs through a variety of prefixes to end at LZ90, although a sub-series exists of NA01 to NC90.

	EF	UNC
— DN01	£60	£125
— NA01	£100	£250
— NC90	£10	£35
— Mid on NB	£12	£20
B344 Somerset £5 OCR EXP	£450	£800

	EF	UNC
B345 Somerset £5 Wide Thread	£10	£15
B346 Somerset £10 LNN	£25	£40
B347 Somerset £10 NNL	£18	£32
B348 Somerset £10 LLNN with "L"	£18	£30
B349 Somerset £10 Window Thread	£14	£30
B350 Somerset £20 LNN	£30	£50
B351 Somerset £20 NNL Window Thread	£35	£45
B352 Somerset £50	£65	£100
B353 Gill £5	£10	£18
—SE90 (last)	£40	£80
B354 Gill £10	£14	£20
B355 Gill £20	£22	£40
— 01L (first)	£40	£110
— 20X (last)	£90	£150
B356 Gill £50 Window Thread	£60	£95
B360— E01	£65	£110

SERIES E—HISTORICAL

	EF	UNC
B357 Gill £5	—	£10
B358 Gill £20	—	£35

SERIES D

	EF	UNC
B359 Kentfield £10	—	£30
B360 Kentfield £50	—	£95

SERIES E

	EF	UNC
B361 Kentfield £5 MKI LNN	—	£9
— W18 (last)	£20	£45
B362 Kentfield £5 MKII LNN	—	£10
— AA01 (first)	£8	£16
B363 Kentfield £5 MKIII LLNN	—	£10
B364 Kentfield £10 MKI LNN	—	£15
B365 Kentfield "B" Ream £10 M/Y/Z LNN	—	£35
B366 Kentfield £10 MKII LLNN	—	£14
B367 Kentfield £20 LNN	—	£30
B368 Kentfield "B" Ream £20 A/B LNN	—	£80
& M/Z LNN	—	£80
B369 Kentfield £20 MKII LNN	—	£30
B370 Kentfield £20 MKII LLNN	—	£25
B371 Kentfield £50 LNN	—	Face
— A01	—	£95
Lowther £5 EA01	—	£10
Lowther £10 KL01	—	£45
Lowther £10 KL low nos	—	£16
Lowther £20 DA01	—	£65
Lowther £50 J01	—	£120
Lowther "Elgar" £20 AA	—	—

Only some prices for true firsts and lasts, i.e. A01s–Z99s, have been quoted as often the price is dictated by availability of the notes which on earlier and some modern material, are often in short supply. Some low numbers on firsts command higher prices.

There is a series of unissued fractional notes, printed during the two wars, which are very scarce and not generally found for anything less than £2,000 in EF. These include Bradbury T21 5/–, T22 2/6, T23 1/–, Fisher T27 5/–, T28 2/6, T29 1/–, Peppiatt B253 5/–, B254 2/6.

Abbreviations

®	Replacement		OCR	Optical Character Recognition
"R"	Research		L	Letter (of serial number)
EXP	Experimental		N	Number (of serial number)
G	Goebel			i.e. LNNL = letter, number, number, letter
W	Webb Off-set		"B"	B Ream

Why not BANK NOTES?

Millions of pounds worth of banknotes exchange hands every day, and yet most of us pay little attention to the coloured pieces of paper we are about to part with. To a collector however, they are to be studied and enjoyed. Sometimes they can be worth many times their face value. A historian, with careful study, can discover much about a county's history from prosperity through war, siege and its inflationary periods. Banknotes have also been used for spreading propaganda. The Gulf war is a recent example. Many banknotes still survive long after the country of issue has disappeared.

So how do you start and where can you get advice on forming a collection? The answers, together with a few interesting facts about paper money can be found here. But remember, this feature can only scratch the surface of this fascinating subject; its aim is to inspire and surprise you.

Paper money is not a modern phenomenon. Its origins can be found in China during the second century BC. Emperor Wu (140–86BC), frustrated with the time taken for heavily laden wagons of copper coins to complete their journey, used deerhide as a kind of tax money. Skins from white stags were cut into pieces each a foot square. The borders were decorated with designs of water plants and each skin was given a value of 40,000 copper coins. Around 105 AD paper, made from broken down plant fibres and old cotton textiles was invented by a Chinese minister of Agriculture. However, true paper money didn't appear in China until the Tang Dynasty somewhere between 650–800 AD. The earliest Chinese notes collectors are likely to come across are from the Ming Dynasty. Made from mulberry bark paper, these notes measure 230mm x 330mm. Although over six hundred years old, these notes can be bought for around £500. An interesting factor is that Asia was using paper money while Britain and Europe were still in the dark ages.

The first European bank to be established was in Stockholm, Sweden in July 1661. Unfortunately its banknotes were not government backed and the

enterprise was forced to close within a few years.

On July 27, 1694 the Bank of England was founded by Royal Charter; the first European bank to survive to the present day. From its temporary offices at the Mercers' Hall, Cheapside, London, the

China is credited with issuing the earliest notes, very few of which survive today.

261

Bank set to work producing its first issues. These have become known as running cash notes. At first they were written out entirely by hand on paper bought by the Bank's staff from local stationers. Forgery however, soon put a stop to this practice. Each note was made out to the bearer for the amount they had on deposit. Although there was no guarantee of conversion into gold, the notes could be cashed in for part of their original value. This led to endorsements appearing on the notes stating the date and amount paid off. The notes would change hands for payment of goods or services just as our modern banknotes do today.

During the last century many private banks were set up in towns and cities throughout Britain. The notes they issued were usually well printed and many carry a motif or vignette identifying with the place of issue. For example coats of arms

Notes issued in Revolutionary France are important historical documents—mostly inexpensive and well worth looking out for.

Provincial banknotes are eagerly sought after by collectors of local history.

often appear, so too do famous buildings. Others simply have embellished initials. It is these simple features that help to make these provincial notes popular with collectors today, coupled with the interest of owning a banknote actually issued in your town! Unfortunately most of these banks went into liquidation and many investors lost their money—it is quite common to find provincial notes with the bankruptcy court stamp or other marks on the reverse. Notes are also encountered which have been rejoined with paper strips as it was often the practice to cut notes in half—sending half by one means and the second portion at a later date, to be joined with its counterpart before it could be redeemed. This lessened the risk of the note being stolen or lost in transit.

The expression "Safe as the Bank of England" is held in high regard today. In reality the Bank has almost collapsed on at least two occasions, and in 1696 it had its first major crisis. An act passed by parliament ordered the recoinage of all metallic currency. As the notes circulated by the Bank had status of legal tender and therefore not legally convertible into gold, people naturally had more confidence in metal currency. Accounts submitted by the Bank to parliament in December of that year showed £764,000 worth of notes in circulation. These were backed by just under £36,000 worth of gold.

The second emergency for the Bank came in 1720 after the "bursting" of the South Sea Bubble. Holding the monopoly of trade with South America, the South Sea Company offered to take on the national debt in return for further concessions. Company shares soared but when the collapse came it was found that government ministers were deeply involved and a political crisis followed. Bankruptcy was rife and people naturally wished to obtain their money. The queue of those wanting to withdraw gold from the Bank of England stretched down Ludgate Hill into Fleet Street.

Notes of the old British Commonwealth are becoming difficult to find in good condition.

The Bank managed to save the situation by employing it own staff to join the queue posing as customers. Each would withdraw large quantities of money and then take it round to the back of the Bank where is was redeposited. This meant the tills were kept opened until the public alarm subsided.

One modern day crisis for the Bank came during the Second World War when Germany decided to forge the large white Bank of England notes in current circulation at the time, in huge quantities. This operation called for around 150 prisoners, each hand picked for their skills in engraving, printing and paper making. The original idea was to drop the undetectable forgeries on the British Isles and neutral nations in an effort to destroy Britain's economy but the plan never came to fruition, although millions of pounds in face value were produced. Most of the notes were dumped into Lake Toplitz, but many have since been recovered and often appear on the market today. When encountering forgeries, collectors are in a difficult position. If they hold a note, knowing it to be a forgery, they are breaking the law. If they have the note checked, they run the risk of having it confiscated!

A banknote need not be old to be worth collecting. Many interesting notes have been issued throughout the world each with their own story to tell. In 1954 the Canadian Central Bank issued notes in which the portrait of the Queen had what appeared to be the hidden face of the Devil in the folds of her hair. The public refused to handle them and the notes were withdrawn. To this day it is not known whether the engraving was done intentionally or not.

Most countries suffer from inflation but in 1923, Germany saw one of the biggest inflationary periods of modern times. On November 1 of that year the average wage packet was 28 million marks, equivalent to 1.3 million pounds at the 1913 exchange rate. This huge sum would not have been enough to buy a newspaper, which would have cost around 3,000 million marks. This period left a legacy of hundreds of different notes for the collector today.

Unlike coins, collecting of paper money is still in its infancy. It is still possible to obtain notes from many different countries for a modest outlay. Some dealers sell starter packs that include 50 uncirculated notes from 50 different counties, all for under £30. One reason why some notes are so cheap is that many countries devalue their currency. When a new set of notes are issued, the old set after a period, become worthless. Dealers can acquire large quantities of these notes for less than the original face value. New collectors will find many books on the subject of paper money. For a detailed look into Treasury and Bank of England issues, including a comprehensive price guide, *English Paper Money* by Vincent Duggleby is essential. The best way to meet fellow collectors is to join an organisation. The International Bank Note Society (IBNS) has over 2,000 members world wide; full details can be obtained from the Assistant General Secretary: Mrs Sally Thowney, 36B Dartmouth Park HIll, London NW5 1HN.

COIN NEWS is also a useful way of keeping in touch with the every day events of the banknote world. There is a dedicated banknote section in the magazine every month often giving vital pieces of information, for example the latest auction prices realised, forthcoming events and fairs and there are also informative articles designed to be of appeal to experienced collectors as well as newcomers.

Coincraft purchased the biggest-ever hoard of banknotes when they bought over 8 tons of British Armed Forces Special Vouchers at auction in 1991. Despite the quantity, these notes are still highly collectable and have all vanished into collections!

MEDAL YEARBOOK 2001

This new edition of the **MEDAL YEARBOOK** contains descriptions and pictures of all British and Empire medals, covering orders (illustrated in full colour, as is the photographic medal ribbon chart), decorations, campaign medals, long service medals, life-saving awards and a host of others. There is a full account of who the medal was awarded to and why and *all the prices have been updated in line with market movements*

Fully revised with new medals, new illustrations, new sections and new information, the MEDAL YEARBOOK is essential reading for the medal collector, military enthusiast, experienced dealer or raw recruit.

The MEDAL YEARBOOK has become a must have for collectors and dealers alike and is recognised throughout the world as having NO EQUAL—*ORDER YOUR COPY TODAY!*

Once again, there is a very limited edition hardback version of the MEDAL YEARBOOK published, early ordering of this is essential to guarantee your copy.

Please tick as appropriate

Please send me .... copy(ies) of the **MEDAL YEARBOOK 2001 @ £16.95 each plus £3.00 p&p** (ISBN: 1 870 192 311) ☐

I would like a special hardbound edition of the **MEDAL YEARBOOK 2001 @ £21.95 each plus £3.00 p&p** (ISBN: 1 870 192 34 6) ☐

I enclose remittance of £....................

Please make cheques payable to "Token Publishing Ltd." US Dollar cheques also acceptable. We also accept Visa/ Mastercard/JCB cards.

To: TOKEN PUBLISHING LTD.,Orchard House, Duchy Road, Heathpark Honiton, Devon, EX14 1YD
Tel: 01404 44166   Fax: 01404 44788
email: sales @medal-news.com. Website: www.medal-news.com

NAME ....

ADDRESS ....

....

POSTCODE ....

TELEPHONE (*in case of query*) ....

Expiry date .... Signature ....   *Please allow 14 days for delivery*   CYB/01

Directory section

ON the following pages will be found the most useful names and addresses needed by the coin collector.

At the time of going to press with this edition of the YEARBOOK the information is correct, as far as we have been able to ascertain. However, people move and establishments change, so it is always advisable to make contact with the person or organisation listed before travelling any distance, to ensure that the journey is not wasted.

Should any of the information in this section not be correct we would very much appreciate being advised in good time for the preparation of the next edition of the COIN YEARBOOK.

Museums *and* Libraries

Listed below are the Museums and Libraries in the UK which have coins or items of numismatic interest on display or available to the general public.

A

Anthropological Museum, University of Aberdeen, Broad Street, **Aberdeen,** AB9 1AS (01224 272014).

Curtis Museum (1855), High Street, **Alton,** Hants (01420 2802). *General collection of British coins.*

Ashburton Museum, 1 West Street, **Ashburton,** Devon. *Ancient British and Roman antiquities including local coin finds.*

Ashwell Village Museum (1930), Swan Street, **Ashwell,** Baldock, Herts. *Roman coins from local finds, local trade tokens, Anglo-Gallic coins and jetons.*

Buckinghamshire County Museum (1862), Church Street, **Aylesbury,** Bucks (01296 88849). *Roman and medieval English coins found locally, 17th/18th century Buckinghamshire tokens, commemorative medals.*

B

Public Library and Museum (1948), Marlborough Road, **Banbury,** Oxon (01295 259855). *Wrexlin Hoard of Roman coins.*

Museum of North Devon (1931), The Square, **Barnstaple,** EX32 8LN (01271 46747). *General coin and medal collection, including local finds. Medals of the Royal Devonshire Yeomanry.*

Roman Baths Museum, Pump Room, **Bath,** Avon (01225 461111 ext 2785). *Comprehensive collection of Roman coins from local finds.*

Bagshaw Museum and Art Gallery (1911), Wilton Park, **Batley,** West Yorkshire (01924 472514). *Roman, Scottish, Irish, English hammered, British and foreign coins, local traders' tokens, political medalets, campaign medals and decorations.*

Bedford Museum (1961), Castle Lane, **Bedford** (01234 353323). *Collections of the Bedford Library and Scientific Institute, the Beds Archaeological Society and Bedford Modern School (Pritchard Memorial) Museum.*

Ulster Museum (1928), Botanic Gardens, **Belfast** BT9 5AB (01232 381251). *Irish, English and British coins and commemorative medals.*

Berwick Borough Museum (1867), The Clock Block, Berwick Barracks, Ravensdowne, **Berwick.** TD15 1DQ (01289 330044). *Roman, Scottish and medieval coins.*

Public Library, Art Gallery and Museum (1910), Champney Road, **Beverley,** Humberside (01482 882255). *Beverley trade tokens, Roman, English, British and foreign coins.*

Bignor Roman Villa (1811), **Bignor,** nr Pulborough, West Sussex (017987 202). *Roman coins found locally.*

City Museum and Art Gallery (1861), Chamberlain Square, **Birmingham** B3 3DH (0121 235 2834). *Coins, medals and tokens, with special emphasis on the products of the Soho, Heaton, Birmingham and Watt mints.*

Blackburn Museum, Museum Street, **Blackburn,** Lancs (01254 667130). *Incorporates the Hart (5,000 Greek, Roman and early English) and Hornby (500 English coins) collections, as well as the museum's own collection of British and Commonwealth coins.*

Museum Collection, Town Hall, **Bognor Regis,** West Sussex. *Roman, English and British coins and trade tokens.*

Museum and Art Gallery,(1893), Civic Centre, **Bolton,** Lancashire (01204 22311 ext 2191). *General collection of about 3000 British and foreign coins, and over 500 British medals. Numismatic library.*

Art Gallery and Museum, Central Library, Oriel Road, **Bootle,** Lancs. *Greek, Roman, English, British and some foreign coins, local trade tokens.*

Roman Town and Museum (1949) Main Street, **Boroughbridge,** N. Yorks. YO2 3PH (01423 322768). *Roman coins.*

The Museum (1929), The Guildhall, **Boston,** Lincs (01205 365954). *Small collection of English coins.*

Natural Science Society Museum (1903), 39 Christchurch Road, **Bournemouth,** Dorset (01202 553525). *Greek, Roman and English hammered coins (including the Hengistbury Hoard), local trade tokens.*

Bolling Hall Museum (1915), Bolling Hall Road, **Bradford,** West Yorkshire BD4 7LP (01274 723057). *Some 2,000 coins and tokens, mostly 18th–20th centuries.*

Cartwright Hall Museum and Art Gallery (1904), Lister Park, **Bradford,** West Yorkshire BD9 4NS (01274 493313). *Roman coins found locally.*

Museum and Art Gallery (1932), South Street, **Bridport,** Dorset (01308 22116). *Roman coins, mainly from excavations at Claudian Fort.*

The City Museum (1820), Queen's Road, **Bristol** BS8 1RL (0117 9 27256). *Ancient British, Roman (mainly from local hoards), English hammered coins, especially from the Bristol mint, and several hundred local trade tokens.*

District Library and Museum (1891), Terrace Road, **Buxton,** Derbyshire SK17 6DU (01298 24658). *English and British coins, tokens and commemorative medals. Numismatic library.*

C

Segontium Museum (1928), Beddgelert Road, **Caernarfon,** Gwynedd (01286 675625) *Roman coins and artifacts excavated from the fort.*

Fitzwilliam Museum (1816), Department of Coins and Medals, Trumpington Street, **Cambridge** (01223 332900). *Ancient, English, medieval European, oriental coins, medals, plaques, seals and cameos.*

National Museum & Galleries of Wales, Cathays Park, **Cardiff** (029 20397951). *Greek, Celtic, Roman and British coins and tokens with the emphasis on Welsh interest. Also military, civilian and commemorative medals.*

Guildhall Museum (1979), Greenmarket, **Carlisle,** Cumbria (01228 819925). *General collection of coins and medals.*

Tullie House (1877), Castle Street, **Carlisle,** Cumbria (01228 34781). *Roman, medieval and later coins from local finds, including medieval counterfeiter's coin-moulds.*

Gough's Caves Museum (1934), The Cliffs, **Cheddar,** Somerset (01934 343). *Roman coins.*

Chelmsford and Essex Museum (1835), Oaklands Park, Moulsham Street, **Cheltenham,** Glos CM2 9AQ (01245 353066). *Ancient British, Roman, medieval and later coins mainly from local finds, local medals.*

Town Gate Museum (1949), **Chepstow,** Gwent. *Local coins and trade tokens.*

Grosvenor Museum (1886), Grosvenor Street, **Chester** (01244 21616). *Roman coins from the fortress site, Anglo-Saxon, English medieval and post-medieval coins of the Chester and Rhuddlan mints, trade tokens of Chester and Cheshire, English and British milled coins.*

Public Library (1879), Corporation Street, **Chesterfield,** Derbyshire (01246 2047). *Roman coins from local finds, Derbyshire trade tokens, medals, seals and railway passes. Numismatic library. Numismatic library and publications.*

Red House Museum (1919), Quay Road, **Christchurch,** Dorset (01202 482860). *Coins of archaeological significance from Hampshire and Dorset, notably the South Hants Hoard, ancient British, Armorican, Gallo-Belgic, Celtic and Roman local trade tokens and medals.*

Corinium Museum (1856), Park Street, **Cirencester,** Glos (01285 655611). *Roman coins from archaeological excavations.*

Colchester and Essex Museum (1860), The Castle, **Colchester,** Essex (01206 712931/2). *Ancient British and Roman coins from local finds, medieval coins (especially the Colchester Hoard), later English coins and Essex trade tokens, commemorative medals.*

D

Public Library, Museum and Art Gallery (1921), Crown Street, **Darlington,** Co Durham (01325 463795). *General collection of coins, medals and tokens.*

Borough Museum (1908), Central Park, **Dartford,** Kent (01322 343555). *Roman, medieval and later English hammered coins, trade tokens and commemorative medals.*

Dartmouth Museum (1953), The Butterknowle, **Dartmouth,** Devon (01803 832923). *Coins and medals of a historical and maritime nature.*

Museum and Art Gallery (1878), The Strand, **Derby** (01332 255586). *Roman coins, English silver and copper regal coins, Derbyshire tradesmen's tokens, British campaign medals and decorations of the Derbyshire Yeomanry and the 9/12 Royal Lancers.*

Museum and Art Gallery (1909), Chequer Road, **Doncaster,** South Yorkshire (01302 734293). *General collection of English and foreign silver and bronze coins. Representative collection of Roman imperial silver and bronze coins, including a number from local hoards. English trade tokens, principally of local issues, medals.*

Dorset County Museum(1846), **Dorchester,** Dorset (01305 262735). *British, Roman, medieval and later coins of local interest.*

Central Museum (1884), Central Library, St James's Road, **Dudley,** West Midlands (01384 453576). *Small general collection of coins, medals and tokens.*

Burgh Museum (1835), The Observatory, Corberry Hill, **Dumfries** (01387 53374). *Greek, Roman, Anglo-Saxon, medieval English and Scottish coins, especially from local hoards. Numismatic library.*

Dundee Art Galleries and Museums (1873). Albert Square, **Dundee** DD1 1DA (01382 23141). *Coins and medals of local interest.*

The Cathedral Treasury (995 AD), The College, **Durham** (0191-384 4854). *Greek and Roman coins bequeathed by Canon Sir George Wheeler (1724), general collection of medals from the Renaissance to modern times, medieval English coins, especially those struck at the Durham ecclesiastical mint.*

Durham Heritage Centre, St Mary le Bow, North Bailey, **Durham** (0191-384 2214). *Roman, medieval and later coins, mainly from local finds.*

E

Royal Museum of Scotland (1781), Queen Street, **Edinburgh** EH1 (0131 225 7534). *Roman, Anglo-Saxon, Englsh and Scottish coins, trade tokens, commemorative medals and communion tokens. Numismatic library. Publications.*

Royal Albert Memorial Museum (1868), Queen St, **Exeter** EX4 3RX (01392 265858). *Roman and medieval. Coins of the Exeter Mint.*

G

Hunterian Museum (1807), Glasgow University, University Avenue, **Glasgow** G12 8QQ (041 339 8855). *Greek, Roman, Byzantine, Scottish, English and Irish coins, Papal and other European medals, Indian and Oriental coins, trade and communion tokens.*

Art Gallery and Museum (1888), Kelvingrove, **Glasgow** G3 (0141 357 3929). *General collection of coins, trade tokens, communion tokens, commemorative and military medals.*

Museum of Transport (1974), Kelvin Hall, Bunhouse Road, **Glasgow** G3 (0141 357 3929). *Transport tokens and passes, commemorative medals, badges and insignia of railway companies and shipping lines.*

City Museum and Art Gallery (1859), Brunswick Road, **Gloucester** (01452 524131). *Ancient British, Roman, Anglo-Saxon (from local finds), early medieval (from local mints), Gloucestershire trade tokens.*

Guernsey Museum and Art Gallery, St Peter Port, **Guernsey** (01481 726518). *Armorican, Roman, medieval and later coins, including the coins, medals, tokens and paper money of Guernsey.*

Guildford Museum (1898), Castle Arch, **Guildford**, Surrey GU1 3SX (01483 444750). *Roman and medieval coins and later medals.*

H

Gray Museum and Art Gallery, Clarence Road, **Hartlepool**, Cleveland (01429 268916). *General collection, including coins from local finds.*

Public Museum and Art Gallery (1890), John's Place, Cambridge Road, **Hastings**, East Sussex (01424 721952). *General collection of English and British coins, collection of Anglo-Saxon coins from Sussex mints.*

City Museum (1874), Broad Street, **Hereford** (01432 268121 ext 207). *Coins from the Hereford mint and local finds, Herefordshire trade tokens, general collection of later coins and medals.*

Hertford Museum (1902), 18 Bull Plain, **Hertford** (01992 582686). *British, Roman, medieval and later English coins and medals.*

Honiton and Allhallows Public Museum (1946), High Street, **Honiton**, Devon (01404 44966). *Small general collection, including coins from local finds.*

Museum and Art Gallery (1891), 19 New Church Road, **Hove**, East Sussex (01273 779410). *English coins, Sussex trade tokens and hop tallies, campaign medals, orders and decorations, commemorative medals.*

Tolson Memorial Museum (1920), Ravensknowle Park, **Huddersfield**, West Yorkshire (01484 541455). *Representative collection of British coins and tokens, Roman and medieval coins, mainly from local finds.*

Hull and East Riding Museum (1928), 36 High Street, **Hull** (01482 593902). *Celtic, Roman and medieval coins and artifacts from local finds. Some later coins including tradesmen's tokens.*

I

The Manx Museum, Douglas, **Isle of Man** (01624 675522). *Roman, Celtic, Hiberno-Norse, Viking, medieval English and Scottish coins, mainly from local finds, Manx traders' tokens from the 17th to 19th centuries, Manx coins from 1709 to the present day.*

J

Jersey Museum, Weighbridge, St Helier, **Jersey** (01534 30511). *Armorican, Gallo-Belgic, Roman, medieval English and French coins, coins, paper money and tokens of Jersey.*

K

Dick Institute Museum and Art Gallery (1893), Elmbank Avenue, **Kilmarnock**, Ayrshire (01563 26401). *General collection of coins and medals, and the Hunter-Selkirk collection of communion tokens.*

L

City Museum (1923), Old Town Hall, Market Square, **Lancaster** (01524 64637). *Roman, Anglo-Saxon, medieval English coins, provincial trade tokens, medals of the King's Own Royal Lancashire Regiment.*

City Museum (1820), Municipal Buildings, The Headrow, **Leeds**, West Yorkshire (01532 478279). *Greek, Roman, Anglo-Saxon, English medieval, Scottish, Irish, British, Commonwealth and foreign coins. Several Roman and Saxon hoards. The Backhouse collection of Yorkshire banknotes, the Thornton collection of Yorkshire tokens, British and foreign commemorative medals.*

Leicester Museum and Art Gallery (1849), New Walk, **Leicester** (01533 554100). *Roman, medieval and later coins, mainly from local finds, tokens, commemorative medals, campaign medals and decorations.*

Pennington Hall Museum and Art Gallery, **Leigh,** Lancashire. *General collection of Roman, English and British coins and medals.*

Museum and Art Gallery (1914), Broadway, **Letchworth**, Herts (01462 65647). *Ancient British coins minted at Camulodunum, Roman, medieval and English coins, Hertfordshire trade tokens, commemorative and campaign medals.*

City Library, Art Gallery and Museum (1859), Bird Street, **Lichfield**, Staffs (01543 2177). *Roman, medieval and later English coins, Staffordshire trade tokens and commemorative medals.*

Liverpool Museum(1851), William Brown Street, **Liverpool** L3 8EN (0151 207 0001). *General collection of Roman, medievaland later British coins, tokens.*

Bank of England Museum, Threadneedle Street, **London** EC2 (020-7601 5545). *Exhibits relating to gold bullion, coins, tokens and medals, the design and manufacture of banknotes, and a comprehensive collection of bank notes dating from the 17th century to the present day.*

British Museum(1752), HSBC Coin Gallery, Great Russell Street, **London** WC1 (020-7636 1555). *Almost a million coins, medals, tokens and badges of all period from Lydia, 7th century BC to the present time. Extensive library of books and periodicals.*

British Numismatic Society (1903), Warburg Institute, Woburn Square, **London** WC1. *Library containing over 5,000 volumes, including sale catalogues, periodicals and pamphlets. Open to members only.*

Cuming Museum (1906), Walworth Road, **London** SE17 (020-7703 3324/5529). *Some 8,000 items, including Greek, Roman, medieval English and modern British coins, English tokens and commemorative medals.*

Gunnersbury Park Museum (1927), Acton, **London** W3. *Ancient British, Greek, Roman, medieval English, British and some foreign coins, tradesmen's tokens and commemorative medals, including local finds. Small numismatic library.*

Horniman Museum and Library (1890), **London** Road, Forest Hill, London SE23 (020-7699 2339). *General collection, primitive currency, some tokens.*

Imperial War Museum, Lambeth Road, **London** SE1 6HZ (020-7416 5000). *Emergency coinage of two world wars, occupation and invasion money, extensive collection of German Notgeld, commemorative, propaganda and military medals, badges and insignia.*

Sir John Soane's Museum (1833), 13 Lincoln's Inn Fields, **London** WC2 (020-7405 2107). *Napoleonic medals and medallic series of the late 18th and early 19th centuries.*

National Maritime Museum, Romney Road, Greenwich, **London** SE10 (020-8858 4422). *Commemorative medals with a nautical or maritime theme, naval medals and decorations.*

Victoria and Albert Museum (1852), South Kensington, **London** SW7 (020-7938 8441). *Byzantine gold and medieval Hispano-Mauresque coins (Department of Metalwork), large collection of Renaissance and later medals (Department of Architecture and Sculpture). Library of numismatic books.*

Ludlow Museum (1833). The Assembly Rooms. Castle Square, **Ludlow** (01584 873857). *Roman and medieval coins from local finds.*

Luton Museum and Art Gallery (1927), Wardown Park, **Luton**, Beds (01582 36941). *Coins, tokens and medals.*

M

Museum and Art Gallery (1858), **Maidstone**, Kent (01622 754497). *Ancient British, Roman, Anglo-Saxon and medieval coins found in Kent, modern British coins, Kent trade tokens, banknotes, hop tallies and tokens, primitive currency, collections of Kent Numismatic Society.*

The Manchester Museum (1868), The University, **Manchester** M13 (0161-275 2634). *Very fine collections of Greek and Roman coins, comprehensive collections of English, European and Oriental coins, over 30,000 in all.*

Margate Museum (1923), The Old Town Hall, Market Place, **Margate**, Kent (01843 225511 ext 2520). *Small collection of coins, including Roman from local finds.*

Montrose Museum and Art Gallery (1836). Panmure Place, **Montrose**, Angus DD10 8HE (01674 73232). *Scottish and British coins.*

N

Newark-on-Trent Museum (1912), Appleton Gate, **Newark**, Notts (01636 702358). *Siege pieces, trade tokens and coins from local finds and hoards.*

Newbury District Museum, The Wharf, **Newbury**, Berkshire (01635 30511). *Ancient British, Roman and medieval coins and artifacts, later coins and tokens.*

The Greek Museum, Percy Building, **Newcastle-upon-Tyne** (0191 2226000 ext 7966). *Ancient coins.*

O

Heberden Coin Room, Ashmolean Museum (1683), **Oxford** (01865 278000). *Extensive collections of all periods, notably Greek, Roman, English and Oriental coins, Renaissance portrait and later medals, tokens and paper money. Large library. Numerous publications.*

P

Peterborough Museum (1881), Priestgate, **Peterborough**, Cambs (01733 340 3329). *Roman (mainly from local hoards and finds), Anglo-Saxon, medieval English, British and modern European coins, English and British commemorative medals and tokens.*

City Museum and Art Gallery (1897), Drake Circus, **Plymouth**, Devon (01752 264878). *General collections of British and Commonwealth coins and tokens, Devon trade tokens and Plymouth tradesmen's checks, Ancient British and Roman coins from local sites.*

Waterfront Museum, 4 High Street, **Poole**, Dorset (01202 683138). *General collection of British and foreign coins, medals and tokens (view by appointment).*

City Museum (1972), Museum Road, Old **Portsmouth** PO1 (023 80827261). *Roman, medieval and later coins mainly from local finds and archaeological excavation, British coins, trade tokens of Hampshire, commemorative medals.*

Harris Museum and Art Gallery (1893), Market Square, **Preston**, Lancashire (01772 58248). *English and British coins, tokens and medals.*

R

Reading Museum and Art Gallery (1883) Blagrave Street, **Reading**, Berks (0118 939 9800). *British, Roman and medieval English coins, mostly from local finds, tradesmen's tokens and commemorative medals.*

Rochdale Museum (1905), Sparrow Hill, **Rochdale**, Lancs (01706 41085). *Roman and medieval coins from local finds, Rochdale trade tokens, miscellaneous British and foreign coins and medals.*

Municipal Museum and Art Gallery (1893), Clifton Park, **Rotherham** (01709382121). *Roman coins from Templeborough Forts, medieval English coins from local hoards and a general collection of British coins.*

S

Saffron Walden Museum (1832) (1939), Museum Street, **Saffron** Walden, Essex (01799 522494). *Ancient British, Roman, medieval and later coins, mainly from local finds and archaeological excavation, trade tokens and commemorative medals.*

Verulamium Museum, St Michael's, **St Albans,** Herts (01727 819339). *Coins and artifacts excavated from the Roman town.*

Salisbury and South Wiltshire Museum (1861), The Cathedral Close, **Salisbury,** Wilts (01722 332151). *Collection of coins minted or found locally, including finds of Iron Age, Roman, Saxon and medieval coins, as well as 18th and 19th century tradesmen's tokens.*

Richborough Castle Museum (1930), **Sandwich,** Kent (0304 612013). *Roman coins of 1st–5th centuries from excavations of the Richborough site.*

Scarborough Museum (1829), The Rotunda, Vernon Road, **Scarborough,** North Yorkshire (01723 374839). *Over 4,000 Roman coins, 1,500 English and 600 coins from local finds, siege pieces and trade tokens.*

Shaftesbury and Dorset Local History Museum (1946), 1 Gold Hill, **Shaftesbury,** Dorset (01747 52157). *Hoard of Saxon coins.*

City Museum (1875), Weston Park, **Sheffield** (0114 2 768588). *Over 5,000 coins of all periods, but mainly English and modern British. European coins, imperial Roman (including three hoards of about 500 coins each), Yorkshire trade tokens, British historical medals, campaign medals. Library.*

Rowley's House Museum, Barker Street, **Shrewsbury,** Salop (01743 361196). *Coins minted at Shrewsbury 925-1180, Civil War coinage of 1642, Shropshire tradesmen's tokens, English coins and medals.*

Museum of Archaeology (1951), God's House Tower, Town Quay, **Southampton,** Hants (023 8022 0007). *Main emphasis lies in Ancient British, Roman and medieval English coins from local archaeological excavations. General collection of later coins and medals.*

Atkinson Art Gallery (1878), Lord Street, **Southport,** Lancs (01704 533133). *Roman coins.*

Botanic Gardens Museum, Churchtown, **Southport,** Lancs (01704 87547). *English and British coins and medals, military medals and decorations.*

Southwold Museum (1933), St Bartholomew's Green, **Southwold,** Suffolk (01502 722375). *General collection of coins, specialised Suffolk trade tokens.*

Stamford Museum (1961), Broad Street, **Stamford,** Lincs (01780 66317). *General collection of coins, medals and tokens, including a selection from the Stamford mint.*

Municipal Museum (1860), Vernon Park, Turncroft Lane, **Stockport,** Cheshire (0161 474 4460) *Miscellaneous general collection of coins, tokens and medals.*

Stroud Museum (1899), Lansdown, **Stroud,** Glos (01453 376394). *Ancient British, Roman, Saxon, Norman, later medieval English, British coins and Gloucestershire trade tokens.*

Museum and Art Gallery (1846), Borough Road, **Sunderland,** Tyne & Wear (0191 514 1235). *Roman imperial, medieval and later English, including examples of the pennies minted at Durham, modern British and foreign coins, 17th-19th century tradesmen's tokens, local medallions and campaign medals.*

Swansea Museum (1835), Victoria Road, **Swansea,** W. Glamorgan, SA1 1SN (0792 653765). *Coins and medals of local interest.*

T

Tamworth Castle and Museum (1899), The Holloway, **Tamworth,** Staffs (01827 63563). *Anglo-Saxon coins, medieval English including coins of the Tamworth mint, later English and British coins, tokens, commemorative medallions and medals.*

Somerset County Museum, Taunton Castle, **Taunton,** Somerset (01823 255510/320200). *Celtic, Roman, Anglo-Saxon, early Medieval, tokens, medallions and banknotes. Strong emphasis on locally-found items.*

Thurrock Local History Museum (1956), Civic Square, **Tilbury,** Essex (01375 390000 ext 2414). *Roman coins.*

Royal Cornwall Museum (1818), River Street, **Truro,** Cornwall (01872 72205). *Coins, tokens and medals pertaining principally to the county of Cornwall.*

W

Wakefield Museum (1919), Wood Street, **Wakefield,** West Yorkshire (01924 295351). *Roman and medieval English silver and copper coins.*

Epping Forest District Museum, 39/41 Sun Street, **Waltham Abbey,** Essex EN 9. *Ancient British, Roman and medieval coins, Essex tradesmen's tokensof local interest.*

Warrington Museum and Art Gallery (1848). Bold Street, **Warrington,** Cheshire, WA1 1JG (01925 30550). *Coins, medals and tokens.*

Worcester City Museum (1833), Foregate Street, **Worcester** (01905 25371). *Roman, medieval and later coins and tokens. Coins of the Worcester mint.*

Wells Museum (18903), 8 Cathedral Green, **Wells,** Somerset (01749 3477). *Ancient and modern British and world coins, local trade tokens and medals.*

Municipal Museum and Art Gallery (1878), Station Road, **Wigan,** Lancashire. *British, Commonwealth and foreign coins from about 1660 to the present. Roman coins from local sites, commemorative medals.*

City Museum (1851), The Square, **Winchester,** Hants (01962 848269). *Roman and medieval coins chiefly from local hoards and finds. Hampshire tradesmen's tokens and commemorative medals. Small reference library.*

Wisbech and Fenland Museum (1835), Museum Square, **Wisbech,** Cambridgeshire (01945 583817), *British Roman, medieval and later coins, medals and tokens.*

Y

The Museum of South Somerset (1928), Hendford, **Yeovil,** Somerset (01935 24774). *Roman coins from local sites, medieval English, modern British coins and medals and a fine collection of tokens (particularly 17th century Somerset).*

Castle Museum (1938), **York** (01904 653611). *English and British coins, campaign medals, orders and decorations, comemorative medals.*

Jorvik Viking Centre (1984), Coppergate, **York** (01904 643211). *Coins and artefacts pertaining to the Viking occupatio of York.*

The Yorkshire Museum (1823), **York** (01904 629745). *Roman imperial, medieval English and later coins, about 12,000 in all.*

Club directory

Details given here are the name of the Numismatic Club or Society, its date of foundation, its venue, days and times of meetings. Meetings are monthly unless otherwise stated. Finally, the telephone number of the club secretary is given; the names and addresses of club secretaries are withheld for security reasons, but full details may be obtained by writing to the Secretary of the British Association of Numismatic Societies, Philip Mernick, c/o Bush Boake Allen Ltd, Blackhorse Lane, London E17 5QP.

Banbury & District Numismatic Society (1967). Banbury British Rail Working Mens Club. 2nd Mon (exc Jul & Aug), 19.45. (01295 254451).

Bath & Bristol Numismatic Society (1950). Ship Inn, Temple Street, Keynsham, Bristol. 2nd Thu, 19.30. (01275 472385).

Bedford Numismatic Society (1966). RAF Association Club, 93 Ashburnham Road, Bedford MK40 1EA. 3rd Mon, 19.30. (01234 228833/ 358369).

Bexley Coin Club (1968). St Martin's Church Hall, Erith Road, Barnehurst, Bexleyheath, Kent. 1st Mon (exc Jan & Aug), 20.00. (020 8303 0510).

Birmingham Numismatic Society (1964). Friend's Meeting House, Linden Road, Bournville, Birmingham 30. 2nd Wed, 19.45. (0121 308 1616).

Matthew Boulton Society (1994). PO Box 395, Birmingham B31 2TB (0121 781 6558 fax 0121 781 6574).

Bradford & District Numismatic Society (1967). East Bowling Unity Club, Leicester Street, Bradford, West Yorkshire. 3rd Mon, 19.00. (01532 677151).

Brighton & Hove Coin Club (1971). Methodist Church Hall, St Patrick's Road, Hove, East Sussex. Last Wed (exc Dec), 20.00. (01273 419303).

British Cheque Collectors' Society (1980). John Purser, 71 Mile Lane, Cheylesmore, Coventry, West Midlands CV3 5GB.

British Numismatic Society (1903). Warburg Institute, Woburn Square, London WC1H 0AB. Monthly (exc Aug & Dec), 18.00.

Cambridgeshire Numismatic Society (1946). Friends' Meeting House, 12 Jesus Lane (entrance in Park Street), Cambridge, CB5 8BA. 3rd Mon, Sept–June, 19.30. (01767 312112).

Chester & North Wales Coin & Banknote Society (1996). Liver Hotel, 110 Brook Street, Chester. 4th Tue, 20.00. (0151 478 4293)

Cheltenham Numismatic Society, The Reddings & District Community Association, North Road, The Reddings, Cheltenham. 3rd Mon, 19.45 (01242 673263)

Coin Correspondence Club (1988). Postal only. A.H. Chubb, 49 White Hart Lane, Barnes, London SW13 0PP. (0181-878 0472).

Cornwall Collectors' Club (1990). The Swan Inn, 40 Bosvigo Road, Truro. 1st Wed, 20.00. (01872 73376).

Crawley Coin Club (1969). Furnace Green Community Centre, Ashburnham Road, Furnace Green, Crawley, West Sussex. 1st Tue, 20.00. (01293 548671).

Crewe & District Coin & Medal Club (1968). Memorial Hall, Church Lane, Wistaston, Crewe, 2nd Tue (exc Jan & July), 19.30. (01270 69836).

Darlington & District Numismatic Society (1968). Darlington Arts Centre, Vane Terrace, Darlington, Co Durhm. 3rd Wed, 19.30. (01609 772976).

Derbyshire Numismatic Society (1964). The Friends' Meeting House, St Helens Street, Derby. 3rd Mon (exc August), 19.45. (01283 211623).

Devon & Exeter Numismatic Society (1965). Red Cross Centre, Butts Road, Heavitree, Exeter, Devon. 3rd Tue, 19.30. (01392 461013).

Edinburgh Numismatic Society (1996). Department of History and Applied Arts, Royal Museum of Scotland, Chambers Street, Edinburgh EH1 1JF. 3rd Mon, 19.30. (0131 225 7534).

Enfield & District Numismatic Society (1969). Millfield House Arts Centre, Silver Street, Edmonton, London N18 1PJ. 3rd Mon, 20.00. (0181-340 0767).

Essex Numismatic Society (1966). Chelmsford & Essex Museum, Moulsham Street, Chelmsford, Essex. 4th Fri (exc Dec), 20.00. (01376 21846).

Glasgow & West of Scotland Numismatic Society (1947). The College Club, University of Glasgow, University Avenue, Glasgow G12. 2nd Thu, Oct-May, 19.30. (0141 633 5422).

Harrow & North West Middlesex Numismatic Society (1968). YWCA, 51 Sheepcote Road, Harrow, Middlesex. 2nd and 4th Tue, 20.00. (020 8952 8765).

Havering Numismatic Society (1967). Fairkytes Arts Centre, Billet Lane, Hornchurch, Essex. 1st Tue, 19.30. (01708 704201).

Hayes & District Coin Club. The United Reformed Church Hall, Swakeleys Road, Ickenham, Middlesex. 3rd Thu, 19.45. (0181-422 9178).

Horncastle & District Coin Club (1963). Bull Hotel, Bull Ring, Horncastle, Lincs. 2nd Thu (exc Aug), 19.30. (01754 2706).

Huddersfield Numismatic Society (1947). Tolson Memorial Museum, Ravensknowle Park, Huddersfield, West Yorkshire. 1st Mon (exc Jul & Aug), 19.30. (01484 226300).

Hull & District Numismatic Society (1967). The Young People's Institute, George Street, Hull. Monthly (exc Aug & Dec), 19.30. (01482 441933).

International Bank Note Society (1961). Victory Services Club, 63–79 Seymour Street, London W1. Last Thu (exc Dec), 18.00. (020-8969 9493).

International Bank Note Society, Scottish Chapter (1995). West End Hotel, Palmerston Place, Edinburgh. Last Sat (exc Dec), 14.30.

Ireland, Numismatic Society of (Northern Branch).Denman International, Clandeboye Road, Bangor or Maysfield Leisure Centre, Belfast. 1st Fri (exc Jan) 19.30. (028 9146 6743)

Ireland, Numismatic Society of. (Southern Branch). Ely House, 8 Ely Place, Dublin. Last Fri, 20.00. (0035 3 283 2027).

Ipswich Numismatic Society (1966). Ipswich Citizens Advice Bureau, 19 Tower Street, Ipswich, Suffolk. Monthly meetings, 19.30. (01473 711158).

Kent Towns Numismatic Society (1913). Adult Education Centre, 9 Sittingbourne Road (Maidstone) and King's School Preparatory School, King Edward Road (Rochester). 1st Fri of month, 19.30 alternately at Maidstone and Rochester. (01622 843881).

Kingston Numismatic Society (1966). King Athel-stan's School, Villiers Road, Kingston-upon-Thames, Surrey. 3rd Thu (exc Dec & Jan), 19.30. (020-8397 6944).

Lancashire & Cheshire Numismatic Society (1933). Manchester Central Library, St Peter's Square, Manchester M2 5PD. Monthly, Sep–June, Wed (18.30) or Sat (14.30). (0161 445 2042).

Lincolnshire Numismatic Society (1932). Grimsby Bridge Club, Bargate, Grimsby, South Humberside. 4th Wed (exc Aug), 19.30.

London Numismatic Club (1947). Institute of Archaeology, 31–34 Gordon Square, London WC1H 0PY. Monthly, 18.30.

Loughborough Coin & Search Society (1964). Wallace Humphry Room, Shelthorpe Community Centre, Loughborough, Leics. 1st Thu, 19.30. (01509 261352).

Merseyside Numismatic Society (1947). The Lecture Theatre, Liverpool Museum, William Brown Street, Liverpool L3 8EN. Monthly (exc July & Aug), 19.00. (0151-929 2143).

Mid Lanark Coin Circle (1969). Hospitality Room, The Civic Centre, Motherwell, Lanarkshire. 4th Thu, Sep–Apr (exc Dec), 19.30. (0141-552 2083).

Morecambe & Lancaster Numismatic Society. Monthly, 19.30. (01524 411036).

Newbury Coin & Medal Club (1971). Monthly, 20.00. (01635 41233).

Northampton Numismatic Society (1969). Old Scouts RFC, Rushmere Road, Northampton. 3rd Mon, 20.00.

Norwich Numismatic Society (1967). Assembly House, Theatre Street, Norwich, Norfolk. 3rd Mon, 19.30. (01493 651577).

Nottinghamshire Numismatic Society (1948). The Cecil Roberts Room, County Library, Angel Row, Nottingham NG1 6HP. 2nd Tue (Sep-Apr), 18.45. (0115 9257674).

Nuneaton & District Coin Club (1968). United Reformed Church Room, Coton Road, opposite Council House, Nuneaton, Warwickshire. 2nd Tue, 19.30. (01203 371556).

Orders & Medals Research Society (1942). National Army Museum, Royal Hospital Road, Chelsea, London SW3. Monthly, 14.30 (020-8680 2701).

Ormskirk & West Lancashire Numismatic Society (1970).The Eagle & Child, Maltkiln Lane, Bispham Green L40 1SN. 1st Thu, 20.15. (01704 531266).

Peterborough Coin & Medal Club (1967). The Club Room, APV-Baker Social Club, Alma Road, Peter-borough, Cambs. Last Tue (exc July & Aug), 19.30.

Plymouth Coin & Medal Club (1970). RAFA Club, 5 Ermington Terrace, Mutley Plain, Plymouth, Devon. 2nd Wed (exc Dec), 19.30. (01752 663803).

Preston & District Numismatic Society (1965). Eldon Hotel, Eldon Street, Preston, Lancs. 1st and 3rd Tue, 20.00. (012572 66869).

Reading Coin Club (1964). Abbey Baptist Church, Abbey Square, Reading. 1st Mon, 19.00. (0118 9332843).

Redbridge Numismatic Society (1968). Gants Hill Library, Cranbrook Road, Ilford, Essex. 4th Wed, 19.30. (020-8554 5486).

Rochford Hundred Numismatic Society. Civic Suite, Rayleigh Town Hall, Rayleigh, Essex. 2nd Thu, 20.00. (01702 230950).

Romsey Numismatic Society (1969). Romsey WM Conservative Club, Market Place, Romsey, Hants SO5 8NA. 4th Fri (exc Dec), 19.30. (01703 253921).

Rotherham & District Coin Club (1982). Rotherham Art Centre, Rotherham, South Yorkshire. 1st Wed, 19.00. (01709 528179).

Royal Mint Coin Club, PO Box 500, Cardiff CF1 1HA (01443 222111).

Royal Numismatic Society (1836). Society of Antiquaries, Piccadilly, London W1. Monthly (Oct-June), 17.30. Joe Cribb, Coins and Medals, British Museum, London WC1B 3DG (020-7323 8585).

Rye Coin Club (1955). Rye Further Education Centre, Lion Street, Rye, East Sussex. 2nd Thu (Oct-Dec, Feb-May), 19.30. (01424 422974).

St Albans & Hertfordshire Numismatic Society (1948). St Michael's Parish Centre, Museum Entrance, Verulamium Park, St Albans, Herts AL3 4SL. 2nd Tue (exc Aug), 19.30. (01727 824434).

Sheffield Numismatic Society. Telephone for venue. 2nd Wed, 19.00. (0114 2817129)

South East Hants Numismatic Society. Different locations. 1st Fri. Contact: Tony Matthews, 8 King George Road, Totton, Southampton SO4 3FE.

South Manchester Numismatic Society (1967). Nursery Inn, Green Lane, Heaton Mersey, Stockport. 1st & 3rd Mondays of each month (excl. Public hols), 20.00. (0161-485 7017).

South Wales & Monmouthshire Numismatic Society (1958). The W. R. Lysaght Institute, Corporation Road, Newport. 2nd Tues, 19.30. (029 20561564).

Thurrock Numismatic Society (1970). Stanley Lazell Hall, Dell Road, Grays, Essex. 3rd Wed, 19.00.

Torbay & District Coin Club (1967). British Rail Social Club, Brunel Road, Newton Abbott, Devon TQ12 4PB. 1st Tue, 19.45. (01803 326497).

Tyneside Numismatic Society (1954). RAFA Club, Eric Nelson House, 16 Berwick Road, Gateshead, Tyne & Wear. 2nd Wed, 19.30. (0191 372 2266).

Wessex NS (1948). Hotel Bristowe, Grange Road, Southbourne, Bournemouth, Dorset. 2nd Thurs (exc Aug), 20.00. (020 7731 1702).

Wiltshire Numismatic Society (1965). Raven Inn, Poulshot, Nr Devizes, Wiltshire. 3rd Mon, Mar-Dec, 20.00. (01225 703143).

Worthing & District Numismatic Society (1967). Kingsway Hotel, Marine Parade, Worthing, West Sussex BN11 3QQ. 3rd Thu, 20.00. (01903 241503).

Yorkshire Numismatic Society (1909). Leeds Museum, The Headrow , Leeds. 1st Sat (exc Jan, Aug & Dec) (0113 286 4914).

Club Secretaries: if your details as listed are incorrect please let us know in time for the next edition of the COIN YEARBOOK

IMPORTANT ORGANISATIONS

ADA
The Antiquities Dealers Association
Secretary: Susan Hadida, Duke's Court, 32 Duke Street, London SW1Y 6DU

BNTA
The British Numismatic Trade Association
Secretary: Carol Carter, PO Box 474A, Thames Ditton, Surrey KT7 0WJ

ANA
The American Numismatic Association
818 North Cascade Avenue, Colorado Springs, CO 80903-3279, USA

IAPN
International Association of Professional Numismatists
Secretary: Jean-Luc Van der Schueren, 14 Rue de la Bourse, B–1000, Brussels.

IBNS
International Bank Note Society
Membership Secretary: Mrs Sally Thowney, 36B Dartmouth Park Hill, London NW5 1HN

Directory of Auctioneers

Listed here are the major UK auction houses which handle coins, medals, banknotes and other items of numismatic interest. Many of them hold regular public auctions, whilst others handle numismatic material infrequently. A number of coin companies also hold regular Postal Auctions—these are marked with a P.

Baldwin's Auctions Ltd
   11 Adelphi Terrace, London WC2N 6BJ (020 7930 9808 fax 020 7930 9450, e-mail auctions@baldwin.sh, website http// www.thesaurus.com/Baldwins)

Banking Memorabilia
   PO Box 14, Carlisle CA3 8DZ (0169 7476465).

A. F. Brock & Company
   269 London Road, Hazel Grove, Stockport, Cheshire SK7 4PL (0161 456 5050 fax 0161 456 5112, website www.afbrock.co.uk, email info@afbrock.co.uk).

Christie, Manson & Wood Ltd
   8 King Street, St James's, London SW1Y 6QT (020 7839 9060).

Christie's Scotland Ltd
   164–166 Bath Street, Glasgow G2 4TG (0141 332 8134 fax 0141 332 5759).

Classical Numismatic Group Inc (Seaby Coins)
   14 Old Bond Street, London W1X 4JL (020 7495 1888 fax 020-7499 5916, Email cng@historicalcoins.com). **P**

Corbitts
   5 Moseley Sreet, Newcastle upon Tyne NE1 1YE (0191-232 7268 fax 0191-261 4130).

Croydon Coin Auctions
   272 Melfort Road, Thornton Heath, Surrey CR7 7RR (020 8240 7924 or 020 8656 4583, website www.eigo.co.uk/cca, email cca@eigo.co.uk).

Dix Noonan Webb
   1 Old Bond Street, London W1XZ 3TD (020 7499 5022 fax 020 7499 5023)

Edinburgh Coin Shop
   11 West Crosscauseway, Edinburgh EH8 9JW (0131 668 2928 fax 0131 668 2926). **P**

Fellows & Sons
   Augusta House, 19 Augusta Street, Hockley, Birmingham B18 6JA (0121-212 2131).

B. Frank & Son
   3 South Avenue, Ryton, Tyne & Wear NE40 3LD (0191 413 8749 fax 0191 413 2957, email bfrankandson@aol.com).

T. Gillingham
   42 Highbury Park, Warminster, Wilts BA12 9JF (01985 216486).

Gillio Coins International
   1013 State Street, Santa Barbara, CA 93101, USA (805 9631345—London contact Eric Green 020-7586 3964).

Glendining & Co
   101 New Bond Street, London W1Y 9LG (020 7 493 2445 fax 020 7491 9181).

Graves, Son & Pilcher Fine Arts
   71 Church Road, Hove, East Sussex BN3 2GL (01273 735266 fax 01273 723813).

Hoods Postal Coin Auctions
   23 High Street, Kilbirnie, Ayrshire KA25 7EX (fax/tel 01505 682157). **P**

Kleeford Coin Auctions
   19 Craythorns Crescent, Dishforth, Thirsk YO7 3LY. (tel/fax 01845 577977). **P**

W. H. Lane & Son
   65 Morrab Road, Penzance, Cornwall TR18 2QT (01736 61447 fax 01736 50097) also: Trafalgar House, Malpas Road, Truro, Cornwall TR1 1QH (01872 223379).

Lawrence Fine Art Auctioneers
   South Street, Crewkerne, Somerset TA18 8AB (01460 73041).

David Lay
   The Penzance Auction House, Alverton, Penzance, Cornwall TR18 4RE (01736 61414 fax 01736 60035).

Lockdale Coins
   36 Upper Orwell Street, Ipswich IP4 1BR. (01473 218588).

London Coin Auctions
   31 Reigate Way, Wallington, Surrey SM6 8NU (020 8688 5297 fax 020 8680 8071, website www.londoncoins.co.uk).

Neales
   192–194 Mansfield Road, Nottingham NG1 3HU (0115 9624141 fax 0115 9856890).

Phillips
101 New Bond Street, London W1S 1SR (020-7468 8345 fax 020-7409 3466, website www.phillips-auctions.com).

R & W Coin Auctions
307 Bretch Hill, Banbury, Oxon OX16 0JD (01295 275128).

Sheffield Coin Auctions
7 Beacon Close, Sheffield S9 1AA (0114 249 0442).

Simmons Gallery
53, Lamb's Conduit Street, Holborn, London WC1N 3NB (020 7831 2080 fax 020 7831 2090). **P**

Sotheby's
34–35 New Bond Street, London W1Y 2AA (020-7408 5312/4 fax 020-7493 6863 Coins. Website www.sothebys.com).

Spink & Son Ltd
69 Southampton Row, Bloomsbury, London. WC1B 4ET (020 7563 2820, fax 020 7563 4066, website www.spink-online.com, email info@spinkandson.com).

Sussex Auction Galleries
59 Perrymount Road, Haywards Heath, West Sussex RH16 3DS (01444 414935 fax 01444 450402).

Wallis & Wallis
West Street, Lewes, East Sussex (01273 480208 fax 01273 476562).

Warwick & Warwick
Chalon House, Scarbank, Millers Road, Warwick CV34 5DB (01926 499031 fax 01926 491906)

Whytes
30 Marlborough Street, Dublin 1, Republic of Ireland (+3531 874 6161 fax 874 6020, website www.whytes.ie, email whytes@iol.ie).

directory of *Fairs*

Listed below are the names of the fair organisers, their venue details where known along with contact telephone numbers. Please call the organisers direct for information on dates etc.

Aberdeen
Jarvis Amatola Hotel, Great Western Road, also venues in **Glenrothes** and **Glasgow.** *Cornucopia Collectors Fairs. (01382 224946)*

Birmingham
National Motor Cycle Museum, Bickenhill, Birmingham. *Midland Stamp & Coin Fair. (024 7671 6587)*

Bristol
Jury's Hotel, Prince Street. *Gold Star Fairs. (01823 251563)*

Cardiff
City Hall. *R. J. Neil Fairs. (01873 854688)*

Cheltenham
Town Hall or White House Hotel. *R. J. Neil Fairs. (01873 854688)*

Exeter
St Georges Hall, George Street. *Gold Star Fairs. (01823 251563)*

Hereford
Holmer Church Hall. *R. J. Neil Fairs. (01873 854688)*

Leeds-Morley
Morley Snooker Centre, Bruntcliffe Lane, * new venue to be announced shortly, *for details contact N. C. S. Promotions. (01552 684681).*

Lichfield
Civic Hall, Castle Dyke, City Centre. *C. S. Fairs. (01562 710424)*

London
The Cumberland Hotel, Marble Arch, London W1. *London Coin Fair. (020 7831 2080)*

London
The Bonnington Hotel, 92 Southampton Row, London WC1. *West Promotions. (020 8641 3224).*

London
The Commonwealth Institute, Kensington High Street, London W8. *Davidson Monk Fairs. (020 8656 4583 or 020 8651 3890)*

Malvern
Lyttleton Rooms. *R. J. Neil Fairs. (01873 854688)*

Newport
The Holiday Inn. *R. J. Neil Fairs. (01873 854688)*

Newtown
Elephant & Castle Hotel. *R. J. Neil Fairs. (01873 854688*

Sutton Coldfield
Fellowship Hall, South Parade. *C. S. Fairs. (01562 710424)*

West Bromwich
Town Hall, High Street. *C. S. Fairs. (01562 710424)*

York
The Grandstand, York Racecourse. *York Coin Fair (01268 726687 or 020 8946 4489)*

Annual events
The B.N.T.A. (Coinex)
Tel: 020 8398 4290 for details

The I.B.N.S. (World Paper Money Fair)
Tel: 020 8360 2759 for details

Directory of **Dealers**

The dealers listed below have comprehensive stocks of coins and medals, unless otherwise stated. Specialities, where known, are noted. Many of those listed are postal dealers only, so to avoid disappointment always make contact by telephone or mail in the first instance, particularly before travelling any distance.

Abbreviations:
ADA—Antiquities Dealers Association
ANA—American Numismatic Association
BADA—British Antique Dealers Association
BNTA—British Numismatic Trade Association
IAPN—International Association of Professional Numismatists
IBNS—International Bank Note Society
P—Postal only
L—Publishes regular lists

A. Ackroyd (IBNS)
 62 Albert Road, Parkstone, Poole, Dorset BH12 2DB (tel/fax 01202 739039, website www.AAnotes.com). *P. L. Banknotes, cheques and related collectables.*

Airedale Coins (ANA, BNTA)
 PO Box 7, Bingley, West Yorkshire, BD16 4ST (01274 770414 fax 01274 563869, website www.airedalecoins.com, email info@airedalecoins.com).
 P. L. British and modern coins of the world.

David Allen Coins and Collectables
 PO Box 125, Pinner, Middlesex HA5 2TX (020 866 6796). *P. L. British and world coins, tokens, banknotes.*

Joan Allen Electronics Ltd
 190 Main Road, Biggin Hill, Kent TN16 3BB (01959 71255). Mon-Sat 09.00–17.00. *Metal detectors.*

Ancient Forum (ADA)
 PO Box 356, Christchurch, Dorset BH23 2YD (01202 478592). *P. L. Greek, Roman and medieval antiquities with occasional groups of coins.*

Ancient World
 16 High Petergate, York, YO1 2EH (01904 624062) 10.30–17.00 weekdays. *Greek, Roman, Celtic and medieval coins, also antiquities.*

Antique Boutique
 54–59 Merrion Centre, Leeds, West Yorkshire (01132 444174). 09.30–17.30 (Wed 09.30 –13.30).

Keith Austin (IBNS)
 PO Box 89, Carlise, Cumbria CA3 0GH (01228 819149, fax 01228 521176, email kaustin@kabc.freeserve.co.uk). L. *Banknotes.*

N. J. Aves
 PO Box 811, Yeovil, Somerset (01935 72368). P. *Coins, tokens and medals.*

Mark Bailey
 120 Sterte Court, Sterte Close, Poole, Dorset BH15 2AY (01202 674936). *P. L. Ancient, modern, world coins and antiquities.*

Baird & Co
 304 High Street, Stratford, London E15 1AJ (020 8555 5217). 09.00–17.30 weekdays. *Bullion and World coins.*

A. H. Baldwin & Sons Ltd (ANA, BADA, BNTA, IAPN)
 11 Adelphi Terrace, London WC2N 6BJ. 09.00–17.00 weekdays. (email coins@baldwin.sh) *Coins, tokens, commemorative medals, war medals and decorations, numismatic books.*

Banking Memorabilia (IBNS)
 PO Box 14, Carlisle, Cumbria (0169 96465). 09.00–18.00 (not Sun). *Cheques, banknotes, related ephemera. auctions.*

Banknotes of Auld Scotland
 Sconser, Isle of Skye IV48 8TD. (01478 650459, website www.scottish-banknotes.com, email johnaunc@aol.com).

D. G. Barney
 Greenfield, Colyton Hill, Colyton, Devon EX24 6HY (01297 552702, email dougbarney@ondigital.com).
 British and world coins, tokens and banknotes.

G. Barrington Smith
 Cross Street, Oadby, Leicestershire LE2 4DD (01533 712114). 08.30–17.15 weekdays. *Albums, catalogues and accessories.*

Bath Stamp and Coin Shop (BNTA)
 Pulteney Bridge, Bath, Avon BA2 4AY (01225 463073). Mon-Sat 09.30–17.30. *British and world coins.*

Baxters Coin & Stamp Exchange
 20–22 Hapworths Arcade, Silver Street, Hull, North Humberside, HU1 1JU (01482 223875). 10.00–17.00 (closed Thurs). *British and world coins.*

Michael Beaumont
 PO Box 8, Carlton, Notts NG4 4QZ (0115 9878361). *P. Coins, medals and tokens of the world.*

Beaver Coin Room (BNTA)
 57 Philbeach Gardens, LondonSW5 9ED (020 7373 4553). *P. European coins and medals.*

R. P. & P. J. Beckett
Maesyderw, Capel Dewi, Llandyssul, Dyfed SA44
4PJ. (Fax only 01559 395631, email
rppjbeckett@btinternet.com) *P. World crowns, coin
sets and banknotes.*

Lloyd Bennett (BNTA)
PO Box 2, Monmouth, Gwent NP5 3YE (01600
890634). Abergavenny Market (Tue), Monmouth
Market (Fri–Sat) 09.00–16.00. *English hammered,
milled and coins of the world.*

Berkshire Coin Centre
35 Castle Street, Reading, Berkshire RG1 7SB
(01734 575593). 10.00–16.00 weekdays, half-day
Sat. *British and world coins.*

Beron Coins
64 Rosewood Close, Glascote, Tamworth, Staffs
B77 3PD (01827 54541). *P. L. British and world
coins.*

Stephen J. Betts
4 Victoria Street, Narborough, Leics LE9 5DP (0116
2864434). *P. L. Medieval and modern coins, counters,
jetons and tokens, countermarks and medals.*

Birchin Lane Gold Coin Company
6 Castle Court, St Michael's Alley (off Cornhill),
London EC3V 9DS (020 7621 0370 and 020 7263
3981). Mon-Fri 10.00–16.30. *Gold and bullion coins.*

Barry Boswell
24 Townsend Lane, Upper Boddington, Daventry,
Northants NN1 6DR (01327 261877, fax 01327
261391, email Barry.Boswell@btinternet.com). *P. L.
British and world banknotes.*

James & C. Brett
17 Dale Road, Lewes, East Sussex BN7 1LH. *P. L.
British and world coins.*

J. Bridgeman Coins
129a Blackburn Road, Accrington, Lancs (01254
384757). 09.30–17.00. *British & World coins.*

Brighton Coin Company (ANA, BNTA)
36 Ship Street, Brighton, Sussex BN1 1AB (01273
733365 Mon-Fri 9.45–17.30, Sat 9.45–15.30. *World
coins.*

Britannia Jewellery Co
234 Yorkshire Street, Rochdale, Lancs OL16 2DP
(01706 341046/55507. Mon-Sat 10.00–17.00.

BRM Coins
3 Minshull Street, Knutsford, Cheshire WA16 6HG
(01565) 651480 and 0606 74522). Mon-Sat 10,00–
17.00. *British coins.*

Peter F. Broadbelt
10 Dragon Road, Harrogate, North Yorkshire HG1
5DF (01423 562037). Mon-Sat 11–18.00. *Specialist in
Foreign coins.*

A. F. Brock & Company
269 London Road, Hazel Grove, Stockport,
Cheshire SK7 4PL (0161 456 5050/5112. Mon-
Sat 09.30–17.30.

E. J. & C. A. Brooks (BNTA, IBNS)
44 Kiln Road, Thundersley, Essex SS7 1TB (01268
753835). Any time up to 23.00. *L. British coins and
banknotes.*

Iain Burn
2 Compton Gardens, 53 Park Road, Camberley,
Surrey GU15 2SP (01276 23304). *Bank of England &
Treasury notes*

Butler & Co
111 Promenade, Cheltenham, Glos GL50 1NN
(01242 522272). Sat only. *World coins.*

BBM Coins
8–9 Lion Street, Kidderminster, Hereford &
Worcester, DY10 1PT (01562 744118). Mon, Wed-
Sat 10.00–17.00. *World coins.*

Cambridge Stamp Centre Ltd
9 Sussex Street, Cambridge CB4 4HU (01223
63980). Mon-Sat 09.00–17.30. *British coins.*

Castle Coins
47a High Street South, Dunstable, Beds LU6 3RZ
(01582 602778). Mon-Sat 10.00–17.00. *English coins.*

Castle Curios
165 Wellgate, Rotherham, South Yorkshire S60
4DT. Wed-Sat 11.00–17.00. *English coins.*

Castle Galleries
81 Castle Street, Salisbury, Wiltshire SP1 3SP
(01722 333734). Tue, Thu Fri 09.00–17.00, Sat
09.30–16.00. *British coins, medals and tokens.*

Cathedral Coins
23 Kirkgate, Ripon, North Yorkshire HG4 1PB
(01765 701400). Mon-Sat 10.00–17.00.

David L. Cavanagh
49 Cockburn Street, Edinburgh EH1 1PB (0131 226
3391). Mon-Sat 10.30–17.00. *British coins.*

Cavendish Coins
14 Longfields, Ongar, Essex CM5 9BZ. *P. Modern
crown-sized coins.*

CCC Coins
PO Box 192, Peterborough, PE2 5DT. *P. L. Roman,
hammered and English milled silver.*

Lance Chaplin
17 Wanstead Lane, Ilford, Essex IG1 3SB (020 8554
7154). *P. L. Roman, Greek, Celtic, hammered coins
and antiquities.*

Chelsea Coins Ltd (BNTA)
PO Box 2, Fulham Road, London SW10 9PQ. (020
8870 5501 Fax 020 8875 1459). *P. World coins.*

Nigel A. Clark
28 Ulundi Road, Blackheath, London SE3 7UG (020
8858 4020). *P. L. Mainly 17th century tokens.*

Classical Numismatic Group
14 Old Bond Street, London W1X 4JL. (020 7495
1888 Fax 020 7499 5916, Email
cng@historicalcoins.com). *P. Ancient and world
coins. Publishers of the Classical Numismatic Review.*

Paul Clayton (BNTA)
PO Box 21, Wetherby, West Yorkshire LS22 5JY.
(01937 72441). *Modern gold coins.*

André de Clermont (BNTA)
PO Box 3615, London, SW10 0YD. (020 7351 5727,
Fax 020 7352 8127). *World coins, especially Islamic &
Oriental coins, Latin America.*

M. Coeshaw
PO Box 115, Leicester LE3 8JJ (01533 873808). *P.*

Philip Cohen Numismatics (ANA, BNTA)
20 Cecil Court, Charing Cross Road, London
WC2N 4HE (020 7379 0615). Mon-Sat 10.30–17.30
(half-days Mon and Sat).

Coin & Collectors Centre
PO Box 22, Pontefract, West Yorkshire WF8 1YT
(01977 704112, website www.coincentre.co.uk,
email sales@coincentre.co.uk). *P. British coins.*

Coincraft (ANA, IBNS)
44/45 Great Russell Street, London WC1B 3LU
(020 7636 1188 and 020 7637 8785 fax 020 7323 2860,
Website www.coincraft.com Email
info@coincraft.com). Mon-Fri 09.30–17.00, Sat
10.00–14.30. *L (newspaper format). Coins and
banknotes.*

277

Coinote Services Ltd
PO Box 53, Sorting Office, Clarke Street,
Hartlepool TS26 NYL (01429 273044). *P. L. Coins
and banknotes 1615 todate. Accessories and books.*

Coins of Beeston
PO Box 19, Beeston, Notts BG9 2NE. *P. L. Tokens,
medals and paranumismatics.*

Coins of Canterbury
PO Box 47, Faversham, Kent ME13 7HX (01795
531980). *P. English coins.*

Coliseum Coins
30 Staunton Avenue, Hayling Island, Hants
PO11 0EN (01705 464332). *P. Greek, Roman,
Oriental coins.*

Collecta Coins Limited
PO Box 101, Northampton NN1 3LT (01604
766607/27076). Mon–Sat 09.00–21.00. *World coins.*

The Collector
242 High Street, Orpington, Kent BR6 0LZ (01689
890045). Mon–Sat 09.45–17.30 (closed Tue). *Coins,
medals, banknotes, badges, militaria, cigarette cards etc*

3CO
PO Box 27, Manchester, M23 9UJ. *English milled
coinage. P.*

Collectors' Corner
East Street, Crescent Road, Faversham, Kent ME13
8AD (01795 539721). Mon–Fri 10.00–15.00 (half-
day Mon, Thu). *Coins and medals.*

Collectors' Corner
Watford Market (off High Street), Watford, Herts
(020 8904 0552). Tue, Fri, Sat 09.00-17.00. *World
coins.*

Collectors' Forum
237 South Street, Romford, Essex RM1 2BE (01708
723357). Mon–Sat 09.30-18.00 Thu 09.30-14.00.
British coins and medals.

Collectors Gallery (BNTA, IBNS)
Castle Hall, Castle Gates, Shrewsbury SY1 2AD
(01743 272140 fax 01743 366041). Mon–Fri 09.00–
18.00, half-day Sat. *Coins, medals and banknotes.
Numismatic accessories and related books. Agents for
the Abafil range of coin cases.*

Collectors' World
188 Wollaton Road, Wollaton, Nottingham NG8
1HJ. (01159 280347). *Coins, Tokens, Banknotes,
Accessories.*

Constantia CB
15 Church Road, Northwood, Middlesex HA6
1AR. *P. Roman and medieval hammered coins.*

Colin Cooke
257 Brooklands Road, Manchester M23 9HF (0161
973 2395 fax 0161 962 2864, email
coins@colincooke.com). *L. British coins.*

Corbitts (BNTA)
5 Mosley Street, Newcastle Upon Tyne NE1 1YE
(0191 232 7268 fax: 0191 261 4130). *Dealers and
auctioneers of all coins and medals.*

G. D. Courtenay
58 New Peachey Lane, Uxbridge, Middlesex UB8
3SX. *P. L. Coins, medals, tokens and banknotes.*

David Craddock
PO Box 3785, Camp Hill, Birmingham B11 2NF.
(0121 733 2259) *L. Crown to farthings. Copper and
bronze specialist. Some foreign.*

K. A. Cudworth
8 Park Avenue, Clayton West, Huddersfield, West
Yorkshire HD8 9PT (01484 862679). *P. British and
world coins.*

John Cummings Ltd (BNTA)
Parthenon Gallery, 25 Bury Place, WC1A 2JH (020
7242 5656). *P. Greek, Roman, Byzantine, Celtic,
Saxon, Viking and English hammered coins. Quarterly
catalogue.*

Mark Davidson
PO Box 197, South Croydon, Surrey CR3 0ZD (020
8651 3890). *Ancient, hammered coinage.*

Davidson Monk Fairs
PO Box 201, Croydon, Surrey CR9 7AQ (020 8656
4583). *Organiser of monthly fairs at the Common
wealth Institute, Kensington High Street, London W8.*

Paul Davies Ltd (ANA, BNTA, IAPN)
PO Box 17, Ilkley, West Yorkshire LS29 8TZ (01943
603116 fax 01943 816326). *P. World coins.*

Paul Davis
PO Box 418, Birmingham B17 0RZ (0121 427 7179).
P. Hammered gold and silver coins.

DD Coins of Windsor
24–28 St Leonards Road, Suite 100, Windsor, Berks
SL4 3BB. (01753 739487). *L. GB milled list.*

B. J. Dawson (Coins) (BNTA)
52 St Helens Road, Lancs BL3 3NH (01204 63732).
Mon Tue Sat 09.30–16.00, Thu Fri 09.30–17.30, Wed
09.30–13.00. *L. Ancient, hammered and milled coins,
tokens and banknotes.*

Patrick Deane
PO Box 76, Orpington, Kent BR6 0UB. (01689
812222 fax 01689 898008, website
www.coinsandmedals.com, email
newissuesbureau@compuserve.com).
By appointment only. British coins.

Decus Coins
The Haven, Brockweir, Chepstow, Gwent NP6
7NN (01291 689216). *P.*

Dei Gratia
PO Box 3568, Buckingham MK18 4ZS (01280
848000). *P. L. Pre-Roman to modern coins,
antiquities, banknotes.*

Den of Antiquity
26 West End, Haddenham, Ely, Cambs CB6 3TE
(01353 741759). *Ancients and Antiquities. L*

Clive & Richard Dennett (BNTA)
66 St Benedicts Street, Norwich, Norfolk NR2 4AR
(01603 624315). Mon–Fri 09.00–17.30, Sat 09.00–
16.00 (closed Thu). *L. World paper money.*

C. J. Denton (ANA, BNTA, FRNS)
PO Box 25, Orpington, Kent BR6 8PU (01689
873690). *P. World coins.*

Michael Dickinson (ANA, BNTA)
Ramsay House, 825 High Road Finchley, London
N12 8UB (0181 441 7175). *P. British and world coins.*

Dolphin Coins (ANA)
22 High Street, Leighton Buzzard, Beds. LU7 7EB.
(01525 383822 fax 01525 383872)
Mon–Fri 09.30– 17.00. Sat appt only. *L. British and
world coins.*

Dorset Coin Co Ltd (BNTA)
193 Ashley Road, Parkstone, Poole, Dorset BH14
9DL (01202 739606, fax 01202 739230). *P. L.
Separate coin and banknote lists.*

Drizen Coins
1 Hawthorns, Leigh-on-Sea, Essex SS9 4JT (01702
521094). *P. L. British, Commonwealth and world
coins.*

Dyas Coins & Medals
30 Shaftmoor Lane, Acocks Green, Birmingham
B27 7RS (0121 707 2808). Fri 10.30–18.30, Sun
10.30–13.00. *World coins and medals.*

Eagle Coins
Winterhaven, Mourneabbey, Mallow, Co. Cork, Ireland (010 35322 29385). *P. L. Irish and English coins.*

East Kent Coins
PO Box 106, Herne Bay, Kent CT6 6GN (01227 365073). *P. L. World coins*

Eden Coins
PO Box 73, Oldbury, Warley, West Midlands B68 0BT (0121 422 5357). *P. English coins, tokens and medals.*

Edinburgh Coin Shop (ANA)
11 West Crosscauseway, Edinburgh EH8 9JW (0131 668 2928 fax 0131 668 2926). Mon-Sat 10.00–17.30. *L. World coins and medals. Postal auctions.*

Christopher Eimer (ANA, BNTA)
PO Box 352 London NW11 7RF (020 8458 9933 fax 020 8455 3535, email art@christophereimer.co.uk). *P. Commemorative medals.*

Elm Hill Stamps & Coins
27 Elm Hill, Norwich, Norfolk NR3 1HN (01603 627413). Mon-Fri 09.00–16.45, half-day Sat. *British and world coins.*

ELM
15 Phillimore Walk, Kensington, London W8 7SA (020 7937 8484)P. *Egyptian Banknotes.*

Ely Stamp & Coin Shop
27 Fore Hill, Ely, Cambs CB7 1AA (01353 663919). Mon, Wed-Sat 09.30–17.30. *World coins, medals and stamps.*

Europa Numismatics (ANA, BNTA)
PO Box 119, High Wycombe, Bucks HP11 1QL (01494 437307). *P. European coins.*

Tim Everson
40 Woodlands Avenue, New Malden, Surrey KT3 3UQ (020 8949 7739) *P. L. Early British coinage.*

Evesham Stamp & Coin Centre
Magpie Antiques, Paris House, 61 High Street, Evesham, Worcs WR11 4DA (01386 41631). Mon-Sat 09.00–17.30. *British coins.*

Michael E. Ewins
Meyrick Heights, 20 Meyrick Park Crescent, Bournemouth, Dorset BH3 7AQ (01202 290674). *P. World coins.*

I. Fine & Son Ltd
Victoria House, 93 Manor Farm Road, Wembley, Middlesex HA10 1XB (020 8997 5055). *P. British & World coins.*

Patrick Finn (BNTA)
PO Box 26, Kendal, Cumbria LA9 7AB (01539 730008, fax 01539 721800). *P. L. Early British, Irish, Scottish and Anglo-Gallic coins.*

Robin Finnegan Stamp Shop
83 Skinnergate, Darlington, Co Durham DL3 7LX (01325 489820/357674). Mon-Sat 10.00–17.30 (closed Wed). *World coins.*

Richard N. Flashman
54 Ebbsfleet Walk, Gravesend, Kent, DA11 9EW. *L. P. British banknotes.*

David Fletcher (Mint Coins) (ANA, BNTA)
PO Box 64, Coventry, Warwickshire CV5 6SN (024 7671 5425, Fax 024 7667 7985). *P. World new issues*

Folley Island Coins
PO Box 361, Dunstable, Bedfordshire LU5 4YU. (01582 667734). *World and English coins.*

Format of Birmingham Ltd (ANA, BNTA, IAPN, IBNS)
18 Bennetts Hill, Birmingham B2 5QJ (0121 643 2058 fax 0121 643 2210). Mon-Fri 09.30-7.00. *L. Coins, tokens and medals.*

B. Frank & Son (ANA, IBNS)
3 South Avenue, Ryton, Tyne & Wear NE40 3LD (0191 413 8749). *P. L. Banknotes and cheques, coins of the world. Organiser of the North of England fair.*

Frank Milward (BNTA)
2 Ravensworth Road, Mortimer, Berks, RG7 3UU (01734 332843). Mon-Sat 09.00-18.00. *British and World coins.*

Dennis Fudge Coins
127 Hadrian Road, Jarrow, Tyne & Wear NE32 3TS (0191 421 6221). *P. L. Ancient coins.*

Galata Coins Ltd (ANA, BNTA)
The Old White Lion, Market Street, Llanfylin, Powys SY22 5BX (01691 648 765). *P. British and world coins.*

G. Gant
Glazenwood, 37 Augustus Way, Witham, Essex CM8 1HH. *P. British and Commonwealth coins.*

James Garriock
38 Hazel Close Bemerton Heath, Salisbury, Wiltshire SP2 977 (01722 500590). *P. L. Mainly hammered coins.*

John Gaunt
21 Harvey Road, Bedford MK41 9LF (01234 217685). By appointment. *Numismatic books.*

Alistair Gibb (IBNS)
5 West Albert Road, Kirkcaldy, Fife KY1 1DL (01592 269045). *P. L. Banknotes and books on banking.*

A. & S. Gillis
20 Howard Street, Darfield, Barnsley, South Yorkshire S73 9JD. (01226 750371, website www.gilliscoins.com,email: catalogues@gilliscoins.com) *P. L. Ancient and medieval coins.*

Richard Gladdle
9 Cork Street, London W1X 1P9. (01327 858511). *Tokens. P. L.*

Glance Back Books
17 Upper Street, Chepstow, Gwent NP6 5EX (01291 626562). 10.30–17.30. *World coins, medals, banknotes.*

Glendining's (ANA, BNTA)
101 New Bond Street, London W1Y 9LG (020 7493 2445). Mon-Fri 08.30-17.00, Sat 08.30–13.00. *Auctioneers.*

Phil Goodwin (ANA)
PO Box 69, Portsmouth, Hants PO1 5SH (02392 423267 or 02392 752006 incl. fax). *P or by appoint ment.L. Ancient coins and antiquities.*

K. Goulborn
12 Sussex Street, Rhyl, Clwyd. (01745 338112 or 01745 344856). *P. L. British coins and banknotes.*

Granta Stamp & Coin Shop
28 Magdalene Street, Cambridge CB3 0AF (01223 315044) Mon-Sat 10.30-18.30. *English coins and medals.*

Grantham Coins (BNTA)
PO Box 60, Grantham, Lincs (01476 870565). *P. L. English coins and banknotes.*

Eric Green—Agent in UK for Ronald J. Gillio Inc,
1013 State Street, Santa Barbara, California, USA 93101 (020 8907 0015, Mobile 0468 454948). *Gold coins, medals and paper money of the world.*

Barry Greenaway
PO Box 2151, Swindon, Wilts SN5 3GT. (01793
771079, fax 01793 772556, email
bdgreenaway@beeb.net). *Tokens, Checks. P.L.*

Grove Philatelics, Coins & Antiquities
Suite 4, Grove House, Blackheath Grove, London
SE3 0DG (020 8463 0063). *P. British coins.*

R. I. Groves
82 Burntscarth Green, Locharbriggs, Dumfries
DG1 1UL (01387 710636). *P. World, esp.
Scandinavian coins.*

Ian Haines
PO Box 45, Hereford, HR2 7YP (01432 268178). *P.
L. British and foreign coins and banknotes.*

Anthony Halse
The Headlands, Chepstow Road, Langstone,
Newport, Gwent NP6 2JN (01633 413238). *P. L.
English and foreign coins and tokens.*

A. D. Hamilton & Co (ANA, BNTA)
7 St Vincent Place, Glasgow G1 5JA (0141 221 5423,
fax 0141 248 6019, website www.adhamiltons.com,
email jeffrey@hamiltons.junglelink.co.uk). Mon-Sat
10.00–17.00. *British and World coins.*

Peter Hancock
40 West Street, Chichester, West Sussex PO19 1RP
(01243 786173). Mon-Sat. *World coins.*

P. Hanson
160 Princess Road, Buckhurst Hill, Essex IG9 5DJ.
P. L. Inexpensive world coins.

J. Hardiman & Son
PO Box 151, London SE20 7YL (020 8778 2678/
4159). *P. Quality world coins, all periods.*

Craig Holmes
6 Marlborough Drive, Bangor, Co Down BT19
1HB. *P. L. Low cost banknotes of the world.*

R. G. Holmes
11 Cross Park, Ilfracombe, Devon EX34 8BJ (01271
864474). *P. L. Coins, modern world crowns and
foreign banknotes.*

John L. Homan
Oxford Grange, Marsh Lane, Barrow Haven,
Barrow-on-Humber, South Humberside DN19 7ER
(01469 32109). *P. Greek, Roman and Byzantine coins.*

Homeland Holding Ltd (IBNS)
Homeland, St John, Jersey, Channel Islands
JE3 4AB (01534 65339). Mon-Fri 09.00-2.00. *World
coins.*

HTSM Coins
26 Dosk Avenue, Glasgow G13 4LQ. *P. L. British
and foreign coins and banknotes.*

T. A. Hull
15 Tangmere Crescent, Hornchurch, Essex RM12
5PL. *P. L. British coins, farthings to crowns, tokens.*

Humber Coins (BNTA)
PO Box 16, Scunthorpe, South Humberside DN15
7AA (01724 763990). *P. British coins.*

J. Hume
107 Halsbury Road East, Northolt, Middlesex UB5
4PY (020 8864 1731). *P. L. Chinese coins.*

D. D. & A. Ingle
380 Carlton Hill, Nottingham (0115 9873325).
Mon-Sat 09.30–17.00. *World coins.*

Rendal Ingram Coins (English)
206 Honeysuckle Road, Bassett, Southampton,
Hants SO16 3BU. (023 8032 4258, website http://
www.angelfire.com/co/RIngramCoins, email
ybu36@dial.pipex.co. *P. L. English
milled and modern coins.*

Intercol London (ANA, BNTA, IBNS)
43 Templars Crescent, London N3 3QR (020 7349
2207). *P. Paper money of the world.*

Peter Ireland Ltd (BNTA, IBNS)
31 Clifton Street, Blackpool, Lancs FY1 1JQ (01253
21588 fax 0253 300232). Mon-Sat 09.00-17.30.*British
and world coins, medals and tokens.*

JAK (IBNS)
31 Vapron Road, Mannamead, Plymouth, Devon
PL3 5NJ (01752 665405). *P. L. GB and Common.
banknotes.*

F. J. Jeffery & Son Ltd
23 Catalina Court, Melksham, Wiltshire SN12 6FA.
(01225 703143). *P. British, Commonwealth and
foreign coins.*

Richard W. Jeffery
Trebehor, Porthcurno, Penzance, Cornwall TR19
6LS (01736 871263). *P. British and world coins.*

Jersey Coin Co Ltd
26 Halkett Street, St Helier, Jersey, Channel Islands
(01534 25743). Mon-Sat 09.00–17.00. *World coins.*

J. G. Coins
PO Box 206, Southshore, Blackpool FY1 6GZ.
(01253 349138). *P. L British Coins.*

Ian Johnson
PO Box 28, Swinton, Manchester M27 3FR (01204
393944). *P. L. Ancient European and Oriental coins.*

I. L. Johnson
63, Sedley Close, Parkwood, Kent ME8 9QZ.
(01634 261037) *P. L. English coins 1672–1967*

Robert Johnson Coin Co
PO Box 194, 15 Bury Place, London WC1A 2JN
(020 7831 0305). Mon-Fri 10.30-18.00, Sat 10.30-
15.00. *British and world coins.*

Ian Jull
PO Box 594, Harrow, Middx, HA2 7SG. (020 8429
3988 fax: 020 8248 1714). *British coins and medals.*

Jumbo Coins
22 Woodend Lane, Stalybridge, Cheshire SK15 2SR
(0161 338 5741). Fri-Sat 14.00-19.00. *World coins,
medals and tokens.*

KB Coins (BNTA)
50 Lingfield Road, Martins Wood, Stevenage,
Herts SG1 5SL (01438 312661, fax 01438 311990).
09.00–18.00 by appointment only. *L. Mainly
British coins.*

Knightsbridge Coins (ANA, BNTA, IAPN)
43 Duke Street, St James's, London SW1Y 6DD (020
7930 8215/7597 Fax 020 7930 8214). Mon-Fri
10.00–17.30. *Quality coins of the world.*

Lancashire Coin & Medal Co
31 Adelaide Street, Fleetwood, Lancs FY7 6AD
(01253 779308). *P. British coins and medals.*

Lennox Gallery Ltd
K12/13, 4 Davies Mews, London, W1Y 1AR. (020
7629 9119 fax 020 7629 9119). *Ancient coins.*

Peter Licence
31 Reigate Way, Wallington, Surrey SM6 8NU (020
8688 5297). *P. British and World coins.*

Lighthouse Publications (UK)
4 Beaufort Road, Reigate, Surrey RH2 9DJ (01737
244222 Fax 0737 24743). *L. Manufacturers and
stockists of coin albums, cabinets and accessories.*

Lindner Publications Ltd
13 Fore Street, Hayle, Cornwall TR27 4DX (01736
751914 fax 01736 751911, email
lindneruk@cs.com). Mon–Fri 09.00–13.00. *L.
Manufacturers of coin albums, cabinets and accessories.*

Jan Lis (BNTA)
Beaver Coin Room, 57 Philbeach Gardens, London SW5 9ED (020 7373 4553 fax 020 7373 4555). *By appointment only. European coins.*

Keith Lloyd
45 Bramblewood, The Beeches, Ipswich, Suffolk IP8 3RS (01473 603067). *P. L. Greek, Roman coins.*

Lockdale Coins
36 Upper Orwell Street, Ipswich. (01473 218588). L. (Shop open 9.30–4.30 Mon–Sat). *World coins, medals, banknotes and accessories.*

Stephen Lockett
59 Cedar Drive, Sutton at Hone, Kent DA4 9EW (01322 861 228). *British and world coins.*

Mike Longfield Detectors
83 Station Road, Balsall Common, nr Coventry, Warwickshire CV7 7FN (01676 533274). Mon-Sat 09.30-17.00. *Metal detectors.*

Richard M. Lubbock (ANA, BNTA, IAPN, IBNS)
315 Regent Street, London W1R 7YB (020 7580 9922, 020 7637 7922 fax 020 7637 7602). *By appointment only. World coins and medals.*

Don MacRae Coins
PO Box 233, Uxbridge, Middlesex UB9 4HY (01895 832625). *P. British and world coins.*

Mannin Collections Ltd
5 Castle Street, Peel, Isle of Man (01624 843897). Mon-Sat 10.00-17.00. Half-day Thu. *British and Isle of Man coins.*

I. Markovits
1-3 Cobbold Mews, London W12 9LB (020 8749 3000). *Enamelled coins.*

Marron Coins
7 Beacon Close, Sheffield, South Yorkshire S9 1AA (0114 2433500, website www.marroncoins.free-online.co.uk, email marronsca@aol.com). *P. English coins.*

C. J. Martin (Coins) Ltd (BNTA)
85 The Vale, Southgate, London N14 6AT (020 8882 1509). .P. L. Bi-monthly catalogue. *Greek, Roman and English hammered coins.*

Clive Maxwell-Yates
21 Nicolas Road, Chorlton Manchester, M21 1LG (0161 881 7015). *P. L. World banknotes.*

M. G. Coins & Antiquities
12 Mansfield, High Wych, Herts cm21 0JT. (01279 721719).

Michael Coins
6 Hillgate Street, London W8 7SR (020 7727 1518). Mon-Fri 10.00-17.00. *World coins and banknotes.*

Midland Medals
12 Commerce House, Vicarage Lane, Water Orton, Birmingham B46 1RR (0121 7475983 fax 01564 784245). *P. Commemorative medals.*

David Miller Coins & Antiquities (ANA, BNTA)
PO Box 711, Hemel Hempstead, HP2 4UH (tel/fax 01442 251492). *Ancient and hammered English coins.*

Frank Milward (ANA, BNTA)
2 Ravensworth Road, Mortimer, Berkshire RG7 3UU (01734 322843). *P. European coins.*

Modern Coins & Stamps
24 Market Hall, Arndale Centre, Luton, Beds LU1 2TA (01582 412839). Mon-Sat 09.00-17.00. Half-day Wed. *Modern world coins.*

Graeme & Linda Monk (ANA, BNTA)
PO Box 201, Croydon, Surrey, CR9 7AQ (020 8656 4583 fax 020 8656 4583). *P. Fair organisers.*

Mike Morey
9 Elmtrees, Long Crendon, Bucks HP18 9DG. *P. L. British coins, halfcrowns to farthings.*

Peter Morris
1 Station Concourse, Bromley North Station, Bromley, BR1 1NN or PO Box 223, Bromley, BR1 4EQ (020 8313 3410 fax 020 8466 8502, website www.petermorris.co.uk, email info@petermorris.co.uk). Mon-Fri 10.00–18.00, Sat 0900-14.00 or by appointment. *L. British and world coins, proof sets and numismatic books.*

James Murphy
PO Box 122, Chorley, Lancashire PR7 2GE. *(01257 274 381). P. L. Ancient coins and antiquities.*

Colin Narbeth & Son Ltd (ANA, IBNS)
20 Cecil Court, Leicester Square, London WC2N 4HE (020 7379 6975 fax 01727 811 244, website http://www.colin-narbeth.com). Mon-Sat 10.30-17.00. *World banknotes.*

New Forest Leaves
Bisterne Close, Burley, Ringwood, Hants BH24 4BA (014253 3315). *Publishers of numismatic books.*

Peter Nichols
2 Norman Road, St Leonards on Sea, East Sussex TN37 6NH. (01424 436682, website www.coincabinets.com, email coincabinets@freezone.co.uk).

Wayne Nicholls
PO Box 44, Bilston, West Midlands. (01543 452476) *L. Choice English coins*

North Wales Coins Ltd (BNTA)
1b Penrhyn Road, Colwyn Bay, Clwyd (01492 533023/532129). Mon-Sat (closed Wed) 09.30–17.30. *British coins.*

Notability (IBNS)
'Mallards', Chirton, Devizes, Wilts SN10 3QX (01380 723961, website www.notability.org.uk, email cmp@notability.prestel.co.uk). *P. L. Banknotes of the world.*

NP Collectables
9 Main Street, Gedney Dyke, Spalding, Lincs PE12 0AJ (01406 365211Ireland (010 35322 29385). *P. L. English Hammered and Milled coins.*

The Numismery
89b Oxford Road, Reading, Berks RG1 7UZ (01734 582145). Mon-Sat 11.00–20.30. *World coins.*

Glenn S. Ogden
Duncraig, Canada Hill, Ogwell, Newton Abbot, Devon TQ12 6AF. (01626 331663) *P. L. English milled.*

John Ogden Coins
Hodge Clough Cottage, Moorside, Oldham OL1 4JW (0161 678 0709) *P. L. Ancient and hammered coins.*

Michael O'Grady (IBNS)
PO Box 307, Pinner, Middlesex HA5 4XT (020 8428 4002). *P. British and world paper money.*

Colin James O'Keefe
5 Pettits Place, Dagenham, Essex RM10 8NL. *P. British and European coins.*

Don Oliver Gold Coins
The Coin Gallery, Stanford House, 23 Market Street, Stourbridge, West Midlands DY8 1AB (01384 373899). Mon-Fri 10.00–17.00, Sat 10.00-13.00 (closed Thu). *Gold coins of the world.*

Ongar Coins
14 Longfields, Marden Ash, Ongar, Essex IG7 6DS. *P.World coins.*

Tim Owen Coins
63 Allerton Grange Rise, Leeds 17, West Yorkshire (0113 2688015). *P. L. Quality hammered coins.*

Oxford Coins
25, Weldon Road, New Marston, Oxford OX3 0HP (01865 726939). *British coins.*

P&D Medallions
PO Box 269, Berkhampstead, Herts HP4 3FT. (01442 865127, email P&D@medallions.freeserve.co.uk). *Historical and Commemorative medals of the world. P.*

Penrith Coin & Stamp Centre
37 King Street, Penrith, Cumbria CA11 7AY (01768 64185). Mon-Sat 09.00–17.30. *World coins.*

Pentland Coins (IBNS)
Pentland House, 92 High Street, Wick, Caithness KW14 L5. *P. British and world coins and world banknotes.*

Phil Phipps
PO Box 31, Emsworth, Hants PO10 7WE (tel/fax 01243 376086, email philip@worldcurrency.cc). *P. L. World and German banknotes.*

David C. Pinder
20 Princess Road West, Leicester LE1 6TP (0116 2702439). *P. Greek, Roman and Byzantine coins.*

Pobjoy Mint Ltd (ANA)
Millennium House, Kingswood Park, Bonsor Drive, Kingswood, Surrey KT20 6AY (01737 818181 fax 01737 818199). Mon-Fri 09.00–17.00. *Europe's largest private mint. New issues.*

S. R. Porter (BNTA)
18 Trinity Road, Headington Quarry, Oxford OX3 8LQ (01865 766851). *P. L. Ancient and British coins, some foreign, tokens, banknotes and accessories.*

David Pratchett
Trafalgar Square Collectors Centre, 7 Whitcombe Street, London WC2H 7HA. (020 7930 1979, fax 020 7930 1152, website www.coinsonline.co.uk, email info@coinsonline.co.uk). Mon-Fri 10.00–7.30. *Specialist in gold and silverworld coins.*

Tony Radman
Westfield House, 2G Westfield Road, Witney, Oxon OX8 5JG (01993 772 705). Mon-Sat 10.00-17.00. *Ancient and World coins.*

George Rankin Coin Co Ltd (ANA, BNTA)
325 Bethnal Green Road, London E2 6AH (020 7729 1280 fax 020 7729 5023). Mon-Sat 10.00-18.00 (half-day Thu). *World coins.*

Mark T. Ray (formerly MTR Coins)
22a Kingsnorth Close, Newark, Notts NG24 1PS. (01636 703152). *P. British coins.*

Regton Ltd
82 Cleveland Street, Birmingham B1 3SN (0121 359 2379). Mon-Sat 09.30-17.00. *Metal detectors.*

Rhyl Coin & Stamp Centre
12 Sussex Street, Rhyl, Clwyd (01745 338112). Mon-Sat 10.00-17.30. *World coins.*

Chris Rigby
PO Box 181, Worcester WR1 1YE (01905 28028). *P. L. Modern British coins.*

Roderick Richardson
The Old Granary Antiques Centre, King's Staithe Lane, King's Lynn, Norfolk. (01553 670833) *L. English, Hammered and early milled coins.*

F. J. Rist
PO Box 4, Ibstock, Leics LE67 6ZJ (01530 264278). *P. L. Ancient and medieval coins, British coins and antiquities.*

Ian Robinson
PO Box 929, Burgess Hill, West Sussex RH15 9FN (01444 242215, website www.iamcoins.co.uk, email ian@iamcoins.co.uk). *P. L. Quality English milled coins.*

S. J. Rood & Co Ltd
52–53 Burlington Arcade, London W1V 9AE (0171 493 0739). Mon-Sat 09.30-17.00. *World gold coins.*

Bill Rosedale
17 Priory Close, Abbots Park, Chester CH1 4BX (01244 382554, email bill@banknotes40freeserve.com) *P. L. World paper money*

Royal Mint Coin Club
PO Box 500, Cardiff CF1 1YY (01433 223366). *P. New issues struck by the Royal Mint.*

Colin de Rouffignac (BNTA)
57, Wigan Lane, Wigan, Lancs WN1 2LF (01942 237927) *P. English and Scottish hammered.*

Chris A. Rudd (IAPN)
PO Box 222, Aylsham, Norfolk, NR11 6TY (01263 735007 fax 01263 731777, website www.celticcoins.com). *P. L. Celtic coins.*

Colin Rumney (BNTA)
26 Caer Felin, Llanrheadr, Denbigh, Clwyd LL16 4PR (074 578621). *All world including ancients.*

R & J Coins
21b Alexandra Street, Southend-on-Sea, Essex SS1 1DA (01702 345995). Mon-Sat 10.00–16.00 (closed Wed). *World coins.*

RJB Coins (BNTA)
R. J. Bayliss, PO Box 95, Cheltenham GL51 9SF (01242 680652). *P. General world coins, especially Western Europe.*

R & L Coins (BNTA)
521 Lytham Road, Blackpool, Lancs FY4 1RJ (01253 43081). Mon-Sat 09.00–17.00 by appointment only. *British, Commonwealth and European coins.*

Safe Albums (UK) Ltd
16 Falcon Business Park, 38 Ivanhoe Road, Finchampstead, Berkshire RG40 4QQ. (0118 932 8976 fax 0118 932 8612).

Saltford Coins
Harcourt, Bath Road, Saltford, Bristol, Avon BS31 3DQ (01225 873512). *P. British, Commonwealth and world coins.*

I. S. Sandiford & Co Ltd
3 Marriotts Court, Brown Street, Manchester M2 1EA (0161 834 9346). Mon-Sat 09.00-16.30. *British and world coins.*

Satin
PO Box 63, Stockport, Cheshire SK4 5BU. (07940 393583 answer machine)

Schwer Coins (ANA, BNTA)
6 South Hill, Felixstowe, Suffolk, IP11 8AA (01394 278580 fax 0394 271348). *P. World coins.*

Seaford Coins
PO Box 2016, Seaford, East Sussex BN25 2PW (01323 491646). *P. L. British and foreign coins.*

David Seaman
160 Holloway Road, London N7. (020 7607 5607, email davidseamancoins@lineone.net). *P. L. Hammered, Milled, Maundy.*

Patrick Semmens
3 Hospital Road, Half Key, Malvern, Worcs WR14 1UZ (0886 33123). *P. European and British coins.*

Mark Senior
553 Falmer Road, Woodingdean, Brighton, Sussex (01273 309359). By appointment only. *P. L. Saxon, Norman and English hammered coins.*

S. E. Sewell
PO Box 104, Ipswich, Suffolk IP5 7QL (01473 626 950). *Mainly British milled coins.*

T. Sexton (IBNS)
19 Great Western Avenue, Bridgend, Mid Glamorgan CF31 1NN (01656 4861). *P. World coins.*

R. D. Shah (BNTA)
9 Lansdowne Grove, Neasden, London NW10 1LP (020 8452 5160). *Ancient India and Indian states.*

Robert Sharman Numismatist (ANA)
36 Dairsie Road, Eltham, London SE9 1XH (020 8850 6450). *P. British coins.*

Shepshed Coins & Jewellery
24 Charnwood Road, Shepshed, Leics LE12 9QF (01509 502511). Mon, Wed-Sat 09.15-16.30. *British coins.*

Simmons Gallery (ANA, BNTA, IBNS)
53 Lamb's Conduit Street, London WC1N 3NB (020 7831 2080 fax 020 7831 2090, website www.simmonsgallery.co.uk, email info@simmonsgallery.co.uk). *Organisers of the London Coin Fair, Cumberland Hotel, Marble Arch, London W1. L. Coins, tokens and medals.*

Raymond J. Sleet (BNTA)
11 Seagull Close, Kempshott, Basingstoke, Hants RG22 5QR (01256 53256 fax 01256 63525) *General world coins and tokens.*

E. Smith (ANA, IBNS)
PO Box 348, Lincoln LN6 0TX (01522 684681 fax 01522 689528). *P. Organisewr of the Morley, Leeds, monthly coin fair. World coins and paper money.*

J. Smith (BNTA)
47 The Shambles, York YO1 2LX (01904 654769). Mon-Sat 09.30–17.00. *World coins.*

Val Smith
170 Derby Road, Nottingham NG7 1LR (0115 9781194). Mon-Sat 11.00–16.30 (cl. Thu). *British and world coins.*

Jim Smythe
PO Box 6970, Birmingham B23 7WD (e-mail Jimdens@aol.com). *P. L. 19th/20th century British and world coins.*

S & B Coins
Grass Walk, Wood Lane, South Heath, Great Missenden, Bucks HP16 0RB (01494 862161). *P. L. British coins and medallions.*

Southern Coins
51 Beach Road, Selsey, West Sussex PO20 0LT (01243 606698). *P. British and world coins.*

George Sowden
Coins Galore, The Lizard, nr Helston, Cornwall TR12 7NU (01326 290300). *P. World coins.*

Spink & Son Ltd (ANA, BNTA, IAPN, IBNS)
69 Southampton Row, Bloomsbury, London. WC1B 4ET (020 7563 2820, fax 020 7563 4066, website www.spink-online.com, email info@spinkandson.com). *Ancient to modern world coins, orders, medals and decorations, banknotes and numismatic books*

SPM Jewellers (BNTA)
112 East Street, Southampton, Hants SO14 3HD (023 80 223255/020 80 227923, fax 023 80 335634, wwbsite www.spmgoldcoins.co.uk, email user@spm.in2home.co.uk). Tue-Sat 09.15–17.00, Sat 09.15–16.00. *World coins and medals.*

Stamp & Collectors Centre
404 York Town Road, College Town, Camberley, Surrey GU15 4PR (01276 32587 fax 01276 32505). Mon, Tue, Thu, Sat 09.00–17.00, Wed, Fri 09.00–1900. *World coins and medals.*

St Edmunds Coins & Banknotes
PO Box 118, Bury St Edmunds IP33 2NE. (01284 761894)

Sterling Coins & Medals
2 Somerset Road, Boscombe, Bournemouth, Dorset BH7 6JH (01202 423881). Mon-Sat 09.30–16.30 (closed Wed). *World coins and medals.*

Strawbridge
Tanglewood, Ivy Tree Hill, Stokeinteignhead, Newton Abbott, Devon TQ12 4QH (01626 873783, emailjim@strawbridge.co.uk). *P. L. Coins, tokens, medals, banknotes.*

Studio Coins (ANA, BNTA)
16 Kilham Lane, Winchester, Hants SO22 5PT (01962 853156 fax 01962 624246). *P. English coins.*

Surena Numismatics (BNTA)
PO Box 2194, London NW8 6QQ (0831 220010). *P. Parthian, Sassanian, Islamic coins.*

Stuart J. Timmins
Smallwood Lodge Bookshop, Newport, Salop (01952 813232). Mon-Sat 09.30–17.00. *Numismatic literature.*

R. Tims
39 Villiers Road, Watford, Herts WD1 4AL. *P. L. Uncirculated world banknotes.*

Trafalgar Square Collectors' Centre (ANA, BNTA, LM, OMRS)
7 Whitcomb Street, Trafalgar Square, London WC2H 7HA (020 7930 1979). Mon-Fri 10.00–17.30. *World coins and commemorative medals. War medals and decorations.*

D. A. Travis
8 Cookridge Drive, Leeds LS16 7LT. *P. L. US coins.*

Michael Trenerry Ltd (BNTA)
PO Box 55, Truro, Cornwall TR1 2YQ (01872 277977 fax 01872 225565). By appointment only. *L. Roman, Celtic and English hammered coins, trade tokens.*

Vera Trinder Ltd
38 Bedford Street, Strand, London WC2E 9EU (020 7836 2365/6). Mon-Fri 08.30-17.30. *L. Coin catalogues and books, albums, envelopes, cases and accessories.*

Robert Tye
Poll Toran, Loch Eynort, South Uist PA81 5SJ. *P. European and Oriental hammered coins.*

Valda Coins
80 Aberfan Road, Aberfan, Mid Glamorgan CF48 4QJ. (01443 690452). *P. L.*

Vale (ADA BNTA)
21 Tranquil Vale, Blackheath, London SE3 0BU (020 8852 9817. Mon-Sat 10.00–17.30 (closed Thu). *British coins and medals.*

Tony Vaughan Collectables
PO Box 364, Wolverhampton, WV3 9PW (01902 27351). *P. L. World coins and medals.*

Victory Coins
184 Chichester Road, North End, Portsmouth, Hants PO2 0AX (01705 751908/663450). Mon-Sat 09.15–17.30. *British and world coins.*

Mark J. Vincenzi (BNTA)
Rylands, Earls Colne, Essex. CO6 2LE (01787 222555). *P. Greek, Roman, Hammered.*

Vista World Banknotes
5 Greenfields Way, Burley-in-Wharfedale, Ilkley, W. Yorks LS29 7RB. (Email vistabanknotes@barclays.net).

Mike Vosper
PO Box 2874, Colchester CO4 5UR (01206 752110, website www.vosper4coins.co.uk, email mikevosper@vosper4coins.co.uk).

Wallis & Wallis
West Street Auction Galleries, Lewes, East Sussex BN7 2NJ (01273 476562). Mon-Fri 09.00–17.30. *Regular auctions of coins, medals and militaria.*

B. M. & S. A. Weeks
PO Box 1447, Salisbury, Wilts SP5 2YG (01725 510311). *L. British coins, world crowns and medals.*

John Welsh
PO Box 150, Burton-on-Trent, Staffs DE13 7LB (01543 73073 fax 0543 473234). *P. L. British coins.*

Pam West (IBNS)
PO Box 257, Sutton, Surrey SM3 9WW (020 8641 3224, website west-banknotes.co.uk, email pamwestbritnotes@compuserve.com). *P. L. English banknotes.*

West Cornwall Stamp Centre
13 Fore Street, Hayle, Cornwall TR27 4DX (01736 751910 fax: 01736 751911. *L. Coin Accessories.*

West Essex Coin Investments (BNTA, IBNS)
Croft Cottage, Station Road, Alderholt, Fordingbridge, Hants SP6 3AZ (01425 656 459). *P. L. British and World coins and paper money.*

R & J White (IBNS)
29 Shortacre, Basildon, Essex SS14 2LR (01268 522923). *P. L. Banknotes and world ephemera.*

Whitmore (BNTA)
Teynham Lodge, Chase Road, Upper Colwall, Malvern, Worcs WR13 6DT (01684 40651). *P. World coins, tokens and medals.*

J. L. Williams
502 Clive Court, Maida Vale, London W9 1SG (020 7286 3461). *P. L. Wholesaler—dealers only.*

A. G. Wilson (BNTA)
PO Box 864, Eastbourne, BN21 4YR (01323 738591 fax 0323 737936). *Rare and choice coins of the world*

World Coins
35–36 Broad Street, Canterbury, Kent CT1 2LR (01227 68887). Mon-Sat 09.30–17.30 (half-day Thu). *World coins.*

World Treasure Books
PO Box 5, Newport, Isle of Wight PO30 5QE (01983 740712). *L. Coins, books, metal detectors*

Barry Wright,
54 Dooley Drive, Bootle, Merseyside. L3O 8RT. *P. L. World banknotes.*

B. N. Yarwood (ANA)
Yarwood Hall, Luttongate Road, Sutton St Edmund, Spalding, Lincs PE12 0LH. *P. British and US coins.*

Banks, Mints and Numismatic
Bureaux
of the world

Many national banks and mints operate numismatic bureaux and sales agencies from which coins, medals and other numismatic products may be obtained direct. The conditions under which purchases may be made vary considerably. In many cases at the present time bureaux will accept orders from overseas customers quoting their credit card number and its expiry date; but in others payment can only be made by certified bank cheque, or international money order, or by girobank. Cash is seldom, if ever, acceptable. It is best to write in the first instance to enquire about methods of payment.

A

National Mint, Baghe Arg, Kabul, Afghanistan

Bank Mille Afghan, Kabul, Afghanistan

Banque d'Algerie, Sucursale d'Alger, 8 Boulevard Carnot, Alger, Algeria

Banco de Angola, Luanda, Daroal, Angola

Casa de Moneda de la Nacion, Avenida Antartica, Buenos Aires, BA, Argentina

Royal Australian Mint, Department of the Treasury, Canberra, ACT, Australia

GoldCorp Australia, Perth Mint Buildings, GPO Box M924, Perth, Western Australia 6001

Oesterreichsiches Hauptmunzamt, Am Heumarkt 1, A-1031 Wien, Postfach 225, Austria

Oesterreichische Nationalbank, A-1090 Wien, Otto Wagner-platz 3, Austria

B

Treasury Department, PO Box 557, Nassau, Bahamas (*coins*)

Ministry of Finance, PO Box 300, Nassau, Bahamas (*banknotes*)

Bank of Bahrain, PO Box 106, Manama, Bahrain

Eastern Bank, PO Box 29, Manama, Bahrain

Monnaie Royale de Belgique, Avenue de Pacheco 32, B-1000 Bruxelles, Belgium

Banque Nationale de Belgique SA, Caisse Centrale, Bruxelles, Belgium

Banque de Bruxelles SA, 2 Rue de la Regence, Bruxelles 1, Belgium

Casa de la Moneda, Potosi, Bolivia

Banco Central de Bolivia, La Paz, Bolivia

Casa da Moeda, Praca da Republica 173, Rio de Janeiro, Brazil

Hemus FTO, 7 Vasil Levski Street, Sofia C-1, Bulgaria

Banque de la Republique, Bujumbura, Burundi

C

Banque Centrale, Douala, Boite Postale 5.445, Cameroun

Royal Canadian Mint, 320 Sussex Drive, Ottawa 2, Ontario, Canada K1A 0G8

Casa de Moneda, Quinta Normal, Santiago, Chile

Casa de Moneda, Calle 11 no 4-93, Bogota, Colombia

Numismatic Section, The Treasury, Avarua, Rarotonga, Cook Islands

Banco Centrale de Costa Rica, Departamento de Contabilidad, San Jose, Costa Rica, CA

Central Bank of Cyprus, PO Box 1087, Nicosia, Cyprus

Artia, Ve Smekach 30, PO Box 790, Praha 1, Czech Republic

D

Den Kongelige Mønt, Amager Boulevard 115, København S, Denmark

Danmarks Nationalbank, Holmens Kanal 17, 1060 København K, Denmark

Banco Central de Santo Domingo, Santo Domingo, Dominican Republic

E

Banco Central, Quito, Ecuador

Mint House, Abbassia, Cairo, Egyptian Arab Republic

Exchange Control Department, National Bank of Egypt, Cairo, Egyptian Arab Republic

Banco Central de la Republica, Santa Isabel, Equatorial Guinea

Commercial Bank of Ethiopia, Foreign Branch, PO Box 255, Addis Ababa, Ethiopia

F

Currency Board, Victoria Parade, Suva, Fiji

Suomen Rahapaja, Katajanokanlaituri 3, Helsinki 16, Finland

Suomen Pankki, PO Box 10160, Helsinki 10, Finland

Hotel de Monnaie, 11 Quai de Conti, 75-Paris 6e, France

G

Banque Centrale Libreville, Boite Postale 112, Gabon

Verkaufstelle fur Sammlermunzen, D-638 Bad Homburg vdH, Bahnhofstrasse 16–18, Germany

Staatliche Munze Karlsruhe, Stephanienstrasse 28a, 75 Karlsruhe, Germany

Staatliche Munze Cannstatt, Taubenheimerstrasse 77, 7 Stuttgart-Bad, Germany

Bayerisches Hauptmunzamt, Hofgraben 4, 8 Munich, Germany

Hamburgische Munze, Norderstrasse 66, 2 Hamburg 1, Germany

Bank of Ghana, PO Box 2674, Accra, Ghana

Pobjoy Mint, Mint House, 92 Oldfields Road, Sutton, Surrey SM1 2NW

Royal Mint, Llantrisant, Mid Glamorgan, Wales, CF7 8YT

Royal Mint Coin Club, PO Box 500, Cardiff, CF1 1HA

Bank of Greece, Treasury Department, Cash, Delivery & Despatch Division, PO Box 105, Athens, Greece

Casa Nacional de Moneda, 6a Calle 4-28, Zona 1, Ciudad Guatemala, Republica de Guatemala CA

States Treasury, St Peter Port, Guernsey, Channel Islands

Bank of Guyana, PO Box 658, Georgetown, Guyana

H

Banque Nationale de la Republique d'Haiti, Rue Americaine et Rue Fereu, Port-au-Prince, Haiti

Banco Central de Honduras, Tegucigalpa DC, Honduras CA

State Mint, Ulloi utca 102, Budapest VIII, Hungary

Artex, PO Box 167, Budapest 62, Hungary

Magyar Nemzeti Bank, Board of Exchange, Budapest 54, Hungary

I

Sedlabanki Islands, Reykjavik, Iceland

Indian Government Mint, Bombay 1, India

Arthie Vasa, Keabajoran Baru, Djakarta, Indonesia

Perum Peruri, Djakarta, Indonesia

National Mint, Tehran, Iran

Bank Markazi Iran, Tehran, IranCentral Bank of Iraq, PO Box 64, Baghdad, Iraq

Central Bank of Ireland, Dublin 2, Republic of Ireland

The Treasury, Government Buildings, Prospect Hill, Douglas, Isle of Man

Israel Stamp and Coin Gallery, 4 Maze Street, Tel Aviv, Israel

Istituto Poligraphico e Zecca dello Stato, Via Principe Umberto, Roma, Italy

J

Decimal Currency Board, PO Box 8000, Kingston, Jamaica

Mint Bureau, 1 Shinkawasakicho, Kita-ku, Osaka 530, Japan

Numismatic Section, Treasury Department, St Helier, Jersey

Central Bank of Jordan, Amman, Jordan

Banque Nationale du Liban, Rue Masraf Loubnan, Beirut, Lebanon

K

Central Bank, PO Box 526, Kuwait

L

Bank of Lithuania, Cash Department, Gedimino av. 6, 2001 Vilius, Lithuania

Caisse Generale de l'Etat, 5 Rue Goethe, Luxembourg-Ville, Grande Duche de Luxembourg

M

Institut d'Emission Malgache, Boite Postale 205, Tananarive, Madagascar

Central Bank of Malta, Valletta 1, Malta

Casa de Moneda, Calle del Apartado no 13, Mexico 1, DF, Mexico

Le Tresorier General des Finances, Monte Carlo, Principaute de Monaco

Banque de l'Etat du Maroc, Rabat, Morocco

Banco Nacional Ultramarino, Maputo, Republica de Mocambique

British Bank of the Middle East, Muscat

N

Royal Mint, Dharahara, Katmandu, Nepal

Nepal Rastra Bank, Katmandu, Nepal

Rijks Munt, Leidseweg 90, Utrecht, Netherlands

Hollandsche Bank-Unie NV, Willemstad, Breedestraat 1, Curacao, Netherlands Antilles

Central Bank of Curacao, Willemstad, Curacao, Netherlands Antilles

The Treasury, Private Bag, Lambton Quay, Wellington, New Zealand

Banco de Nicaragua, Departamento de Emison, La Tresoria, Apartada 2252, Managua, Nicaragua

Nigerian Security Printing and Minting Corporation, Ahmadu Bello Road, Victoria Island, Lagos, Nigeria

Central Bank of Nigeria, Tinubu Square LB, Lagos, Nigeria

Norges Bank, Oslo, Norway

Den Kongelige Mynt, Hyttegaten, Konigsberg, Norway

P

Pakistan State Mint, Baghban Pura, Lahore 9, Pakistan

National Development Bank, Asuncion, Paraguay

Casa Nacional de Moneda, Calle Junin 791, Lima, Peru

Central Bank of the Philippines, Manila, Philippines

Bank Handlowy w Warszawie, Ul. Romuald Traugutta 7, Warsaw, Poland

Desa Foreign Trade Department, Al. Jerozolimskie 2, Warszawa, Poland

Casa da Moeda, Avenida Dr Antonio Jose de Almeida, Lisbon 1, Portugal

R

Cartimex, 14-18 Aristide Briand St, PO Box 134-135, Bucharest, Roumania

Bank of Foreign Trade, Commercial Department, Moscow K 16, Neglinnaja 12, Russian Federation

Banque Nationale du Rwanda, Boite Postale 351, Kigali, Republique Rwandaise

S

Numismatic Section, Box 194, GPO, Apia, Samoa

Azienda Autonoma di Stato Filatelica-Numismatica, Casalla Postale 1, 47031 Repubblica di San Marino

Banque Internationale pour le Commerce, 2 Avenue Roume, Dakar, Senegal

Bank of Yugoslavia, PO Box 1010, Belgrade, Serbia

The Treasury, PO Box 59, Victoria, Seychelles

Bank of Sierra Leone, PO Box 30, Freetown, Sierra Leone

The Singapore Mint, 249 Jalan Boon Lay, Jurong, Singapore

South African Mint, PO Box 464, Pretoria, South Africa

Government Printing Agency, 93 Bukchang Dong, Chungku, Seoul, Republic of South Korea

Fabrica Nacional de Moneda y Timbre, Jorge Juan 106, Madrid 9, Spain

Bank of Sri Lanka, PO Box 241, Colombo, Sri Lanka

Hong Kong and Shanghai Banking Corporation, PO Box 73, Colombo 1, Sri Lanka

Sudan Mint, PO Box 43, Khartoum, Sudan

Bank of Sudan, PO Box 313, Khartoum, Sudan

Bank of Paramaribo, Paramaribo, Suriname

Kungelige Mynt och Justeringsverket, Box 22055, Stockholm 22, Sweden

Eidgenossische Staatskasse, Bundesgasse 14, CH-3003, Berne, Switzerland

Central Bank of Syria, Damascus, Syrian Arab Republic

T

Central Mint of China, 44 Chiu Chuan Street, Taipei, Taiwan, ROC

Royal Thai Mint, 4 Chao Fah Road, Bangkok, Thailand

Numismatic Section, The Treasury, Nuku'alofa, Tonga

Central Bank of Trinidad and Tobago, PO Box 1250, Port of Spain, Trinidad

Banque Centrale de Tunisie, Tunis, Tunisia

State Mint, Maliye Bakanligi Darphane Mudurlugu, Istanbul, Turkey

U

Bank of Uganda, PO Box 7120, Kampala, Uganda

Numismatic Service, US Assay Office, 350 Duboce Avenue, San Francisco, CA, 94102, USA

Office of the Director of the Mint, Treasury Department, Washington, DC, 20220, USA

Philadelphia Mint, 16th and Spring Garden Streets, Philadelphia, PA, 19130, USA

Franklin Mint, Franklin Center, Pennsylvania, 19063, USA

Banco Central del Uruguay, Cerrito 351, Montevideo, RO del Uruguay

V

Ufficio Numismatico, Governatorato dello Stato della Citta de Vaticano, Italy

Banco Central de Venezuela, Caracas, Venezuela

Y

Yemen Bank, Sana'a, Yemen.

Z

Bank of Zambia, PO Box 80, Lusaka, Zambia

Chief Cashier, Reserve Bank, PO Box 1283, Harare, Zimbabwe

Numismatics and
The Law

Counterfeit Currency

A counterfeit is a forgery or imitation of a coin or banknote produced with the intention of defrauding the revenue of the State or deceiving members of the public. By the Coinage Offences Act (1861) it was a felony to counterfeit gold or silver coins. Lesser offences included the gilding of farthings and sixpences to pass them off as half-sovereigns, the possession of moulds, machines or tools clandestinely removed from the Royal Mint, the impairment or diminution of gold or silver coins by filing or clipping (or even the possession of such filings and clippings).

The Coinage Act of 1870 made provision for the counterfeiting of base-metal coins, or the stamping of letters or words on coins of any kind, or the forging of colonial coinage. The most celebrated prosecution under this Act occurred in 1930 when Martin Coles Harman was convicted and fined £5 for issuing bronze coins resembling the British penny and halfpenny for the island of Lundy of which he was then the proprietor. Interestingly, no attempt was made to prosecute the Birmingham Mint which actually struck the coins (prudently omitting the H mintmark).

The making of medals or coins resembling current coin became a misdemeanour under the Counterfeit Medal Act of 1883. This Act is invoked from time to time against manufacturers or distributors of medallic pieces or coin jewellery. Such pieces, often struck in 9 carat gold, are deemed to infringe the Act if, for example, they have a figure even vaguely resembling St George and the Dragon on one side. The use of the royal effigy, however, without due authorisation, is regarded as a misdemeanour punishable by an unlimited fine and the confiscation of tools, dies and instruments. At the present time it is a serious offence to make a counterfeit of a currency note or coin with the intention of passing it off or tendering it as genuine. This offence carries a maximum penalty of ten years' imprisonment or an unlimited fine, or both. Making a counterfeit of a currency note or coin without lawful authority incurs a penalty up to two years' imprisonment or an unlimited fine, or both.

Passing or tendering as genuine anything which is known or believed to be a counterfeit of a currency note or coin renders the criminal on conviction to a term of ten years' imprisonment or an unlimited fine, or both. The mere possession of any forged note or coin is itself a criminal offence. Possessing countertfeits without authority or permission so to do, and doing so knowingly, renders the possessor liable to two years' imprisonment or an unlimited fine, or both. The Act also stipulates that the reproduction of a current banknote—of the Bank of England or of the Scottish and Northern Irish banks is a serious offence. This clause covers even such apparently innocent acts as making a photocopy (whether in black and white or full colour) of a current banknote, the photography of such a note or the illustration of such a note in any book, magazine or newspaper. Strict regulations are laid down concerning the legitimate illustration of notes, whether current or not, in books and periodicals; such illustrations must be either greatly reduced or enlarged *and* must bear a prominent defacement, such as SPECIMEN or CANCELLED. It is also a serious offence to utilise a reproduction of a current British banknote in any medium. Theoretically this includes such things as tea-towels, T-shirts, mugs, plates and other souvenirs in glass or ceramics, but in practice the law seems to turn a blind eye to such practices. Imitations and parodies of notes and coins are also regarded as infringements of the law, but in these instances prosecution of the offender seldom proceeds; a warning is generally regarded as sufficient, provided that the offending article or articles are withdrawn and suppressed.

The advent of high-definition colour photocopying in recent years has brought the offence of reproduction into prominence once more. The regulations have been tightened considerably and there have been several cases of successful prosecution. In each case, however, the intent deliberately to deceive the public by uttering a colour photocopy as a genuine note was proved.

Technically the offence takes places as soon as the photocopy is made, for whatever purpose, but as a rule only those cases in which an element of fraudulent deception subsequently arose were pursued with the full rigour of the law. The law is quite clear, however, and it is a criminal offence to make a colour photocopy or photograph of any current British note unless permission to do so has been obtained from the Treasury. The maximum penalty on conviction is an unlimited fine.

The note-issuing banks have, of course, taken steps in recent years to incorporate further security devices into their notes, notably the use of latent images and underprints in colours which are difficult, if not impossible to photocopy accurately. At the same time, the adoption of metal strips and more complex watermark devices has theoretically made the task of the forger much more difficult. If, by some unlucky chance, someone passes a dud note on to you, you must make no attempt to pass it in turn. To do so renders you liable to prosecution for uttering a forgery. Forged notes must be handed over to the police as soon as possible. If you receive a forged note in payment for goods or services you are entitled to claim its face value from the person who gave it to you. Even if the person giving you the note did not realise that it was counterfeit, it is assumed in law that he or she represented to you that the note was worth its face value at the time the note was passed. If the tenderer knew that the note was forged, he can be prosecuted; but at the end of the day he is still liable to you for the fraud and can be sued in the civil courts for the recovery of the sum involved. If, on the other hand, you received the money as a gift, you have no legal claim against the person who gave it to you. If you pay someone with a counterfeit note or coin unknowingly, you have committed no offence, but you must pay again. The degree of culpability is often difficult to prove or disprove, but it is unlikely that a prosecution would be initiated on the basis of a single note or a solitary coin.

It is also a serious offence to manufacture blanks, discs or washers which are intended to defraud the proprietors of vending machines, or to possess tools and equipment for the dishonest manufacture or alteration of such blanks for this purpose. Under the Gold and Silver Export Control Act (1920) melting down gold or silver coins to extract their precious metal content is an offence punishable by a fine of £100 or two years' imprisonment, or both.

Legal Tender

The dictionary defines this as currency which a creditor is bound by law to accept as payment of a money debt. Debts and purchases must be paid for in cash of legal tender unless the creditor or seller is willing to accept payment in another form, such as a postal order, money order, cheque or, nowadays, credit card. Bank of England notes of any denomination are legal tender in England and Wales. Formerly Bank of England pound notes (but no other) were legal tender in Scotland. Technically, since the demise of the pound note, no Bank of England notes are legal tender in Scotland, although in practice they circulate freely north of the Border. Even more surprisingly, Scottish banknotes are not legal tender anywhere, not even in Scotland! The subtle difference is reflected in the actual wording of the promise on English and Scottish banknotes. Thus English notes are inscribed *"I promise to pay the bearer on demand the sum of . . ."* without stipulating any specific place, the promise being made by the Chief Cashier. Scottish notes, on the other hand, have the promise in the third person. It is the bank itself which makes the promise *"to pay the bearer on demand . . . pounds sterling at their head office here in Edinburgh, by order of the Board"*. In practice, however, Scottish banknotes are accepted without question, not only throughout Scotland but also in parts of England, and are generally accepted in London, although there is no obligation on the part of a creditor so to do.

Apart from gold coins, the base-metal pound coin is legal tender for payment of any amounts. So, too, presumably, are the various two-pound and five-pound base-metal coins of recent years, even though they have been struck as commemoratives and not intended for general circulation in the ordinary sense. Smaller denominations are only legal tender up to a maximum value in each case. In the case of 50p coins, 25p crowns and 20p coins, they may be used alone, or in combination with each other, in payment of amounts up to £10. 10p and 5p coins, alone or in combination, may be used for sums up to £5. Bronze 1p and 2p coins, however, can only be used for payment of amounts up to 20p. In practice, of course, you can probably get away with making payment in larger quantities (within reason!) although strictly speaking there is no obligation on the part of your creditor to accept them.

An Offence to Possess Legal Tender Coins

From the foregoing it will be seen that gold coins are, and always have been, legal tender. Since 1817 the legal tender gold coin of the United Kingdom has been the sovereign (with its sub-division and multiples). Yet there have been times when actual possession of these legal tender coins has been, *per se*, an illegal act. The first attempt to regulate the movement and possession of gold coins arose in 1947 with the passage of the Exchange Control Act which made it illegal to buy, borrow, lend or sell any gold or foreign currency, unless authorised to deal in gold. Moreover it was stipulated that *"any person possessing gold should offer it for sale to an authorised dealer at a price not exceeding the authorised price, unless the Treasury consented to this retention of the gold"*. The serious implications of this Act were mitigated in the case of numismatists by the Exchange Control (Collectors' Pieces Exemption) Order 1947, which allowed collectors to hold on to *"any gold coin which was minted in 1816 or earlier, and any gold coin which was minted after 1816 and which has a numismatic value greater than the value of the gold content which would have been received if the coin had been sold to an authorised (bullion) dealer"*. In effect this meant that numismatists and coin dealers were not hindered from buying and selling gold coins as long as the coins were in collectable condition and possessed numismatic interest. This loophole was brazenly breached in the 1960s and led to the Exchange Control (Gold Coins Exemption) Order of 1966 which aimed to prevent the loss of currency reserves caused by the import of gold coins from abroad, and to eliminate the hoarding of gold by speculators. By the terms of this Order no one was permitted to hold more than four gold coins minted after 1837 unless he had received express permission from the Treasury. The maximum was set at four coins so that people who had one or two sovereigns as mementoes could keep them without breaking the law. Numismatists who possessed more than four post-1837 gold coins on April 27, 1966 had to apply to the Treasury for permission to retain them. To do so they had to prove that they were *bona fide* collectors by completing form GC 1, providing a detailed list of the coins in their possession—not only in gold, but also in silver (pre-1816, 1816–1919 and post-1919) and base metals (before and after 1860). Several individuals were successfully prosecuted under this draconian legislation and their holdings of gold sovereigns confiscated, although no one was imprisoned or heavily fined as the legislation provided. The 1966 order was rescinded in 1970, re-imposed in a modified form in 1975, and finally revoked in 1979. Since that date numismatists and speculators alike have been free to collect (or hoard) gold to their hearts' content.

Value Added Tax

This is a matter which primarily concerns dealers, but it also applies to those who dabble in coins on a part-time basis, and has implications for collectors at all levels. Briefly, anyone conducting a business,

or in self-employment, who has a turnover in excess of £43,000 per annum, must register with HM Customs and Excise for the collection and payment of Value Added Tax. Anyone whose turnover is less than £43,000 is exempt from the obligation to register, but is at liberty to register if he or she feels that this would be advantageous. It is nice to think that there is an element of choice in this, although one would be hard pressed to think why anyone would voluntarily register for VAT unless they absolutely had to! Incidentally, the government raised the VAT registration level by 40 per cent to £35,000 in March 1991 with the avowed intention of relieving a large number of businesses from this burden, at a time when the rate of tax was increased from 15 per cent to 17.5 per cent. Assuming that you are a dealer with a turnover above the magic limit, then you are committing a serious offence if you fail to register. Registration then lays you open to the full machinery of the system. You have to charge VAT on all goods and services, issuing VAT invoices and receipts and keeping detailed accounts which are liable to snap inspection at any time. You have to make quarterly returns to Customs and Excise of the amount of tax you have collected. From this you are allowed to deduct the VAT which you yourself have paid out in the course of your business, and you then have to remit the difference to the VAT collector. Of course, should the amount you have paid exceed the tax you have collected, you receive a repayment in due course. This arises in businesses which handle zero-rated goods and services, but coins and medals do not come within that category.

For dealers in gold bullion, coins or medals, there is a special VAT leaflet which covers regulations specific to such matters. Since January 2000 investment gold has been exempt from VAT. A coin is classified as investment gold if it satisfies the following conditions: 1. Minted after 1800; 2. At least .900 fine; 3. Is or has been legal tender of its country of origin; 4. Is of a description of coin that is normally sold at a price that does not exceed 180% of the open market value of the gold contained in the coin. This is a complicated issue and further advice can be obtained from Customs & Excise Public Notice 701/21/99. A list of coins qualifying as investment gold is published in Public Notice 701/21A/99. When VAT is applicable of course it needs to be accounted for on the profit margin. It is vital therefore to maintain accurate records of all buying and selling, and which coins and medals are subject to VAT and which are exempt. Furthermore, the onus is on you to ensure that the source of the gold you bring into the country is impeccable. There are extremely heavy penalties for smuggling gold, and ignorance of the law, or apparently innocent handling of smuggled gold subsequently, are no defence.

From January 1, 1995 the special margin scheme of accounting for VAT currently available for certain second-hand goods, such as cars, was extended to almost all second-hand goods. The scheme allows businesses buying and selling eligible goods to account for VAT only on the difference between the buying and selling prices of these items.

A special system of accounting exists which enables some dealers to account for VAT without the need to keep a detailed record of every transaction. Certain works of art, antiques and collector's items, including "secondhand" coins, defined in Notice 712 *Second-hand goods*, were exempt from VAT at import. From January 1, 1996 these items became subject to VAT at import at an effective rate of 2.5 per cent.

Export and Import

Some coins do require an export licence before they can be taken out of the country and unfortunately these controls have been extended during the past year. Following the lifting of the export regulations relating to gold coins in 1979, then prior to April 1, 1993 the only coins which required any export licence were those with a value in excess of £35,000. However the agreement by the UK to implement an EC directive on the removal of cultural goods has resulted in a fresh interpretation of previous UK legislation on these coins which are on the market as a result of an archaeological find. Therefore as from April 1, 1993, any coin *whatever its value* which has come from an archaeological source within the UK will require an export licence even to take it to another EC country. Certain other coins of EC provenance other than the UK will now require an EC export licence. The value limit for non-archaeological source coins has been increased to £39,600 (Ecu 50,000). Both types of licence are issued by the Department of National Heritage, 2–4 Cockspur Street, Trafalgar Square, London SW1Y 5DH who can also supply a handy flow-chart to enable you to tell at a glance whether a licence is needed and what type. These new regulations are imposing an enormous additional burden on the trade and the British Numismatic Trade Association has held numerous meetings with the authorities in an attempt to reduce to a minimum the number of licence applications needed. Hopefully, by next year's edition there will be better news.

The restrictions applied to the importation of gold coins were removed in 1979, as previously mentioned. Coins of any kind are now permitted under Open General Import licence from any country and a specific or individual licence is no longer required. Details of any duties which may be payable on imported coins can be obtained from HM Customs and Excise, King's Beam House, Southwark, London SE1 or any local Customs and Excise office. Until recently, the only gold coins under embargo were Krugerrands. This was a political decision, aimed at tightening sanctions against South Africa, and applied to the importation of new gold coins from that country, but not to Krugerrands which had been brought into the United Kingdom, or any of the countries of the European Community, prior to the imposition of sanctions. In practice, it was very difficult to regulate the movement, let alone the importation, of Krugerrands, and with the relaxation of Apartheid this regulation has been lifted.

Importing Coins by Mail

Elsewhere in this volume will be found the names and addresses of mints, banks and numismatic bureaux around the world from whom it may be possible to obtain currency direct. It is a wise precaution to write to these bodies in the first instance for details of their sales and distribution. In some cases they appoint a dealer in Britain as an agent and this is a method of purchase that removes a great deal of the hassle and red tape. Nowadays, however, many mints and banks are quite happy to use the credit card system to make it easy to part you from your money. The problem arises, however, when the coins are despatched. As a rule, banks and mints stipulate quite clearly that they will not accept orders prepaid in cash, and it is an offence to send coins or banknotes out of the country as payment, except through banks authorised for this purpose. Cheques drawn on British banks should not be used. Indeed, this may be actively discouraged by the imposition of heavy clearance and handling charges at the other end. The converse is also true, although Americans seem to think that dollar cheques drawn on some obscure mid-West bank will be eagerly accepted here, and are consequently aggrieved when it is tactfully pointed out to them that this creates enormous problems—to say nothing of the swingeing bank charges incurred in converting such cheques to sterling. Other than credit cards, the Girobank system is probably the best method of remitting currency from one country to another; full details may be obtained from any post office. Details on the preferred method of sending remittances, or transferring cash to another country, as well as the transmission of coins by post to different countries, will be found in the *Royal Mail International Service Guide*. This also lists, among the prohibitions pertaining to each country, which countries accept gold or silver, and which ban the transmission of precious metals by post.

The receipt of postal packets containing coins from abroad makes you liable for Value Added Tax on their importation. As a rule, the despatching mint or bank will have affixed a Customs declaration to the packet, listing the contents, their weight and value, and it is on that basis that VAT will be calculated. The position regarding the import and export of coins by post is more complicated, and applies also to goods sent on approval. In such cases you must consult your Customs and Excise office who will advise you on the correct procedure and what your liabilities will be to tax in either case. This also applies to dealers taking stock out of the country to a coin show and then re-importing the unsold stock afterwards, or importing material purchased at the show.

Buying and Selling

When goods are sold, the seller and the buyer enter into a contract which confers rights and imposes obligations on both parties. The contract need not be in writing. There is no law governing the quality of goods sold by a private individual. If you purchase a coin from a fellow-collector as a result of an informal meeting at the local numismatic society it is incumbent on you to ensure that what you buy is what you think you are buying. If you purchase something from a dealer or shopkeeper, however, you are entitled under the Sale of Goods Act to goods of "merchantable quality" which means that they must be reasonably fit for their purpose. Items sold under a specific description, on the other hand, must correspond exactly with that description. If they do not, the seller *even a private individual* can be sued under the Sale of Goods Act. This is an important distinction because there is an erroneous notion that the Act does not apply to transactions between private individuals. If A sells a coin to B, purporting it to be a rare date, and B subsequently discovers that the date has been deliberately altered, then B can sue A. Even if A claims that he made the sale in good faith, believing the coin to be a genuine rare date, he will still be liable for restitution (giving B his money back) and may also face a claim for damages. The Sale of Goods Act thus overturns the traditional adage *caveat emptor* which, in its full formula, translates as "let the buyer beware for he ought not to be ignorant of the nature of the property which he is buying from another party". Traditionally this was the maxim applicable at auctions. Once the auctioneer's gavel had dropped, the successful bidder had, in effect, made a contract with the vendor and was bound to pay for the lot, even if he subsequently discovered that what he had purchased was not what he had imagined. The view was that it was up to the purchaser to ensure beforehand that what he purchased was genuine and answered the description in the sale catalogue.

Because of vexatious disputes arising from questions of authenticity, and with the Sale of Goods Act breathing down their necks, many auctioneers now have a safety net, in the form of extensions. These enable successful bidders to delay payment for two or three weeks while they seek expertisation of doubtful material. In other words, the law allows a cooling-off period, but only for he legitimate purpose of verifying the authenticity of items over which there may be some doubt. This is only operative in cases where a coin or medal is sold as genuine, and described and estimated in value accordingly. In many doubtful cases, however, an auctioneer will cover himself by adding the crucial words "as is" to the description of a lot. Then, indeed, it is a case of *caveat emptor*. The auctioneer has done everything humanly possible to draw attention to the controversial nature of the item, and it must then rest on the judgment of the purchaser.

On the subject of auctions there are legal aspects which are not always apparent, as well as subtle differences in law and practice between England and Scotland. These tend to arise in cases where coins and medals come up for sale at provincial general mixed auctions, rather than in the sales conducted by numismatic auctioneers. Goods up for auction may be subject to an upset price which is made public as the price at which the bidding will start. A reserve price, on the other hand, is known only to the auctioneer, and if it is not reached, the goods will not be sold. Upset prices are common in Scotland, reserve prices in England. If no upset price is specified and the goods are not subject to a reserve price then the highest bid secures them, even though it may not be as high as the vendor hoped for. If a seller notifies other bidders that he is bidding for his own goods, or that he has employed an agent to bid for him, the bidding is legal. If he does not give notice and bids himself, or gets someone to bid for him, thus forcing up the price, the sale is fraudulent, and the buyer can purchase the goods for the amount of the last bid he made before fraudulent bidding started.

One frequently hears dark, but usually apocryphal, tales of "the ring" in action to depress the bidding and secure items below the price commensurate with their actual value. This is a fraudulent practice and in law is regarded as a criminal conspiracy. In practice, however, it would be very difficult for a group of dealers or other individuals to keep the bidding down merely by sitting on their hands. This practice could only operate successfully in sales which were largely, if not entirely, frequented by dealers. But coin sales, like other specialist collector-orientated auctions, are characterised by a high proportion of private bidders in attendance. Any conspiracy by a ring would merely allow some private bidder to step in and secure the lot at a bargain price. Rings are illegal, but in practice prosecutions are very rare as it is extremely difficult to obtain proof of their operations. What is more likely to happen is that dealers have been known to act in concert to force up the bidding to frighten off some unwelcome interloper. Here again, such tales are legion, but astonishingly lacking in specific details. The golden rule in attending auctions is to know what you are going after, and to have a pretty precise idea of how much you are prepared to pay. Do not be stampeded in the heat of the moment into going way beyond your limit.

Taxation of Profits on Disposal

The Inland Revenue define an asset as "any form of property (other than sterling) wherever situated". A disposal includes a sale, exchange or gift of an asset, or the receipt of a capital sum in respect of them. In layman's terms you dispose of an asset when you sell it, give it away, exchange it or lose it. A transfer of assets between husband and wife doesn't count (unless they are legally separated), nor does the transfer of an asset you leave when you die. If a disposal results in a profit you could be liable to tax. Any profit made on the sale of certain assets, including coins, medals and other collectables, constitutes a capital gain and is subject to Capital Gains Tax (CGT) which is now charged at the same 25% and 40% rates as income tax. However the government allows you to make a total capital gain in the current tax year of £5,500 before tax becomes chargeable. If this is the case, and the total proceeds from disposal do not exceed £10,000, then a simple declaration to this effect is all you need to make in the relevant section of your annual tax return.

Computing the actual capital gain is a complicated matter. Suppose you purchased a coin in 1960 for £5,000 and sold it in 1993 for £12,000. On the face of it, you've made a capital gain of £7,000 and you might think that you were liable to CGT

because the gain was over £5,500. However, the *length of time* you've held the asset also has to be taken into consideration. From April 6, 1988 the law was altered so that only gains made after March 31, 1982 are now taxable. In effect, you are taxed as if you acquired the coin on March 31, 1982. The initial value of the coin is deemed to be its market value at that date. If the gain from March 1982 to the time of disposal is greater than the overall gain from acquisition in 1960 to disposal in 1993, you take the lesser of the two figures. If this produces a gain, whereas the old method of working it out would have produced a loss, you will be regarded, for tax purposes, as having made neither a gain nor a loss on disposal. You have a choice of opting for computing from the time of actual acquisition or from March 1982, whichever seems the more advantageous; but once you've made your choice you cannot subsequently change your mind.

How do you establish what the coin was worth in March 1982? The Inland Revenue tend to regard Seaby, Krause or other relevant catalogues as their yardstick. The difference between the nominal or catalogue value in 1982 and what you eventually got for the coin *assuming that the latter was greater*, might be regarded as the capital gain, but even then the position is complicated by inflation in the intervening years eroding the real value of the coin.

At this stage things get really complicated as you have to work out the indexation allowance. This is determined by the Retail Prices Index (RPI), and you need to know the RPI for (a) the month of disposal, and (b) the month in which you acquired the asset, or March 1982, if later. The RPI is announced each month by the Departmenrt of Employment and is published in its *Employment Gazette* which ought to be available in your local public library. Take the RPI for the month of the disposal and subtract the RPI for the month when indexation commenced. Then divide the result by the RPI for the month when indexation began, and work out this figure to the nearest third decimal place. This is known as the indexation factor, which you then multiply by the initial value of your coin. Simple isn't it? In most cases, however, I expect you will have made a capital loss in real terms, so these sums, though necessary to satisfy the Inland Revenue, are largely academic.

Treasure
and the Law

Until the introduction of the new Treasure Act, the legal position regarding articles of value, found long after they were hidden or abandoned, was not as simple and straightforward as it might be supposed. Furthermore, this was a case where the law in England and Wales differed fundamentally from that in Scotland.

Treasure Trove was one of the most ancient rights of the Crown, deriving from the age-old right of the monarch to grave treasure. In England and Wales, the law applied only to objects made of, or containing, gold or silver, whether in the form of coin, jewellery, plate or bullion. Moreover, the object had to be shown to have been deliberately hidden and the owner could not be readily found. The English law therefore excluded precious stones and jewels set in base metals or alloys such as bronze or pewter. It also took no account of artifacts in pottery, stone, bone, wood or glass which might be of immense antiquarian value.

In recent years, as a result of the rise in metal-detecting as a hobby, the archaeological lobby brought pressure to bear on Parliament to change the law and bring it into line with Scotland where the rules on Treasure Trove were far more rigorously interpreted. In Scotland the Crown is entitled to *all* abandoned property, even if it has not been hidden and is of little value. This applies even to objects dumped in skips on the pavement. Strictly speaking you would be committing a criminal offence if you removed an old chair from a skip without the owner's permission, although in practice such helping oneself rarely proceeds to a prosecution. In 1958 an archaeological expedition

Metal detecting can be fun—but be sure you know the rules!

294

from Aberdeen University found several valuable artifacts on St Ninian's Isle, Shetland. These included silver vessels and ornaments, as well as a porpoise bone which had incised decoration on it. The archaeologists challenged the rights of the Crown to this treasure, arguing that the Crown would have to prove that the articles had been deliberately hidden, and that a porpoise bone was in any case not valuable enough to count as treasure. The High Court, however, decided that as long as the property had been abandoned, it belonged automatically to the Crown. Its value, intrinsic or otherwise, or whether or not it was hidden, did not make any difference. Since then, as a result of this decision in case law, the criteria for Treasure Trove have been very strictly applied in Scotland. It would have only required a similar test case in England or Wales to result in a similar tightening of the rules. This has been resisted, mainly by the detectorist lobby, but inevitably the government considered legislation to control the use of metal detectors, if not to ban them altogether.

In England and Wales a find of gold or silver coins, artifacts or ornaments, or objects which contain some of these metals, which appears to have been concealed by the original owner, was deemed to be Treasure Trove. It was not even necessary for the articles to be buried in the ground; objects concealed in thatched roofs or under the floorboards of buildings have been judged to be Treasure Trove. Such finds had to be notified immediately to the police who then informed the district coroner. He then convened an inquest which decided whether all or part of the find was Treasure Trove. Establishing the gold or silver content was straightforward, but the coroner's inquest had to decide whether the material was hidden deliberately and not just lost or abandoned, and that the owner could not be located. A gold coin found on or near a country footpath might reasonably have been dropped by the original possessor through a hole in pocket or purse and in such cases it was very unlikely that it would be deemed Treasure Trove, even if the coin turned out to be very rare. In this instance the coroner would then have had to determine who was the lawful owner of the find: the actual finder, the owner of the land where it was found or even the tenant of the land. As a rule, however, it was left to the finder and landowner to decide between them who the owner of the coin should be, and in some cases the matter could only be resolved by referring to a civil court. For this reason it was vital that metal detectorists should secure permission *in writing* from landowners before going on to their land, defining rights and obligations on both sides, in order to determine

The Snettisham torcs—one of our country's greatest finds.

the disposal or share-out of any finds or proceeds from the sale of finds, *beforehand*.

If the coroner decided that the articles were deliberately concealed, and declared them to be Treasure Trove, the find automatically reverted to the Crown. In practice the find was considered by the Treasure Trove Reviewing Committee of the Treasury. They might decide that although the articles *invariably coins* were gold or silver, they were so common that they were not required by the British Museum or one of the other great national collections, and would return them to the finder to dispose of at his discretion. If some or all of the coins were deemed vital for inclusion in a national collection the finder was recompensed with the full market value of the material. On the other hand, if someone found gold or silver which might be Treasure Trove and failed to declare it at the time, that person was liable to prosecution under the Theft Act should the find subsequently come to light. Not only could he face a heavy fine but the articles would be forfeit to the Crown, and of course no reward or recompense was then payable either.

The anomalies and inconsistencies of existing law on Treasure Trove were eliminated and the position considerably tightened up by the passage, on July 5, 1996, of the Treasure Act.

Announcing that the Treasure Act had received the Royal Assent, Lord Inglewood, National Heritage Minister, said, "This represents the first legislation on treasure trove to be passed in England and Wales and will replace common law precedents and practices dating back to the

Middle Ages. The Act, which offers a clearer definition of treasure and simplified procedures for dealing with finds, will come into force after a code of practice has been drawn up and agreed by both Houses of Parliament". The Act came into force in England, Wales and Northern Ireland on September 24, 1997, replacing the common law of treasure trove.

The act was introduced as a Private Member's Bill by Sir Anthony Grant, after the failure of an earlier attempt by Lord Perth. For the first time, it would be a criminal offence to fail to report within 14 days the discovery of an item which would be declared Treasure Trove. Finders will continue to be rewarded for reporting their discoveries promptly, while landowners and occupiers will also be eligible for rewards for the first time.

The Treasure Act covers man-made objects and defines treasure as objects other than coins which are at least 300 years old and contain at least 10 per cent by weight of gold or silver; coins more than 300 years old which are found in hoards (a minimum of two coins if the precious metal content is more than 10 per cent, and a minimum of 10 coins if the precious metal content is below 10 per cent). The act also embraces all objects found in clear archaeological association with items which are treasure under the above definitions. It also covers any object which would have been Treasure Trove under the previous definitions (e.g. hoards of 19th century gold or silver coins).

The maximum penalty for failing to report the discovery of treasure within 14 days will be a fine of £50,000 or three months imprisonment, or both.

In Scotland the police pass the goods on to the procurator fiscal who acts as the local representative of the Queen's and Lord Treasurer's Remembrancer. If the articles are of little value, historically or intrinsically, the finder will usually be allowed to keep them. If they are retained for the appropriate national collection then a reward equal to the market value is payable.

A favourite haunt of metal-detectorists these days is the beach, and many hobbyists make quite a lucrative living by sweeping the beaches especially just after a Bank Holiday. It's surprising how much loose change gets lost from pockets and handbags over a holiday weekend. Technically the coins recovered from the beach are lost property, in which case they ought to be surrendered to the police, otherwise the finder may be guilty of theft. In practice, however, the law turns a blind eye to coins, on the sensible grounds that it would be impossible to prove ownership. On the other hand, banknotes are treated as lost property since someone could in theory at least identify a note as his by citing the serial number.

In the case of other objects, such as watches and jewellery, of course the law governing lost property is enforced, and the old adage of "finders keepers" does not apply. Any object of value, identifiable as belonging to someone, that is washed up on the foreshore or found in territorial waters is known technically as "wreck". This includes not just a wrecked ship, but any cargo that was being carried by a ship.

If wreck is not claimed by its owner, it falls to the Crown. In this case it is not necessary to prove deliberate concealment, as in the case of Treasure Trove. This law has a specific numismatic application in the case of the gold and silver coins washed up after storms around our shores, from Shetland to the Scillies. Such coins, emanating from wrecks of Spanish treasure ships and Dutch East Indiamen in particular, are well documented, and any such finds ought to be reported immediately to the police.

Stray finds of coins, as well as other objects of value, on public places, such as the street, a public park or a sports ground, are also subject to law. In this case the finder must take all reasonable steps to locate the owner. Anyone who keeps a coin without making reasonable effort to find the owner could be prosecuted for theft. As with the beach, however, such "reasonable effort" would clearly be impractical. Finding coins on private premises is another matter. In this case large bodies, such as the Post Office, British Rail, the British Airports Authority, bus companies, municipal authorities, hospitals, the owners of department stores, theatre and cinema proprietors and the like, may have bye-laws, rules and regulations for dealing with lost property found within their precincts, or in their vehicles. If you found a purse or wallet on a bus or train, or in a telephone kiosk or a shop, common sense (and your conscience) would tell you to hand it over to the driver, conductor, shopkeeper or official in charge. As a rule, unclaimed lost property reverts eventually to the finder, but not always; British Rail and some other organisations have a rule that in such cases the property reverts to the organisation. In any event, failure to disclose the find immediately might render you liable to prosecution for stealing by finding.

Treasure Act
Code of Practice
—a summary

For easy reference a summary of the main points of the new law is reproduced here*. Further information will be found in the *Code of Practice on the Treasure Act*, which can be obtained free of charge from the Department for Culture, Media and Sport (formerly the Department of National Heritage) (telephone: 020 7211 6200). Metal detectorists are strongly advised to obtain a copy of the Code of Practice which, among other things, contains guidance for detectorists, sets out guidelines on rewards, gives advice on the care of finds and has lists of useful addresses.

What is the definition of treasure?

The following finds are treasure under the Act (more detailed guidance is given in the Code of Practice):

1. *Objects other than coins:* any object other than a coin provided that it contains at least 10 per cent of gold or silver and is a least 300 years old when found (objects with gold or silver plating normally have less than 10 per cent of precious metal).

2. *Coins:* all coins from the same find provided they are at least 300 years old when found (but if the coins contain less than 10 per cent of gold or silver there must be at least 10 of them; there is a list of these coins in the Code of Practice).

An object or coin is part of the same find as another object or coin if it is found in the same place as, or had previously been left together with, the other object. Finds may have become scattered since they were originally deposited in the ground.

Only the following groups of coins will normally be regarded as coming from the "same find":

(a) hoards that have been deliberately hidden;
(b) smaller groups of coins, such as the contents of purses, that may have been dropped or lost and
(c) votive or ritual deposits.

Single coins found on their own are not treasure and groups of coins lost one by one over

a period of time (for example those found on settlement sites or on fair sites) will not normally be treasure.

3. *Associated objects:* any object, whatever it is made of, that is found in the same place as, or that had previously been together with, another object that is treasure

4. *Objects that would have been treasure trove:* any object that would previously have been treasure trove, but does not fall within the specific categories given above. These objects have to be made substantially of gold or silver; they have to have been buried with the intention of recovery and their owner or his/her heirs cannot be traced. The following types of find are not treasure:

(a) objects whose owners can be traced;
(b) unworked natural objects, including human and animal remains, even if they are found in association with treasure;
(c) objects from the foreshore, which are wreck.

If you are in any doubt, it will probably be safest to report your find.

What about objects found before the Act came into force?

You should report objects that come into any of the four categories just described (if found after September 23, 1997). There is no need to report any objects found before that date unless they may be treasure trove (see 4 above)

What should I do if I find something that may be treasure?

You must report all finds of treasure to the coroner for the district in which they are found *either* within 14 days after the date on which you made the find *or* within 14 days after the day on which you realised that the find might be treasure (for example, as a result of having it identified). The obligation to report finds applies to everyone, including archaeologists.

How do I report a find of treasure?

Very simply. You may report your find to the coroner in person, by letter, telephone or fax. The coroner or his officer will send you an acknowledgement and tell you where you should deliver your find. The Code of Practice has a list of all coroners with their addresses, telephone and fax numbers.

There are special procedure for objects from a few areas for which treasure franchises exist, but they should be reported to the coroner in the usual way. The main franchise-holders (the Duchies of Lancaster and Cornwall, the Corporation of London and the City of Bristol) have confirmed that they will pay rewards for finds of treasure from their franchises in the normal way.

Where will I have to take my find?

You will normally be asked to take your find to a local museum or archaeological body. Local agreements have been drawn up for each coroner's district in England and Wales to provide the coroner with a list of such museums and archaeological organisations. The Department is publishing a series of leaflets, roughly one for each country of England and one for Wales, listing the relevant coroners, museums and archaeological services in each area.

The body which receives the find on behalf of the coroner will give you a receipt. Although they will need to know where you made the find, they will keep this information confidential if you or the landowner wish—and you should do so too.

The body receiving the find will notify the Sites and Monuments Record as soon as possible (if that has not already happened), so that the site where the find was made can be investigated by archaeologists if necessary. A list of Sites and Monuments Records is in Appendix 3 of the Code of Practice.

What if I do not report a find of treasure?

If you fail to report a find that you believe or have reasonable grounds for believing to be treasure without a reasonable excuse you may be imprisoned for up to three months or receive a fine of up to level 5 on the standard scale (currently £5,000) or both. You will not be breaking the law if you do not report a find because you do not initially recognise that it may be treasure, but you should report it once you do realise this.

What happens if the find is not treasure?

If the object is clearly not treasure, the museum or archeological body will inform the coroner, who may then decide to give directions that the find should be returned without holding an inquest.

What happens if the find is treasure?

If the museum curator or archaeologist believes that the find may be treasure, they will inform the British Museum or the National Museums & Galleries of Wales. The museums will then decide whether they or any other museum may wish to acquire it.

If no museum wishes to acquire the find, the Secretary of State will be able to disclaim it. When this happens, the coroner will notify the occupier and landowner that he intends to return the object to the finder after 28 days unless he receives an objection. If the coroner receives an objection, the find will be retained until the dispute has been settled.

What if a museum wants to acquire my find?

If a museum wants to acquire part or all of a find, then the coroner will hold an inquest to decide whether it is treasure. The coroner will inform the finder, occupier and landowner and they will be able to question witnesses at the inquest. Treasure inquest will not normally be held with a jury.

If the find is declared to be treasure, then it will be taken to the British Museum or the National Museums & Galleries of Wales, so that it can be valued by the Treasure Valuation Committee.

How do I know that I will receive a fair price for my find?

Any find of treasure that a museum wishes to acquire must be valued by the Treasure Valuation Committee, which consists of independent experts. The Committee will commission a valuation from one or more experts drawn from the trade. You, together with the museum that wishes to acquire the find and any other interested party, will have an opportunity to comment on the valuation and to send in a separate valuation of your own, before the Committee makes its recommendation. If you are dissatisfied you can appeal to the Secretary of State.

What if the coroner or museum loses or damages my find?

They are required to take reasonable steps to ensure that this does not happen; but, if it does, you should nonetheless be compensated.

Who will receive the reward?

This is set out in detail in the Code of Practice. To summarise:

— where the finder has permission to be on the land, rewards should continue to be paid in full to him or her (the burden of proof as to whether he or she has permission will rest with the finder). If the finder makes an agreement with the occupier/landowner to share a reward, the Secretary of State will normally follow it;

— if the finder does not remove the whole of a find from the ground but allows archaeologists to excavate the remainder of the find, the original finder will normally be eligible for a reward for the whole find;

— rewards will not normally be payable when the find is made by an archaeologist;

— where the finder has committed an offence in relation to a find, or has trespassed, or has not followed best practice as set out in the Code of Practice, he or she may expect no reward at all or a reduced reward. Landowners and occupiers will be eligible for rewards in such cases.

How long will it take before I receive my reward?

The Code of Practice states that you should receive a reward within one year of you having delivered your find, although this may take longer in the case of very large finds or those that present special difficulties. If no museum wants to acquire the find it should be disclaimed within six months or within three months if it is a single object.

Reproduced from "The Treasure Act, Information for Finders of Treasure (England and Wales)" leaflet DCMSJ0229NJ, published by the Department for Culture, Media and Sport.

Hoard of Civil War coins found in Yorkshire—picture courtesy of Spink.

Index
to COIN NEWS

Once again, in response to popular demand, we have included this basic subject index to the COIN YEARBOOK's parent magazine COIN NEWS, covering the period from October 1999 to September 2000. Entries are indicated by numbers signifying the month (e.g. 10–12 relate to October to December 1999 and 1–9 signify January to September 2000), followed by the page number.

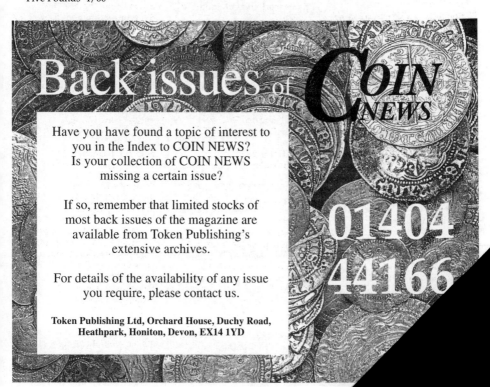

AIREDALE COINS

P.O. BOX 7, BINGLEY, WEST YORKSHIRE BD16 4ST
–WHOLESALE–   TEL: BRADFORD (01274 770414   –RETAIL–
E-MAIL: info@airedalecoins.com   Web pages www.airedalecoins.com

OUR MAIN SPECIALIST AREAS ARE:-

BRITISH NEW ISSUES/COINS BACK TO 1800

SILVER CROWN SIZE COINS

AUSTRALIAN NEW ISSUES

CANADIAN NEW ISSUES

USA NEW ISSUES

FREE LIST AVAILABLE ON REQUEST

FAST MAIL ORDER SERVICE

MOST ORDERS SHIPPED WITHIN 1 DAY

COMPETITIVE PRICES

MEMBERS OF THE AMERICAN NUMISMATIC

OCIATION (ANA)

ANTEE OF A FAIR DEAL

303

90% OF ORDERS DESPATCHED WITHIN 1 WORKING DAY.
ANTEE. MASTERCARD, VISA AND SWITCH ACCEPTED.
S OF THE BRITISH NUMISMATIC TRADE ASSOCIATION